Approximate Methods
for Solution of Differential
and Integral Equations

MODERN ANALYTIC AND COMPUTATIONAL METHODS IN SCIENCE AND MATHEMATICS

A Group of Monographs and Advanced Textbooks

MODERN ANALYTIC AND COMPUTATIONAL METHODS IN SCIENCE AND MATHEMATICS

MÉTHODES MODERNES D'ANALYSE ET DE COMPUTATION EN SCIENCE ET MATHÉMATIQUE

NEUE ANALYTISCHE UND NUMERISCHE METHODEN IN DER WISSENSCHAFT UND DER MATHEMATIK

НОВЫЕ АНАЛИТИЧЕСКИЕ И ВЫЧИСЛИТЕЛЬНЫЕ МЕТОДЫ В НАУКЕ И МАТЕМАТИКЕ

Editorial Board

Approximate Methods for Solution of Differential and Integral Equations

by

S. G. MIKHLIN AND K. L. SMOLITSKIY
Leningrad State University

Translated by *Scripta Technica, Inc.*

Translation Editor: ROBERT E. KALABA
The RAND *Corporation*

AMERICAN ELSEVIER PUBLISHING COMPANY INC.
NEW YORK 1967

ORIGINALLY PUBLISHED AS
Priblizhennyye Metody Reshenya Differentsyalnykh i Integralnykh
Uravneniy
Nauka Press, Moscow 1965

SOLE DISTRIBUTORS FOR GREAT BRITAIN
ELSEVIER PUBLISHING COMPANY, LTD.
Barking, Essex, England

SOLE DISTRIBUTORS FOR THE CONTINENT OF EUROPE
ELSEVIER PUBLISHING COMPANY
Amsterdam, The Netherlands

Library of Congress Catalog Card Number: 67-22421

EDITOR'S PREFACE

The authors have produced a work that is rich in both theoretical and practical aspects of the computational solution of the differential and integral equations of mathematical physics. Of particular interest to non-Russian readers are the sections devoted to Chaplygin's train of ideas, to the method of lines, and to a detailed treatment of the Rayleigh-Ritz method.

Professor Mikhlin very kindly provided us with a number of corrections which have been incorporated into this English edition.

R. Kalaba

Santa Monica
April 1967

PREFACE

The aim of this book is to acquaint the reader with the most important and powerful methods of approximate solution of boundary-value problems (including the Cauchy problem) for differential equations, both ordinary and partial, as well as approximate methods for solution of the most frequently encountered types of integral equations: Fredholm, Volterra and singular one-dimensional. This covers the entire domain of classical applications of mathematical analysis to mechanics, engineering, and mathematical physics.

The methods for approximate solution of differential and integral equations are divided into two large groups—numerical and analytical methods. The most important and highly developed part of the first group is the family of the various *grid methods;* the most important analytical methods are the *variational methods.* The "line method" occupies a position midway between the analytical and grid methods. Recently, this method has attracted the attention of increasing numbers of both theoretical and applied mathematicians; however, it has not yet matured to the point of deserving a separate classification, and the authors have included it among the analytical methods.

The book is organized basically in accordance with the separation of approximate methods into numerical and analytical classes. The main chapters of the book, Chapters II and III, correspond to the basic groups of approximate methods—grid and variational (the latter including the line method)—and are in no way related to the type of equation to which a given method can be applied. The methods presented in each of the two chapters can be applied equally well to ordinary differential equations, partial differential equations, and integral equations; similarly, these methods can be applied to both linear and nonlinear problems. The authors did, however, find it desirable to concentrate on two problems in two special chapters because of their extremely specific nature.

Thus, there are two relatively small chapters; the chapter on the Cauchy problem (Chapter I), and the chapter on approximate solution of integral equations (Chapter IV). The fact is that it is frequently difficult (or impossible) to classify the numerical or analytical methods developed for these problems as either grid or variational. It is, however, true that part of the material of Chapter I and IV could have been placed in Chapters II and III—difference methods for ordinary differential equations and quadrature methods for solution of integral equations could have been included in Chapter II, while the method of least squares and the Ritz and Bubnov-Galerkin methods for integral equations could have been included in Chapter III. This approach, however, would have made the exposition difficult and disjointed.

The separation of methods into two groups is preserved in Chapter I: Section 1 of this chapter considers analytical methods for solution of the Cauchy problem, while Section 2 considers numerical methods. Strict separation of the material into groups was abandoned in the chapter on integral equations, where such a division would have been unjustified, Here, the material is organized according to the major problems in the field: computation of eigenvalues and eigenfunctions of a symmetric kernel (Section 1), solution of Fredholm and Volterra equations (Sections 2–5), and solution of singular equations (Section 6).

Chapter I was written jointly by the authors, Chapter II by Kh. L. Smolitskiy, and Chapters III and IV by S. G. Mikhlin.

S. G. Mikhlin
Kh. L. Smolitskiy

CONTENTS

Chapter One

APPROXIMATE SOLUTION OF THE CAUCHY PROBLEM FOR ORDINARY DIFFERENTIAL EQUATIONS

In this chapter we will discuss the Cauchy problem for one ordinary differential equation and for systems of such equations. Relative to methods of approximate solution, boundary-value problems for ordinary differential equations are little different from analogous problems for partial differential equations: As a rule, both are solved either by grid or variational methods. We therefore leave boundary-value problems for ordinary differential equations to Chapters two and three.

In Section 1 of this chapter we will consider analytic approximate methods for obtaining solutions to the Cauchy problem in the form of some analytic expression; Section 2 deals with numerical methods that, as solutions to the Cauchy problem, provide answers in the form of a table of approximate values for the desired function.

The Cauchy problem for the first-order differential equation

$$y' = f(x, y) \qquad (1.1)$$

consists in finding, in some interval $x_0 \leqslant x \leqslant x_0 + a$, an integral of this equation, that satisfies the initial condition

$$y \big|_{x=x_0} = y_0. \qquad (1.2)$$

Assume that a region G in the (x, y) plane contains the point (x_0, y_0), and assume that in this region the function $f(x, y)$ is continuous and, say, has a continuous partial derivative $\partial f/\partial y$. Under these conditions we can guarantee the existence and uniqueness of solutions to the Cauchy Problem (1.1)–(1.2) in some interval $x_0 - A < x < x_0 + A$, and we will assume that A is the largest of the numbers for which Problem (1.1)–(1.2) has a solution in the interval $x_0 - A < x < x_0 + A$. If it turns out that $a < A$, the initially stated Cauchy problem also has a solution, indeed, a unique one; if, however, $a > A$, the problem we have posed has no solution—instead of existing in the interval $x_0 - a \leqslant x \leqslant x_0 + a$, we desire, the solution exists only in the smaller interval $x_0 - A' \leqslant x \leqslant x_0 + A'$, where A' is any number smaller than A. Thus, for example, the Cauchy problem

$$y' = y^2 + 1, \quad y \big|_{x=0} = 0$$

1

has the unique solution $y = \text{tg } x$, which is defined and continuous only in the interval $-\pi/2 < x < \pi/2$, although the function $1 + y^2$ is continuous and differentiable everywhere in the (x, y) plane. The problem of finding a solution to the Cauchy problem we have just stated for the interval $-a \leqslant x \leqslant a$, where $a \geqslant \pi/2$, has no solution.

In subsequent discussions of approximate methods for solution of the Cauchy problem, we will assume that an exact solution exists everywhere in the interval in which an approximate solution is sought.

I. ANALYTIC METHODS

1.1 Expansion of solutions in Taylor series.   Let the function $f(x, y)$ in the right-hand side of Eq. (1.1) be analytic in the neighborhood of the point (x_0, y_0); this means that the indicated function can be expanded in a double power series

$$f(x, y) = \sum_{k \ m=0}^{\infty} a_{km}(x - x_0)^k(y - y_0)^m, \tag{1.3}$$

that converges in the neighborhood of the point (x_0, y_0), i.e., converges for x and y sufficiently close to x_0 and y_0. Then, as we know (see [18], pp. 224–326, as well as Section 32 of [120]), a solution to the Cauchy Problem (1.1)–(1.2) exists for x sufficiently close to x_0, is unique, and is an analytic function of x; as a result, it has the Taylor series expansion

$$y(x) = \sum_{k=0}^{\infty} \frac{y^{(k)}(x_0)}{k!} (x - x_0)^k \tag{1.4}$$

in the neighborhood of x.

It is possible to find a disk in the complex x plane (and, consequently, an interval on the real x axis) in which Series (1.4) definitely converges. Namely, let the function $f(x, y)$ be analytic when the *complex* variables x and y satisfy the inequalities

$$|x - x_0| \leqslant \alpha, |y - y_0| \leqslant \beta, \tag{1.5}$$

where α and β are constants. In the closed region (1.5) the variables x and y of the function $f(x, y)$ are always continuous and therefore bounded; assume that in this region $|f(x, y)| \leqslant \mu$. Then Series (1.4) converges in the disk

$$|x - x_0| \leqslant \rho, \qquad \rho = \min\left(\alpha, \frac{\beta}{\mu}\right). \tag{1.6}$$

Choose a natural number N and retain only terms of order $\leqslant N$ in Series (1.4). The approximate formula

$$y(x) \approx y_N(x) = \sum_{k=0}^{N} \frac{y^{(k)}(x_0)}{k!} (x - x_0)^k \tag{1.7}$$

furnishes us with an approximate solution for Problem (1.1)–(1.2) if we can compute $y^{(k)}(x_0)(k = 0, 1, 2, \ldots, N)$. But this can easily be done by starting from Eqs. (1.1) and (1.2). Indeed, it follows immediately from initial condition (1.2) that

$$y(x_0) = y_0.$$

Now, if we set $x = x_0$, in Eq. (1.1), we find that

$$y'(x_0) = f(x_0, y_0).$$

Differentiating (1.1), we find that

$$y'' = f_x(x, y) + f_y(x, y)y',$$
$$y''' = f_{xx}(x, y) + 2f_{xy}(x, y)y' + f_{yy}(x, y)y'^2 + f_y(x, y)y'',$$
$$\cdots \cdots \cdots \cdots \cdots \cdots \cdots \cdots \cdots \cdots \cdots \cdots$$

If we again set $x = x_0$, here, we can successively compute $y''(x_0)$, $y'''(x_0)$, $\ldots$, $y^{(N)}(x_0)$. We should note that approximate Formula (1.7) is applicable in the disk (1.6) of the complex plane and, consequently, it also applies to the interval $|x - x_0| \leqslant \rho$ of the real x axis.

EXAMPLE 1: Find the approximate solution corresponding to $N = 7$ in Formula (1.7) for the Cauchy problem

$$y' = x^2 + y^2, \quad y\big|_{x=0} = 0. \tag{1.8}$$

It immediately follows from the given data that

$$y(0) = 0, \ y'(0) = 0.$$

Differentiation of Eq. (1.8) yields

$$y'' = 2x + 2yy', \ y''' = 2 + 2yy'' + 2y'^2,$$
$$y^{(4)} = 2yy''' + 6y'y'', \ y^{(5)} = 2yy^{(4)} + 8y'y''' + 6y''^2,$$
$$y^{(6)} = 2yy^{(5)} + 10y'y^{(4)} + 20y''y''',$$
$$y^{(7)} = 2yy^{(6)} + 12y'y^{(5)} + 30y''y^{(4)} + 20y'''^2.$$

If we set $x = 0$ here and use the already known values $y(0) = y'(0) = 0$, we successively find that

$$y''(0) = 0, \ y'''(0) = 2, \ y^{(4)}(0) = y^{(5)}(0) = y^{(6)}(0) = 0, \ y^{(7)}(0) = 80.$$

The desired approximate solution is

$$y_7(x) = \frac{x^3}{3} + \frac{x^7}{63}. \tag{1.9}$$

In our case it is not difficult to estimate the radius of convergence of Series (1.4) and, consequently, the region in which approximate solution (1.9) holds.

The function $x^2 + y^2$ is analytic for all values of x and y, so the constants α and β of Formula (1.5) can be chosen arbitrarily. We take $\beta = k\alpha$, where k is some constant and α is arbitrary. Then $|x^2 + y^2| \leqslant \alpha^2(1 + k^2)$ and we can set $\mu = \alpha^2(1 + k^2)$. Now, by Formula (1.6),

$$\rho = \min\left(\alpha, \frac{k}{\alpha(1 + k^2)}\right).$$

If k is fixed, the largest value of ρ, which is equal to $\sqrt{\dfrac{k}{1 + k^2}}$, is obtained when $\alpha = \sqrt{\dfrac{k}{1 + k^2}}$. By changing k, we can see that ρ achieves its largest value, which is $1/\sqrt{2}$, at $k = 1$. Thus, Problem (1.8) has a solution at least in the interval $|x| \leqslant 1/\sqrt{2}$.

We will now consider an equation of order $n > 1$:

$$y^{(n)} = f(x, y', \ldots, y^{(n-1)}), \tag{1.10}$$

and state a Cauchy problem for this equation: find the integral satisfying the initial conditions

$$y\big|_{x=x_0} = y_0,\, y'\big|_{x=x_0} = y'_0,\, \ldots,\, y^{(n-1)}\big|_{x=x_0} = y_0^{(n-1)}. \tag{1.11}$$

If the right-hand side of Eq. (1.10) is an analytic function of its arguments in the neighborhood of $(x_0, y_0, y'_0, \ldots, y_0^{(n-1)})$, a solution of Cauchy Problem (1.10)–(1.11) exists for all x sufficiently close to x, is unique, and can be expanded in a Taylor series of the form (1.4). As before, we can construct an approximate solution in the form (1.7); the quantities $y^{(k)}(x_0)$ for $k \leqslant n - 1$ are given by initial conditions (1.11), and for $k \geqslant n$ are recurrently determined by differentiation of Eq. (1.10) with subsequent substitution of $x = x_0$.

EXAMPLE 2: Solve the Cauchy problem

$$y'' = x + y^2,\, y\big|_{x=0} = 0,\, y'\big|_{x=0} = 1.$$

We will attempt to find an approximate solution with Formula (1.7) and $N = 8$. It immediately follows from the given that

$$y(0) = 0,\, y'(0) = 1,\, y''(0) = 0.$$

Differentiating the equation $y'' = x + y^2$, we find that

$$y''' = 1 + 2yy',\, y^{(4)} = 2yy'' + 2y'^2,$$
$$y^{(5)} = 2yy''' + 6y'y'',$$
$$y^{(6)} = 2yy^{(4)} + 8y'y''' + 6y''^2,$$
$$y^{(7)} = 2yy^{(5)} + 10y'y^{(4)} + 20y''y''',$$
$$y^{(8)} = 2yy^{(6)} + 12y'y^{(5)} + 30y''y^{(4)} + 20y'''^2.$$

When $x = 0$ we find, by using the values we found above for $y(0)$, $y'(0)$, and $y''(0)$, that
$$y'''(0) = 1, \quad y^{(4)}(0) = 2, \quad y^{(5)}(0) = 0, \quad y^{(6)}(0) = 8,$$
$$y^{(7)}(0) = 20, \quad y^{(8)}(0) = 20.$$

Now Formula (1.7) yields the approximate solution
$$y_8(x) = x + \frac{x^3}{6} + \frac{x^4}{12} + \frac{x^6}{90} + \frac{x^7}{252} + \frac{x^8}{2016}.$$

We now turn to systems of ordinary differential equations. We will only consider first-order systems for, as we know, the general case can easily be reduced to this one.

We will attempt to solve the system
$$y_j = f_j(x, y_1, y_2, \ldots, y_m) \qquad (j = 1, 2, \ldots, m), \tag{1.12}$$

under the initial conditions
$$y_j \big|_{x=x_0} = y_{j0}. \tag{1.13}$$

If the right-hand side of Eqs. (1.12) are analytic functions of their arguments in the neighborhood of the point $(x_0, y_{10}, y_{20}, \ldots, y_{m0})$, a solution for the Cauchy Problem (1.12)–(1.13) exists for all x close to x_0, is unique, and can be represented by Taylor series expansions
$$y_j(x) = \sum_{n=0}^{\infty} \frac{y_j^{(n)}(x_0)}{n!} (x - x_0)^n \qquad (j = 1, 2, \ldots, m). \tag{1.14}$$

If we hold these series to terms of order $\leqslant N$, we obtain the approximate solution
$$y_{jN}(x) = \sum_{n=0}^{N} \frac{y_j^{(n)}(x_0)}{n!} (x - x_0)^n \qquad (j = 1, 2, \ldots, m). \tag{1.15}$$

The values of $y_j^{(n)}(x_0)$ are obtained from initial conditions (1.13), Eqs. (1.12), and relations obtained by differentiating these equations with subsequent substitution of $x = x_0$.

EXAMPLE 3. Solve the Cauchy problem for the system
$$y' = x + z^2, \quad z' = y^2 \tag{1.16}$$
with the initial conditions
$$y \big|_{x=0} = 1, \quad z \big|_{x=0} = 0. \tag{1.17}$$

For the sake of economy, we will limit the discussion to a rough approximation and set $N = 2$ in (1.15), so that
$$y(x) \approx y_2(x) = y(0) + xy'(0) + \frac{x^2}{2} y''(0),$$
$$z(x) \approx z_2(x) = z(0) + xz'(0) + \frac{x^2}{2} z''(0).$$

Initial conditions (1.17) and Eqs. (1.16) yield

$$y(0) = 1, \quad y'(0) = 0, \quad z(0) = 0, \quad z'(0) = 1.$$

Differentiating Eqs. (1.16), we find that

$$y'' = 1 + 2zz', \quad z'' = 2yy'$$

so that

$$y''(0) = 1, \quad z''(0) = 0$$

and, finally,

$$y_2(x) = 1 + \frac{x^2}{2}, \qquad z_2(x) = x,$$

It is possible to find a domain of convergence (not generally the largest) for Series (1.14). Let $f_j(x, y_1, y_2, \ldots, y_m)$ $(j = 1, 2, \ldots, m)$ be analytic in the region

$$|x - x_0| \leqslant \alpha, \quad |y_1 - y_{10}| \leqslant \beta,$$

$$|y_2 - y_{20}| \leqslant \beta, \ldots, |y_m - y_{m0}| \leqslant \beta$$

in the domain of the complex variables $x, y_1, y_2, \ldots, y_m$, and assume that

$$|f_j(x, y_1, y_2, \ldots, y_m)| \leqslant \mu$$

in this same region. Then Series (1.14) converges [120] in the disk $|x - x_0| \leqslant \rho$, where

$$\rho = \min\left(\alpha, \frac{\beta}{\mu}\right).$$

1.2 The method of successive approximations. (a) *First-Order Equations.* Consider the Cauchy problem for Eq. (1.1) under initial condition (1.2). We will no longer assume that the function $f(x, y)$ in the right-hand side of Eq. (1.1) is analytic; instead, we will consider the more general case, in which, in the closed rectangle defined by the inequalities

$$|x - x_0| \leqslant a, \quad |y - y_0| \leqslant b, \tag{1.18}$$

in the (x, y) plane, where a and b are positive constants, the function $f(x, y)$ is continuous and satisfies the Lipschitz condition relative to y:

$$|f(x, y_1) - f(x, y_2)| \leqslant K|y_1 - y_2|, \quad K = \text{const}. \tag{1.19}$$

It is known that the Lipschitz condition (1.19) is satisfied if the derivative $\partial f/\partial y$ of the function $f(x, y)$ is such that $\left|\dfrac{\partial f}{\partial y}\right| \leqslant K$.

Since $f(x, y)$ is continuous in the closed region (1.18), it is bounded there: there exists a constant M such that if x and y satisfy inequalities (1.18), then $|f(x, y)| \leqslant M$.

It is known (see [93], Paragraph 51, or [99]) that if $f(x, y)$ satisfies the requirements we have just stated, a solution for Cauchy problem (1.1)–(1.2) exists and is unique in the interval

$$|x - x_0| \leqslant c, \qquad c = \min \left(a, \frac{b}{M} \right). \tag{1.20}$$

This solution can be found as the limit of the sequence of successive approximations constructed with the recurrence relation

$$y_n(x) = y_0 + \int_{x_0}^{x} f(t, y_{n-1}(t)) \, dt. \tag{1.21}$$

The initial approximation can be selected arbitrarily, and it is simplest to use y_0 for this purpose.

We now fix some number n and take the right-hand side of Formula (1.21) for the approximate solution, thus obtaining the approximate equation

$$y(x) \approx y_n(x) = y_0 + \int_{x_0}^{x} f(t, y_{n-1}(t)) \, dt. \tag{1.22}$$

The error can be estimated with the inequality

$$|y(x) - y_n(x)| \leqslant \frac{M}{K} \frac{(Kc)^n}{n!}. \tag{1.23}$$

It is, however, necessary to remember that estimate (1.23) tends to be extremely pessimistic; in using the method of successive approximations it is usual to take an n for which y_{n-1} and y_n coincide to within the permissible error.

A disadvantage of the method of successive approximations is the necessity of evaluating integrals that depend on a parameter.

EXAMPLE 4: We will apply the method of successive approximations to Problem (1.8). As we noted in Example 1, this problem has a solution everywhere in the closed interval $|x| \leqslant 1/2^{1/2}$. In this case, the solution also lies within the interval $|y| \leqslant 1/2^{1/2}$.

We will now estimate the constant K in the Lipschitz condition (more briefly, the *Lipschitz constant*) for the function $f(x, y) = x^2 + y^2$: in the rectangle

$$|x| \leqslant \frac{1}{\sqrt{2}}, \qquad |y| \leqslant \frac{1}{\sqrt{2}}$$

$$K = \max_{|x| \leqslant \frac{1}{\sqrt{2}}, \; |y| \leqslant \frac{1}{\sqrt{2}}} \frac{\partial f}{\partial y} = \sqrt{2}.$$

To apply the method of successive approximations to problem (1.8), we choose $y_0 = y(0) = 0$ as the initial approximation. Then

$$y_1(x) = \int_0^x t^2 \, dt = \frac{1}{3} x^3,$$

$$y_2(x) = \int_0^x \left(t^2 + \frac{1}{9} t^6 \right) dt = \frac{1}{3} x^3 + \frac{1}{63} x^7,$$

$$y_3(x) = \int_0^x \left(t^2 + \frac{1}{9} t^6 + \frac{2}{189} t^{10} + \frac{1}{3969} t^{14} \right) dt$$

$$= \frac{1}{3} x^3 + \frac{1}{63} x^7 + \frac{2}{2079} x^{11} + \frac{1}{59,535} x^{15}.$$

When $|x| \leqslant 1/\sqrt{2}$ the difference between $y_2(x)$ and $y_3(x)$ is sufficiently small, i.e., does not exceed

$$\frac{2}{2079} \left(\frac{1}{\sqrt{2}} \right)^{11} + \frac{1}{59,535} \left(\frac{1}{\sqrt{2}} \right)^{15} < 0.000022,$$

and we can set

$$y(x) \approx y_2(x) = \tfrac{1}{3} x^3 + \tfrac{1}{63} x^7,$$

which coincides with the approximate solution obtained with Taylor's formula.

Formula (1.23) yields

$$|y(x) - y_3(x)| \leqslant \frac{1}{3! \sqrt{2}} = 0.118,$$

which, as we will see below, is considerably larger than the real error.

(b) *Differential Equations of Order Greater Than One.* This case can easily be reduced to the case of a system of first-order differential equations.

(c) *Systems of First-Order Differential Equations.* For Cauchy Problem (1.12)–(1.13), successive approximations can be computed with the formula

$$y_{jn}(x) = y_{j0} + \int_{x_0}^x f_j(t, y_{1,n-1}(t), y_{2,n-1}(t), \ldots, y_{m,n-1}(t)) \, dt \quad (1.24)$$

$$(j = 1, 2, \ldots, m)$$

Here it is assumed that the functions f_j are continuous and satisfy the Lipschitz condition relative to the variables y_k in the parallelepiped

$$|x - x_0| \leqslant a, \quad |y_j - y_{j0}| \leqslant b \quad (j = 1, 2, \ldots, m).$$

If M is a constant such that in this parallelepiped

$$|f_j(x, y_1, y_2, \ldots, y_m)| \leqslant M,$$

Problem (1.12)–(1.13) has a solution in the interval (1.20), and in this interval the successive approximations uniformly converge to the solution.

Fixing some n we obtain the approximate solution

$$y_j(x) \approx y_{jn}(x) = y_{j0} + \int_{x_0}^{x} f_j(t, y_{1,n-1}(t), y_{2,n-1}(t), \ldots, y_{m,n-1}(t)) \, dt \quad (1.25)$$

$$(j = 1, 2, \ldots, m);$$

the error of this approximation can be estimated with the inequality

$$|y_j(x) - y_{jn}(x)| \leqslant \frac{M}{K} \frac{(mKc)^n}{n!}. \tag{1.26}$$

1.3 Chaplygin's method. Here we will limit the discussion to the case of first-order equations. Consider Cauchy Problem (1.1)–(1.2) and assume that the right-hand side $f(x, y)$, of the equation satisfies the conditions of Paragraph 1.2. Moreover, assume that $y = y(x)$ is the solution of our Cauchy problem; in the (x, y) plane, this solution is a curve passing through the point $M_0(x_0, y_0)$. At the basis of this method lies

Chaplygin's theorem. If curves $y = u(x)$ and $y = v(x)$ pass through a point M_0, and if the differential inequalities

$$u'(x) - f(x, u(x)) < 0,$$

$$v'(x) - f((x, v(x))) > 0, \quad x > x_0, \tag{1.27}$$

hold, then

$$u(x) < y(x) < v(x) \tag{1.28}$$

for all $x > x_0$.

Thus, if it has been possible to find two functions, $u(x)$ and $v(x)$, satisfying inequalities (1.27), and the equations $u(x_0) = v(x_0) = y_0$, a two-sided estimate for the desired function $y(x)$ will have been obtained. The method then proceeds by improving this estimate as fast as it was obtained. We assume that the second derivative $\partial^2 f/\partial^2 y$ does not change sign in the rectangle (1.18). In the (x, y, z) space we consider the surface $z = f(x, y)$ and the curves along which it intersects the planes $x = \text{const}$; these curves always either have their convexity directed downward, if $\partial^2 f/\partial^2 y > 0$, or have their convexity directed upwards, if $\partial^2 f/\partial y^2 < 0$. Consequently, any arc along this curve lies between its cord and a tangent drawn through an arbitrary point on the arc. On the curve $z = f(x, y)$, $x = \text{const}$, we take the arc corresponding to the values of y in the interval $u(x) \leqslant y \leqslant v(x)$, and we write the equations of the cord and the tangent drawn through the point $y = u(x)$:

$$z = f(x, u(x)) + \frac{f(x, v(x)) - f(x, u(x))}{v(x) - u(x)} (y - u(x)) = M(x)y + N(x),$$

$$z = f(x, u(x)) + f_y(x, u(x))(y - u(x)) = \tilde{M}(x)y + \tilde{N}(x).$$

The curve is located between the tangent and its cord, which means that the function $f(x, y)$ lies between the functions $M(x)y + N(x)$ and $\tilde{M}(x)y + \tilde{N}(x)$. If we assume, for example, that $\partial^2 f/\partial y^2 > 0$, we find that the curve lies below the cord and above the tangent, i.e.,

$$\tilde{M}(x)y + \tilde{N}(x) < f(x, y) < M(x)y + N(x).$$

We write the linear first-order differential equations

$$y' = \tilde{M}(x)y + \tilde{N}(x), \quad y' = M(x)y + N(x),$$

and we find integrals (this is not difficult) that satisfy initial condition (1.2); let these integrals be $y = u_1(x)$ and $y = v_1(x)$. It turns out that we have the inequalities

$$u(x) < u_1(x) < y(x) < v_1(x) < v(x), \tag{1.29}$$

which show that the new functions $u_1(x)$ and $v_1(x)$ yield more exact approximations of the unknown function $y(x)$. Now, beginning with the approximations $u_1(x)$ and $v_1(x)$, we can construct new, still more accurate approximations $u_2(x)$ and $v_2(x)$, etc. The process converges very rapidly, for we have the inequality

$$v_n(x) - u_n(x) \leqslant \frac{C}{2^{2^n}}, \tag{1.30}$$

where C depends on neither x nor n.

There is another method (see [2]) for refining the approximations $u(x)$ and $v(x)$. In this method the assumption is not required that the second derivative $\partial^2 f/\partial y^2$ does not change sign. Let K be the Lipschitz constant of the function $f(x, y)$ [see Formula (1.19)], Then the functions

$$\left.\begin{array}{l} u_1(x) = u(x) + \displaystyle\int_{x_0}^{x} e^{-K(x-t)}[\, f(t, u(t)) - u'(t)]\, dt, \\[3mm] v_1(x) = v(x) - \displaystyle\int_{x_0}^{x} e^{-K(x-t)}[v'(t) - f(t, v(t))]\, dt \end{array}\right\} \tag{1.31}$$

satisfy inequalities (1.29). As above, we can construct a sequence of improving approximations $u_n(x)$, $v_n(x)$, by repeatedly applying formula (1.31); and, as before, $u_n(x)$ and $v_n(x)$ uniformly approach $y(x)$ as $n \to \infty$, but the rate of convergence is less than the rate given by Formula (1.30).

The fundamental difficulty in applying Chaplygin's method lies in construction of the initial pair of approximations $u(x)$ and $v(x)$ for the literature does not contain prescriptions for constructing such approximations.

EXAMPLE 5:   We will use Chaplygin's method to solve Problem (1.8), assuming that a solution is to be found in the interval $0 < x \leqslant 1/\sqrt{2}$.

It is not difficult to see that we can set

$$u(x) = \tfrac{1}{3}x^3, \quad v(x) = \tfrac{11}{30}x^3.$$

Indeed,

$$u'(x) - x^2 - u^2(x) = -\tfrac{1}{9}x^6 < 0,$$

$$v'(x) - x^2 - v^2(x) = \tfrac{1}{10}x^2 - \tfrac{121}{900}x^6 = (\tfrac{1}{91} - \tfrac{121}{900}x^4)x^2$$

$$\geqslant (\tfrac{1}{10} - \tfrac{121}{900} \cdot \tfrac{1}{4})x^2 > 0.06x^2 > 0.$$

Computation of the functions $M(x)$, $N(x)$, $\tilde{M}(x)$, and $\tilde{N}(x)$ presents no difficulty:

$$M(x) = \tfrac{7}{10}x^3, \qquad N(x) = x^2 - \tfrac{11}{90}x^6,$$

$$\tilde{M}(x) = \tfrac{2}{3}x^3, \qquad \tilde{N}(x) = x^2 - \tfrac{1}{9}x^6.$$

In our case $\partial^2 f/\partial y^2 = 2 > 0$ and, consequently, $u_1(x)$ and $v_1(x)$ are the integrals of the equations

$$u_1' = \tfrac{2}{3}x^3 y + x^2 - \tfrac{1}{9}x^6,$$

$$v_1' = \tfrac{7}{10}x^3 y + x^2 - \tfrac{11}{90}x^6,$$

that vanish at $x = 0$. These integrals are

$$u_1(x) = e^{(1/6)x^4} \int_0^x \left(z^2 - \frac{1}{9}z^6\right) e^{-(1/6)z^4}\, dz,$$

$$v_1(x) = e^{(7/40)x^4} \int_0^x \left(z^2 - \frac{11}{90}z^6\right) e^{-(7/40)z^4}\, dz$$

Expanding the exponential functions in power series and preserving terms of only up to 11-th order in x and z, we find that

$$u_1(x) \approx \bar{u}_1(x) = \frac{x^3}{3} + \frac{x^7}{63} + \frac{2}{2079}x^{11},$$

$$v_1(x) \approx \bar{v}_1(x) = \frac{x^3}{3} + \frac{x^7}{63} + \frac{1}{990}x^{11};$$

the value of $\bar{u}_1(x)$ coincides with the value of $y_3(x)$, obtained by the method of successive approximations, up to terms of order greater than 11.

The functions $\bar{u}_1(x)$ and $\bar{v}_1(x)$ also form the Chaplygin boundaries for the desired solution, since

$$\bar{u}_1' - x^2 - \frac{\bar{u}_1^2}{\bar{u}_1^2} = -\left[\left(\frac{1}{63^2} + \frac{4}{3 \cdot 2079}\right)x^{14} + \frac{4}{63 \cdot 2079}x^{18} + \frac{4}{2079^2}x^{22}\right] < 0,$$

$$\bar{v}_1' - x^2 - \bar{v}_1^2 = \frac{x^{10}}{9}\left\{\frac{1}{210} - \left[\left(\frac{1}{21^2} + \frac{1}{165}\right)x^4 + \frac{2}{7 \cdot 990}x^8 + \frac{1}{330^2}x^{12}\right]\right\}$$

for $0 < x \leqslant 1/\sqrt{2}$.

The derivative of the expression in braces is negative when $0 < x \leqslant 1/\sqrt{2}$, and the indicated expression is minimal when $x = 1/\sqrt{2}$, so

$$v_1' - x^2 - \bar{v}_1^2 \geqslant \frac{x^{10}}{9}\left[\frac{1}{210} - \left(\frac{1}{441} + \frac{1}{165}\right)\frac{1}{4} - \frac{1}{7\cdot 990}\cdot\frac{1}{8} - \frac{1}{330^2}\cdot\frac{1}{64}\right] > 0.$$

It follows that

$$\frac{x^3}{3} + \frac{x^7}{63} + \frac{2}{2079}x^{11} < y(x) < \frac{x^3}{3} + \frac{x^7}{63} + \frac{1}{990}x^{11}, \quad 0 < x < \frac{1}{\sqrt{2}}.$$

If either of the functions $\bar{u}_1(x)$ or $\bar{v}_1(x)$ is taken for the approximate solution of Problem (1.8), the error in the approximation is no larger than

$$\left(\frac{1}{990} - \frac{2}{2079}\right)x^{11} \leqslant \frac{1}{20,790}\frac{1}{\sqrt{2^{11}}} \approx 0.000001,$$

which is considerably less than the value given by Formula (1.23) in Paragraph 1.2.

By starting with the approximations $u(x) = \dfrac{x^3}{3}$, $v(x) = \dfrac{11}{30}x^3$, we can also construct more exact approximations with Formulas (1.32). Recalling that the Lipschitz constant for this case is $K = \sqrt{2}$, we find that

$$u_1(x) = \frac{x^3}{3} + \frac{1}{9}\int_0^x t^6 e^{-\sqrt{2}(x-t)}\,dt,$$

$$v(x) = \frac{11}{30}x^3 - \int_0^x\left(\frac{t^2}{10} - \frac{121}{900}t^6\right)e^{-\sqrt{2}(x-t)}\,dt;$$

evaluation of these integrals is elementary, and hence we omit it.

1.4 The Newton-Kantorovich method. By this we mean the well-known method developed by Kantorovich for solution of very general nonlinear problems. This method goes back to Newton's method of tangents for solution of algebraic equations. The special property of the method lies in the fact that if some not-too-crude initial approximation to the solution of a given problem is presented, it is possible to construct increasingly accurate approximations that are each obtained as the solution of some *linear* equation.

The Newton-Kantorovich method is discussed in detail in [23] and [24]. Thus instead of considering the foundations of the method, we will limit our discussion to techniques for applying it and the conditions required for convergence in the Cauchy problem for one first-order differential equation [Problem (1.1)–(1.2)] or systems of such equations [Problem (1.12)–(1.13)].

(a) *One First-Order Differential Equation.* Assuming that some function $y_0(x)$ satisfies initial condition (1.2), so that $y_0(x_0) = y_0$, we will treat this function as the initial approximation to the solution $y(x)$ of Problem (1.1)–(1.2). The next approximation $y_1(x)$ is constructed as the integral of the linear equation

$$y_1' - f_y(x, y_0(x))y_1 = f(x, y_0(x)) - f_y(x, y_0(x))y_0(x),$$

that satisfies initial condition (1.2); more generally, if the approximation $y_n(x)$ is constructed, the following approximation, $y_{n+1}(x)$, is constructed as the integral of the linear equation

$$y_{n+1}' - f_y(x, y_n(x))y_{n+1} = f(x, y_n(x)) - f_y(x, y_n(x))y_n(x) \qquad (1.32)$$

that satisfies condition (1.2.) It is very simple to construct such an integral: If we write

$$f_y(x, y_n(x)) = p_n(x),$$

$$f(x, y_n(x)) - f_y(x, y_n(x))y_n(x) = q_n(x),$$

then

$$y_{n+1}(x) = e^{\int_{x_0}^{x} p_n(t)\,dt}\left\{ y_0 + \int_{x_0}^{x} q_n(z)\, e^{-\int_{x_0}^{z} p_n(t)\,dt}\, dz \right\}. \qquad (1.33)$$

We will now present a condition for convergence of the method and estimate the error in the approximate solution $y_n(x)$. We assume that in rectangle (1.18) the function $f(x, y)$ and its derivatives $f_y(x, y)$ and $f_{y^2}(x, y)$ are continuous and, consequently, bounded; let

$$|f_y(x, y)| \leqslant M_1, \quad |f_{y^2}(x, y)| \leqslant M_2.$$

We also assume that the initial approximation $y_0(x)$ is defined when $|x - x_0| \leqslant a$ and that $|y_0(x) - y_0| \leqslant b$. Notation:

$$\rho = \max_{|x-x_0|\leqslant a} \left| y_0(x) - y_0 - \int_{x_0}^{x} f(t, y_0(t))\, dt \right|. \qquad (1.34)$$

If the initial approximation is close to the exact solution, ρ is small. We also set

$$\gamma = a\rho M_2 e^{2M_1 a}. \qquad (1.35)$$

Assume that the inequalities

$$\gamma \leqslant \tfrac{1}{2} \qquad (1.36)$$

and

$$\frac{2\rho}{1 + \sqrt{1 - 2\gamma}} \leqslant b \qquad (1.37)$$

are satisfied. Then the successive approximations (1.33) constructed with the Newton-Kantorovich method satisfy the inequality $|y_n(x) - y_0| \leqslant b$ and uniformly converge to the exact solution of the problem in the interval $|x - x_0| \leqslant a$; the rate of convergence can be estimated with the inequality

$$|y_n(x) - y(x)| \leqslant \frac{1}{2^{n-1}} (2\gamma)^{2^n - 1}\, \rho. \qquad (1.38)$$

The Newton-Kantorovich method also makes it possible to estimate how far the exact solution is from the initial approximation. We have the inequality

$$|y(x) - y_0(x)| \leqslant \frac{2\rho}{1 + \sqrt{1 - 2\gamma}}. \tag{1.39}$$

EXAMPLE 6:   We will apply the Newton-Kantorovich method to Problem (1.8), constructing the solution on the segment $|x| \leqslant \dfrac{1}{\sqrt{2}}$.

For the initial approximation we take

$$y_0(x) = \frac{x^3}{3}.$$

Then

$$\rho = \max_{|x| \leqslant \frac{1}{\sqrt{2}}} \left| \frac{x^3}{3} - \int_0^x \left(t^2 + \frac{t^6}{9} \right) dt \right| = \frac{2^{-7/2}}{63} = 0.0014,$$

$$M_1 = \max_{|y| \leqslant \frac{1}{\sqrt{2}}} |2y| = \sqrt{2} = 1.4142, \quad M_2 = 2.$$

It follows that

$$\gamma = \frac{1}{\sqrt{2}} 0.0014 \cdot 2 \cdot e^2 = 0.015.$$

We will now compute the first approximation with the Newton-Kantorovich method. We have

$$p_0(x) = \tfrac{2}{3}x^3, \quad q_0(x) = x^2 - \tfrac{1}{9}x^6$$

and, by Formula (1.33),

$$y_1(x) = e^{(1/6)x^4} \int_0^x \left(z^2 - \frac{1}{9} z^6 \right) e^{-z^4/6} \, dz.$$

By Formula (1.38) the error in this approximation is no larger than

$$0.03 \cdot 0.0014 = 0.000042.$$

The approximation $y_1(x)$ that we have constructed coincides with the expression for $u_1(x)$ obtained above with Chaplygin's method. Recall that with accuracy up to terms of order no less than 11, we have

$$u_1(x) = \frac{x^3}{3} + \frac{x^7}{63}$$

and that the last expression coincides with the second approximation obtained above with the method of successive approximations.

The Newton-Kantorovich method sometimes permits solution of the Cauchy problem in an interval larger than the interval permitted by the method of successive approximations.

In the above example, therefore, consider the function $f(x, y) = x^3 + y^2$ in the square $|x| \leqslant 1$, $|y| \leqslant 1$. Then $M_1 = 2$, and $M_2 = 2$. For the initial approximation we take the function $\dfrac{x^3}{3} + \dfrac{x^7}{63}$. This yields

$$\max_{|x| \leqslant 1} \left| \frac{x^3}{3} + \frac{x^7}{63} - \int_0^x \left(t^2 + \frac{t^6}{9} + \frac{2t^{10}}{189} + \frac{t^{14}}{3969} \right) dt \right| = \frac{2}{2079} + \frac{1}{59{,}535} < 0.001,$$

and we can set $\rho = 0.001$. Now,

$$\gamma = 0.001 \cdot 1 \cdot 2 \cdot e^4 < 0.110;$$

from which it follows that

$$\frac{2\rho}{1 + \sqrt{1 - 2\gamma}} < \frac{2 \cdot 0.001}{1 + \sqrt{1 - 0.220}} < 0.00107.$$

It is now clear that our problem can be solved when $|x| \leqslant 1$, and that the solution lies within the interval defined by the inequality

$$\left| y(x) - \frac{x^3}{3} - \frac{x^7}{63} \right| \leqslant 0.00107.$$

(b) *Systems of First-Order Equations.* We consider Problem (1.12)–(1.13), choosing a system of functions $y_{1,0}(x)$, $y_{2,0}(x)$, ..., $y_{m,0}(x)$, satisfying initial conditions (1.13), and we will treat this system as the initial approximation to the exact solution of the problem. Then the first Newton-Kantorovich approximation is the integral of the system of linear differential equations

$$y'_{j,1} - \sum_{k=1}^m \left(\frac{\partial f_j}{\partial y_k} \right)_0 y_{k,1} = (f_j)_0 - \sum_{k=1}^m \left(\frac{\partial f_j}{\partial y_k} \right)_0 y_{k,0} \qquad (1.40)$$

$$(j = 1, 2, \ldots, m),$$

that satisfies initial conditions (1.13); the symbol $(\ )_0$ indicates that $y_{1,0}(x)$, $y_{2,0}(x)$, ..., $y_{m,0}(x)$ are substituted for $y_1(x)$, $y_2(x)$, ..., $y_m(x)$. If $y_{j,n}(x)$ $(j = 1, 2, \ldots, m)$ have already been constructed, then the $(n + 1)$-th approximation $y_{j,n+1}(x)$ is the integral of the linear system

$$y'_{j,n+1} - \sum_{k=1}^m \left(\frac{\partial f_j}{\partial y_k} \right)_n y_{k,n+1} = (f_j)_n - \sum_{k=1}^m \left(\frac{\partial f_j}{\partial y_k} \right)_n y_{k,n} \qquad (1.41)$$

$$(j = 1, 2, \ldots, m);$$

that satisfies conditions (1.13); by analogy to the preceding case, the symbol $(\ )_n$ indicates that $y_{j,n}(x)$ has been substituted for $y_j(x)$.

Generally speaking, the coefficients of system (1.41) are variable, and integration of this sytem is rather difficult. Application of the Newton-Kantorovich method to system (1.12) may prove to be rather difficult, even more so because the matrix $(\partial f_j/\partial y_k)_n$ changes in each step. However, this last difficulty can be eliminated by using the *modified Newton-Kantorovich method*. In this method the $(n + 1)$-th approximation to the solution of Problem (1.12)–(1.13) is constructed as the solution of the linear system

$$y'_{j,n+1} - \sum_{k=1}^{m} \left(\frac{\partial f_j}{\partial y_k}\right)_0 y_{k,n+1} = (f_j)_n - \sum_{k=1}^{n} \left(\frac{\partial f_j}{\partial y_k}\right)_0 y_{k,n} \qquad (1.42)$$

that satisfies the initial conditions; only the slack terms of system (1.42) change with n.

In view of their obvious cumbersomeness, we will not present conditions for convergence or estimates of the error for a system.

1.5 The method of small parameters. This method has been applied in a large variety of forms, so we will present only two of them, and the second only by example.

Given an equation

$$y' = f(x, y; \lambda), \qquad (1.43)$$

whose right-hand side depends on, in addition to x and y, some parameter λ, assume that it is required to find the integral of this equation that satisfies the initial condition $y|_{x=x_0} = y_0$. We assume that the solution $y = \varphi(x)$ of this problem is known for $\lambda = \lambda_0$. The substitutions

$$\tilde{x} = x - x_0, \quad \tilde{y} = y - \varphi(x), \quad \tilde{\lambda} = \lambda - \lambda_0$$

does lead to the case in which $x_0 = y_0 = \lambda_0 = 0$ and $\varphi(x) \equiv 0$; we will therefore immediately assume that Eq. (1.43) must be solved under the initial condition

$$y|_{x=0} = 0 \qquad (1.44)$$

and that, at $\lambda = 0$, the desired solution is $y \equiv 0$. Among other things, it follows that we must have $f(x, 0; 0) \equiv 0$.

We now assume that the function $f(x, y; \lambda)$ can be expanded in a power series in y and λ, that converges close to $y = 0$ and $\lambda = 0$:

$$f(x, y; \lambda) = \sum_{j,k=0}^{\infty} a_{jk}(x) y^j \lambda^k, \quad a_{00} = 0.$$

We will attempt to find the solution of Problem (1.43)–(1.44) in the form of a series

$$y(x) = \sum_{k=1}^{\infty} \lambda^k y_k(x);$$

this series begins with the first power of λ, since $y(x) \equiv 0$ when $\lambda = 0$. It follows from condition (1.44) that we have the initial conditions

$$y_k|_{x=0} = 0 \qquad (k = 1, 2, \ldots). \qquad (1.44')$$

Substituting the last series into Eq. (1.43) and equating coefficients of like powers of λ on the left and right, we find that

$$y'_1 = a_{10}(x)y_1 + a_{01}(x),$$
$$y'_2 = a_{10}(x)y_2 + a_{20}y_1^2 + a_{11}y_1 + a_{02},$$

etc. In general, the kth equation is of the form

$$y'_k = a_{10}(x)y_k + u_k(x),$$

where, in addition to x, $y_k^{(x)}$ depends on $y_1(x), \ldots, y_{k-1}(x)$.

We find $y_1(x)$ by solving the first equation under the initial condition $y_1|_{x=0} = 0$. We substitute $y_1(x)$ into the second equation and integrate under the initial condition $y_2|_{x=0} = 0$, thus finding $y_2(x)$, etc.

The method we have presented easily extends to systems of differential equations and to higher-order equations, as well as to the case in which the equation (or system of equations) contains more than one parameter.

EXAMPLE 7 [31]:   Consider the second-order equation

$$y'' + (1 + 0.1 \cdot x)y + 0.1 \cdot y'^2 = 0 \tag{1.45}$$

under the initial conditions

$$y|_{x=0} = 1, \quad y'|_{x=0} = 2.$$

We replace the given differential equation by the following more general equation, which contains two parameters α and β:

$$y'' + y + \alpha xy + \beta y'^2 = 0; \tag{1.46}$$

the given equation is obtained from Eq. (1.46) by setting $\alpha = \beta = 0.1$. We obtain the first approximation from the equation obtained with $\alpha = \beta = 0$:

$$y'' + y = 0.$$

Its integral satisfying the initial conditions is $y_1 = \cos x + 2 \sin x$. The next approximation is taken in the form $y_2 = y_1 + \eta_1$, where η_1 is a linear function of the parameters α and β:

$$\eta_1 = -\alpha p(x) - \beta q(x).$$

We substitute y_2 for y in Eq. (1.46) and retain only terms of first order with respect to the parameters. Setting the factors containing α and β equal to zero, we obtain linear equations for $p(x)$ and $q(x)$:

$$p'' + p = x \cos x + 2x \sin x;$$
$$q'' + q = \tfrac{5}{2} + \tfrac{3}{2} \cos 2x - 2\sin 2x.$$

These equations must be integrated under the initial conditions

$$x = 0, \quad p = p' = q = q' = 0,$$

which yields

$$p(x) = -\tfrac{1}{2}x^2 \cos x + \tfrac{1}{4}x \cos x + \tfrac{1}{4}x^2 \sin x + \tfrac{1}{2}x \sin x - \tfrac{1}{4} \sin x,$$
$$q(x) = -2 \cos x - \tfrac{4}{3} \sin x - \tfrac{1}{2} \cos 2x + \tfrac{2}{3} \sin 2x + \tfrac{5}{2}.$$

To construct the next approximation we represent it in the form $y_3 = y_2 + \eta_2$, where η_2 is a quadratic function of the parameters:

$$\eta_2 = \alpha^2 P(x) + \alpha\beta Q(x) + \beta^2 R(x).$$

Substituting y_3 for y in Eq. (1.46) and equating the coefficients containing α^2, $\alpha\beta$, and β^2, to zero, we obtain linear equations for $P(x)$, $Q(x)$, and $R(x)$. These equations must be integrated under the initial conditions

$$x = 0, \quad P = P' = Q = Q' = R = R' = 0.$$

This process can be continued.

1.6 Estimating errors in terms of residuals. Let $Y(x)$ be a function that, for one reason or another, we can treat as an approximate solution of Cauchy Problem (1.1)–(1.2). We will call the difference $\Delta(x) = Y(x) - y(x)$ the *error of the approximate solution* $Y(x)$, and the difference $\tau(x) = Y'(x) - f(x, Y(x))$ its *residual;* $y(x)$ denotes the exact solution of the problem. It turns out that under certain conditions, it is possible to estimate the error of the approximate solution in terms of its residual, which, of course, is a known function of x.

Assume that we have been able to find a function $A(x)$ that is continuous on the segment $x_0 \leqslant x \leqslant x_0 + a$, and is such that in this segment the inequality

$$f_y(x, y(x)) \leqslant A(x) \tag{1.47}$$

holds, where, as we have already noted, $y(x)$ denotes the exact solution of our problem. We write the linear equation

$$\frac{dz}{dx} = A(x)z + |\tau(x)|$$

and find its integral $z(x)$ that, when $x = x_0$ takes the value $|Y(x_0) - y_0|$. Then, on the segment $x_0 \leqslant x \leqslant x_0 + a$, we have the estimate

$$|\Delta(x)| \leqslant z(x). \tag{1.48}$$

In the general case, it is difficult to use estimate (1.48) because the function $A(x)$, in terms of which $z(x)$ is represented, must satisfy inequality (1.47), whose left-hand side is unknown.

2. NUMERICAL METHODS

In Section 1 we considered analytic approximate methods for solving the Cauchy problem. In the present section we will consider numerical methods, attempting to obtain solutions in the form of tables of approximate values of the unknown function $y(x)$ for a series of values of the independent variable x in the interval $x_0 \leqslant x \leqslant x_0 + a$. These values of x are either chosen before or selected successively as the approximate solution is constructed. We will call these values of the variable x pivot points and denote them by $x_0, x_1, x_2, \ldots, x_N$, assuming that $x_n < x_{n+1}$. Here y_n will denote the approximate value of $y(x_n)$, where $y(x)$ is the exact solution of the Cauchy problem.

For $y(x)$ we have the equation

$$y(x_0) = y_0, \qquad y(x_{n+1}) = y(x_n) + \int_{x_n}^{x_{n+1}} f(t, y(t))\, dt$$

$$(n = 0, 1, \ldots, N - 1).$$

(1.49)

The numerical methods discussed below for solution of the Cauchy problem differ from each other fundamentally in their approach to the approximate evaluation of the integral in Formula (1.49).

2.1 Euler's method. The quantity $h_n = x_{n+1} - x_n$ is usually called the *integration increment* and is chosen sufficiently small. Euler's method consists in the fact that in the interval $x_n \leqslant t \leqslant x_n + h_n$ the function $f(t, y(t))$ is approximately replaced by a constant, $f(x_n, y_n)$, which is known, provided that x_n has been chosen and y_n has already been determined. Then, together with Eq. (1.49), we have the equation

$$y_{n+1} = y_n + h_n f(x_n, y_n) \quad (n = 0, 1, \ldots, N - 1), \tag{1.50}$$

which makes it possible to determine $y_1, y_2, \ldots, y_N$, if x_0 and y_0 are given and the pivot points have been selected.

2.2 The trapezoid method. Euler's method can be called the rectangle method, since substitution of the product $h_n f(x_n, y_n)$ for the integral in Eq. (1.49) is equivalent to replacing a curvilinear trapezoid under the graph of the function $f(t, y(t))$ by a rectangle. A more accurate technique is provided by substituting a rectilinear trapezoid for a curvilinear trapezoid, which leads to the equation

$$y_{n+1} = y_n + \frac{h_n}{2} \left[f(x_n, y_n) + f(x_{n+1}, y_{n+1}) \right]$$

$$(n = 0, 1, \ldots, N - 1).$$

(1.51)

If x_n, y_n, and x_{n+1} are known, Eq. (1.51) can be treated as an equation for determination of y_{n+1}. For sufficiently small h_n the set of roots of this equation has one closest to y_n, and we will denote this root by y_{n+1}. This root can be found by simple iteration. Various methods have been proposed for selection of the initial approximation $y_{n+1}^{(0)}$ [60], and the simplest of all is to use Formula (1.50) of Euler's method for this purpose. The next approximation is given by the formula

$$y_{n+1}^{(m)} = y_n + \frac{h_n}{2} [f(x_n, y_n) + f(x_{n+1}, y_{n+1}^{(m-1)})]$$

$$(m = 1, 2, \ldots).$$

(1.52)

Because h_n is small, a relatively small number of iterations is required for computation of y_{n+1} to the required accuracy.

2.3 The-Runge-Kutta method.   To simplify the notation, we will substitute x, y, and h for x_n, y_n, and h_n. Let $r \geqslant 2$ be a positive integer, $\alpha_1, \alpha_2, \ldots \alpha_{r-1}$ be positive numbers, and assume that the numbers $\beta_{sm}(s = 1, 2, \ldots, r - 1$; $m = 1, 2, \ldots, s)$ and $\gamma_1, \gamma_2, \ldots, \gamma_r$, satisfy the conditions

$$\sum_{m=1}^{s} \beta_{sm} = \alpha_s \qquad (s = 1, 2, \ldots, r - 1),$$

(1.53)

$$\sum_{j=1}^{r} \gamma_j = 1.$$

(1.54)

One step of the Runge-Kutta method (the transition form x_n to x_{n+1}) is as follows:

(1) One of the following r numbers is computed:

$$\left.\begin{aligned}
k_1 &= hf(\bar{x}, \bar{y}), \\
k_2 &= hf(\bar{x} + \alpha_1 h, \bar{y} + \beta_{11} k_1), \\
k_3 &= hf(\bar{x} + \alpha_2 h, \bar{y} + \beta_{21} k_1 + \beta_{22} k_2), \\
& \cdots \cdots \cdots \cdots \cdots \cdots \cdots \cdots \cdots \cdots \cdots \cdots \cdots \\
k_{j+1} &= hf(\bar{x} + \alpha_j h, \bar{y} + \beta_{j1} k_1 + \beta_{j2} k_2 + \cdots + \beta_{jj} k_j), \\
& \cdots \cdots \cdots \cdots \cdots \cdots \cdots \cdots \cdots \cdots \cdots \cdots \cdots \\
k_r &= hf(\bar{x} + \alpha_{r-1} h, \bar{y} + \beta_{r-1,1} k_1 + \beta_{r-1,2} k_2 + \cdots + \beta_{r-1,r-1} k_{r-1}).
\end{aligned}\right\}$$

(1.55)

(2) The sum

$$k = \sum_{i=1}^{r} \gamma_j k_j$$

(1.56)

is computed.

(3) y_{n+1} is computed with the formula

$$y_{n+1} = y_n + k.$$

(1.57)

The numbers α_s, β_{sm}, and γ_j for a given r are chosen so that, when treated as a function of h, the difference

$$\int_{\bar{x}}^{\bar{x}+h} (f(t, \tilde{y}(t)))\, dt - k$$

($\tilde{y}(x)$ is the solution of Eq. (1.1) that satisfies the condition $\tilde{y}(\bar{x}) = \bar{y}$), is as small as possible at some order l of h when $h \to 0$. Generally speaking, these requirements do not determine the numbers α_s, β_{sm}, and γ_j uniquely, and the need to keep Formulas (1.55) and (1.56) simple must be kept in mind when these numbers are selected. Below are examples of several systems of such numbers and the corresponding values of l:

(1) $r = 2$, $\alpha_1 = \beta_{11} = 1$, $\gamma_1 = \gamma_2 = \frac{1}{2}$, $l = 3$;

(2) $r = 2$, $\alpha_1 = \beta_{11} = \frac{1}{2}$, $\gamma_1 = 0$, $\gamma_2 = 1$, $l = 3$;

(3) $r = 3$, $\alpha_1 = \beta_{11} = \frac{1}{2}$, $\alpha_2 = 1$, $\beta_{21} = -1$, $\beta_{22} = 2$,

$$\gamma_1 = \gamma_3 = \tfrac{1}{6},\ \gamma_2 = \tfrac{2}{3},\ l = 4;$$

(4) $r = 3$, $\alpha_1 = \beta_{11} = \frac{1}{3}$, $\alpha_2 = \frac{2}{3}$, $\beta_{21} = 0$, $\beta_{22} = \frac{2}{3}$,

$$\gamma_1 = \tfrac{1}{4},\ \gamma_2 = 0,\ \gamma_3 = \tfrac{3}{8},\ l = 4;$$

(5) $r = 4$, $\alpha_1 = \beta_{11} = \frac{1}{2}$, $\alpha_2 = \beta_{22} = \frac{1}{2}$, $\beta_{21} = 0$, $\alpha_3 = \beta_{33} = 1$,

$$\beta_{31} = \beta_{32} = 0,\ \gamma_1 = \gamma_4 = \tfrac{1}{6},\ \gamma_2 = \gamma_3 = \tfrac{1}{3},\ l = 5;$$

(6) $r = 4$, $\alpha_1 = \beta_{11} = \frac{1}{3}$, $\alpha_2 = \frac{2}{3}$, $\beta_{21} = -\frac{1}{3}$, $\beta_{22} = 1$,

$$\alpha_3 = 1,\ \beta_{31} = \beta_{33} = 1,\ \beta_{32} = -1,$$

$$\gamma_1 = \gamma_4 = \tfrac{1}{8},\ \gamma_2 = \gamma_3 = \tfrac{3}{8},\ l = 5;$$

(7) $r = 6$, $\alpha_1 = \beta_{11} = \frac{1}{3}$, $\alpha_2 = \frac{2}{5}$, $\beta_{21} = \frac{4}{25}$, $\beta_{22} = \frac{6}{25}$,

$$\alpha, = 1,\ \beta_{31} = \tfrac{1}{4},\ \beta_{32} = -3,\ \beta_{34} = \tfrac{15}{4},$$

$$\alpha_4 = \tfrac{2}{3},\ \beta_{41} = \tfrac{6}{81},\ \beta_{42} = \tfrac{90}{81},\ \beta_{43} = -\tfrac{50}{18},\ \beta_{44} = \tfrac{8}{18},$$

$$\alpha_5 = \tfrac{4}{5},\ \beta_{51} = \tfrac{6}{75},\ \beta_{52} = \tfrac{36}{75},\ \beta_{53} = \tfrac{10}{75},\ \beta_{54} = \tfrac{8}{75},\ \beta_{55} = 0,$$

$$\gamma_1 = \tfrac{23}{192},\ \gamma_2 = 0,\ \gamma_3 = \tfrac{125}{192},\ \gamma_4 = 0,\ \gamma_5 = -\tfrac{81}{192},\ \gamma_6 = \tfrac{125}{192},$$

$$l = 7.$$

We have not given all known systems of such numbers.

Detailed discussions of the Runge-Kutta formulas may be found in [2] and [41].

System (7) was given in [60]. A more convenient system is (5). We will call the corresponding approach the fundamental Runge-Kutta method. Below is the sequence of computations for this case:

(1) $k_1^{(n)} = h_n f(x_n, y_n)$ is computed.

(2) $k_2^{(n)} = h_n f\left(x_n + \dfrac{h_n}{2}, y_n + \dfrac{k_1^{(n)}}{2}\right)$ is computed.

(3) $k_3^{(n)} = h_n f\left(x_n + \dfrac{h_n}{2}, y_n + \dfrac{k_2^{(n)}}{2}\right)$ is computed.

(4) $k_4^{(n)} = h_n f(x_n + h_n, y_n + k_3^{(n)})$ is computed.

(5) $k^{(n)} = \frac{1}{6}(k_1^{(n)} + 2k_2^{(n)} + 2k_3^{(n)} + k_4^{(n)})$ is computed.

(6) $y_{n+1} = y_n + k^{(n)}$ is computed.

We should also note case (2), which is sometimes called the improved Euler method; here the computation proceeds as follows:

(1) $k_1^{(n)} = h_n f(x_n, y_n)$;

(2) $k^{(n)} = k_2^{(n)} = h_n f\left(x_n + \dfrac{h_n}{2}, y_n + \dfrac{k_1^{(n)}}{2}\right)$;

(3) $y_{n+1} = y_n + k^{(n)}$.

In conclusion, we will present a computation scheme for Euler's method and the Runge-Kutta method for solution of the Cauchy problem for systems of first-order differential equations. For the sake of simplicity, we will limit the discussion to the case of two equations.

Let

$$\left.\begin{aligned} y' &= f(x, y, z), \\ z' &= g(x, y, z) \end{aligned}\right\} \tag{1.58}$$

be a system for which it is required to find the solution $y(x)$, $z(x)$, satisfying the condition

$$y\big|_{x=x_0} = y_0, \qquad z\big|_{x=x_0} = z_0. \tag{1.59}$$

(a) *Euler's Method.* The computation is carried out with the formulas

$$\left.\begin{aligned} y_{n+1} &= y_n + h_n f(x_n, y_n, z_n), \\ z_{n+1} &= z_n + h_n g(x_n, y_n, z_n) \\ &(n = 0, 1, 2, \ldots, N-1). \end{aligned}\right\} \tag{1.60}$$

(b) *The Fundamental Runge-Kutta Method.* The computation follows the formulas

(1) $k_1^{(n)} = h_n f(x_n, y_n, z_n),$

$\quad m_1^{(n)} = h_n g(x_n, y_n, z_n);$

(2) $k_2^{(n)} = h_n f\left(x_n + \dfrac{h_n}{2}, y_n + \dfrac{k_1^{(n)}}{2}, z_n + \dfrac{m_1^{(n)}}{2}\right),$

$\quad m_2^{(n)} = h_n g\left(x_n + \dfrac{h_n}{2}, y_n + \dfrac{k_1^{(n)}}{2}, z_n + \dfrac{m_1^{(n)}}{2}\right);$

(3) $k_3^{(n)} = h_n f\left(x_n + \dfrac{h_n}{2}, y_n + \dfrac{k_2^{(n)}}{2}, z_n + \dfrac{m_2^{(n)}}{2}\right),$

$\quad m_3^{(n)} = h_n g\left(x_n + \dfrac{h_n}{2}, y_n + \dfrac{k_2^{(n)}}{2}, z_n + \dfrac{m_2^{(n)}}{2}\right);$

(4) $k_4^{(n)} = h_4 f(x_n + h_n, y_n + k_3^{(n)}, z_n + m_3^{(n)}),$

$\quad m_4^{(n)} = h_n g(x_n + h_n, y_n + k_3^{(n)}, z_n + m_3^{(n)});$

(5) $k^{(n)} = \tfrac{1}{6}(k_1^{(n)} + 2k_2^{(n)} + 2k_3^{(n)} + k_4^{(n)}),$

$\quad m^{(n)} = \tfrac{1}{6}(m_1^{(n)} + 2m_2^{(n)} + 2m_3^{(n)} + m_4^{(n)});$

(6) $y_{n+1} = y_n + k^{(n)},$

$\quad z_{n+1} = z_n + m^{(n)}.$

The authors of [2, 30] considered other possible methods of Runge-Kutta computation for solution of systems of first-order equations and one equation of higher order.

EXAMPLE 8: For Cauchy Problem (1.8), find an approximate solution, using the fundamental Runge-Kutta method with $h = 0.1$.

The results of the computation are given in Table 1. The computation was carried out to six decimal places, and it can be seen that all of the digits are exact.

Table I

x_n	y_n	$k_1^{(n)}$	$k_2^{(n)}$	$k_3^{(n)}$	$k_4^{(n)}$	$k^{(n)}$
0.0	0.000000	0.000000	0.000250	0.000250	0.001000	0.000333
0.1	0.000333	0.001000	0.002250	0.002250	0.004001	0.002334
0.2	0.002667	0.004001	0.006252	0.006253	0.009008	0.006336
0.3	0.009003	0.009008	0.012268	0.012273	0.016045	0.012356
0.4	0.021359	0.016046	0.020336	0.020349	0.025174	0.020432
0.5	0.041791	0.025175	0.030546	0.030576	0.036524	0.030657
0.6	0.072448					

On the errors of Euler's method and the Runge-Kutta method. Let y_n be an approximate value of $y(x_n)$ [$y(x)$ is the exact solution of Problem (1.1)–(1.2)]. By $\tilde{y}_n(x)$ we denote the exact solution of Eq. (1.1) that becomes y_n when $x = x_n$, i.e., the exact solution that satisfies the condition $\tilde{y}_n(x_n) = y_n$. Then the difference

$$y_{n+1} - \tilde{y}_n(x_{n+1}) = y_{n+1} - \left[y_n + \int_{x_n}^{x_{n+1}} f(t, \tilde{y}_n(t))\, dt \right]$$

$$= (y_{n+1} - y_n) - \int_{x_n}^{x_{n+1}} f(t, \tilde{y}_n(t))\, dt$$

is called the error at the nth step in numerical integration. A simple estimate for this error is given below [30].

In what follows, $C_1, C_2, \ldots$ will denote positive constants determined by $f(x, y)$ and its derivatives in some neighborhood of the point (x_n, y_n).

For Euler's method,

$$|y_{n+1} - \tilde{y}_n(x_{n+1})| \leqslant C_1 h_n^2 .$$

For the fundamental Runge-Kutta method,

$$|y_{n+1} - \tilde{y}_n(x_{n+1})| \leqslant C_2 h_n^5.$$

Comparison of these estimates shows that for sufficiently small h_n the Runge-Kutta formula is, generally speaking, more accurate than Euler's method.

Error accumulates from step to step in numerical solution of the Cauchy problem: Even if y_0 is given exactly, y_1 is obtained with some error, which can be estimated as the error of one step; the deviation $y_2 - y(x_2)$ is due to the superimposition of errors in determination of y_1 and in determination of y_2 in terms of y_1 (the error in one step); the deviation $y_n - y(x_n)$ is the result of superposition of a large number of errors.

For Euler's method (under the assumption that $h_i = h = $ const), we have the estimate

$$|y_n - y(x_n)| \leqslant C_3 h (e^{C_4(x_n - x_0)} - 1),$$

from which it follows that $y_n \to y(x)$ uniformly as $h \to 0$ $(nh \to x)$. This estimate assumes that all computations required for determination of y_n are carried out exactly (without rounding off). There is no such simple estimate for the Runge-Kutta method. The author of [113] gave several estimates for the Runge-Kutta method that imply that y_n converges to $y(x)$ as $h \to 0$. Estimates of the error when the computational results are rounded off are also given there.

2.4 Difference methods. The Adams extrapolation formula.   The following simple consideration lies at the basis of difference methods for solving Cauchy

Problem (1.1)–(1.2). Assume that some method has been used to compute approximate values $y_1, y_2, \ldots, y_n$ of the desired function $y(x)$ at the values $x_1, x_2, \ldots, x_n$ of the independent variable, and assume that these values are equidistant, so that $x_{j+1} - x_j = h$, where h is constant. An approximate value y_{n+1} of $y(x_{n+1})$ can be computed with the formula

$$y_{n+1} = y_n + \int_{x_n}^{x_{n+1}} f(x, y(x))\, dx. \tag{1.61}$$

We replace the function $f(x, y(x))$ in the integrand by an interpolation polynomial, which takes the values

$$f_j = f(x_j, y_j). \tag{1.62}$$

at the points $x = x_j$ $(j = n - k, n - k + 1, \ldots, n)$. This polynomial is of the form

$$L_{n,k}(x) = \sum_{j=0}^{k} f_{n-j} P_{kj}(x), \tag{1.63}$$

where $P_{kj}(x)$ is a polynomial of degree k. We should note that $L_{n,k}(x)$ only approximately coincides with the interpolation polynomial of the function $f(x, y(x))$ since, in the general case, $y_j \neq y(x_j)$ and, therefore, $f_j \neq f(x_j, y(x_j))$.

Assume that polynomial (1.63) provides a sufficiently accurate extrapolation of the function $f(x, y(x))$ in the interval $x_n \leqslant x \leqslant x_{n+1}$. We substitute the polynomial $L_{n,k}(x)$ for the function $f(x, y(x))$ in integral (1.61) and set $x = x_n + th$. We thus obtain the approximation formula

$$y_{n+1} = y_n + h \sum_{j=0}^{k} b_{kj} f(x_{n-j}, y_{n-j}), \tag{1.64}$$

where the constants b_{kj} are given by the formula

$$b_{kj} = \frac{(-1)^j}{j!(k-1)!} \int_0^1 \frac{t(t+1)\ldots(t+k)}{t+j}\, dt.$$

Formula (1.64) is called *Adams extrapolation formula*. Below we will present values for the first several coefficients b_{kj} (see Table 2).

Table 2. Values of b_{kj}

k \ j	0	1	2	3	4
0	1				
1	$\frac{3}{2}$	$-\frac{1}{2}$			
2	$\frac{23}{12}$	$-\frac{4}{3}$	$\frac{5}{12}$		
3	$\frac{55}{24}$	$-\frac{59}{24}$	$\frac{37}{24}$	$-\frac{3}{8}$	
4	$\frac{1721}{720}$	$-\frac{1967}{360}$	$\frac{109}{30}$	$-\frac{637}{360}$	$\frac{251}{720}$

Table 3. Values of b_k

k	1	2	3	4	5	6	7	8	9
b_k	$\dfrac{1}{2}$	$\dfrac{5}{12}$	$\dfrac{3}{8}$	$\dfrac{251}{720}$	$\dfrac{95}{288}$	$\dfrac{19,087}{60,480}$	$\dfrac{5275}{17,280}$	$\dfrac{1,070,017}{3,628,800}$	$\dfrac{1,082,753}{7,257,600}$

We can obtain different Adams formulas by setting k equal to different values; when $k = 0$ we obtain Formula (1.50) of Euler's method, but with h constant.

Formula (1.64) can be put in a more convenient form by introducing the differences of the function $f(x, y(x))$:

$$\Delta f_j = f(x_{j+1}, y_{j+1}) - f(x_j, y_j),$$
$$\Delta^2 f_j = \Delta(\Delta f_j) = f(x_{j+2}, y_{j+2}) - 2f(x_{j+1}, y_{j+1}) + f(x_j, y_j),$$
$$\Delta^3 f_j = \Delta(\Delta^2 f_j) = f(x_{j+3}, y_{j+3}) - 3f(x_{j+2}, y_{j+2}) + 3f(x_{j+1}, y_{j+1}) - f(x_j, y_j),$$

etc. We then obtain

$$y_{n+1} = y_n + h(f_n + b_1 \Delta f_{n-1} + b_2 \Delta^2 f_{n-2} + \cdots + b_k \Delta^k f_{n-k}), \quad (1.65)$$

where

$$b_j = \frac{1}{j} \int_0^1 t(t + 1) \cdots (t + j) \, dt. \quad (1.66)$$

See Table 3.

We will now present a computation scheme for Adams Formula (1.65). Here, for definiteness we set $k = 3$, so that the Adams formula takes the form

$$\Delta y_n = \eta_n + \tfrac{1}{2}\Delta\eta_{n-1} + \tfrac{5}{12}\Delta^2\eta_{n-2} + \tfrac{3}{8}\Delta^3\eta_{n-3}; \quad (1.67)$$

here we have set

$$\eta_j = hf(x_j, y_j). \quad (1.68)$$

To use Formula (1.67) for computations we must know, in addition to y_0, the values of y_1, y_2, and y_3, corresponding to $x_1 = x_0 + h$, $x_2 = x_0 + 2h$, and $x_3 = x_0 + 3h$. This data can be used to compute the quantities shown in Table 4.

If we know the quantities located along any diagonal, we can use Formula (1.67) to find Δy_3, and then $y_4 = y_3 + \Delta y_3$. Knowing y_4, we compute $\eta_4 = hf(x_4, y_4)$. Now we can compute the following diagonal:

$$\Delta\eta_3 = \eta_4 - \eta_3, \quad \Delta^2\eta_2 = \Delta\eta_3 - \Delta\eta_2, \quad \Delta^3\eta_1 = \Delta^2\eta_2 - \Delta^2\eta_1;$$

we obtain a new table (Table 5) by writing the computed quantities in the corresponding places of Table 4.

The new diagonal makes it possible to use formula (1.67) to compute Δy_4. Now $y_5 = y_4 + \Delta y_4$, and the process is repeated.

Table 4

x	y	Δy	η	$\Delta\eta$	$\Delta^2\eta$	$\Delta^3\eta$
x_0	y_0		η_0			
		Δy_0		$\Delta\eta_0$		
x_1	y_1		η_1		$\Delta^2\eta_0$	
		Δy_1		$\Delta\eta_1$		$\Delta^3\eta_0$
x_2	y_2		η_2		$\Delta^2\eta_1$	
		Δy_2		$\Delta\eta_2$		
x_3	y_3		η_3			
x_4						
...	...	...	...	...	...	...
x^n						

If general formula (1.65) is used instead of (1.67), initiation of the process requires us to have the values of $y_1, y_2, \ldots, y_k$, corresponding to $x = x_0 + h$, $x_2 = x_0 + 2h, \ldots, x_k = x_0 + kh$. One possible method of computing $y_j (j = 1, 2, \ldots, k)$ will be stated in the following example; there is a more detailed discussion of the construction of the initial Adams table in Paragraph 8 of the present section.

EXAMPLE 9:   Solve the Cauchy Problem (1.8) with Formula (1.67).

We set $h = 0.1$. To compute y_1, y_2, and y_3 we use the approximate solution $y \approx x^3/3$, obtained as the first approximation with the method of successive approximations. The initial table is of the form shown at top of page 28.

Table 5

x	y	Δy	η	$\Delta\eta$	$\Delta^2\eta$	$\Delta^2\eta$
x_0	y_0		η_0			
		Δy_0		$\Delta\eta_0$		
x_1	y_1		η_1		$\Delta^2\eta_0$	
		Δy_1		$\Delta\eta_1$		$\Delta^3\eta_0$
x_2	y_2		η_2		$\Delta^2\eta_1$	
		Δy_2		$\Delta\eta_2$		$\Delta^3\eta_1$
x_3	y_3		η_3		$\Delta^2\eta_2$	
		Δy_3		$\Delta\eta_3$		
x_4	y_4		η_4			
x_5						
...	...	...	...	...	...	...
x_n						
...	...	...	...	...	...	...

Table 6

x	y	Δy	η	$\Delta \eta$	$\Delta^2 \eta$	$\Delta^3 \eta$
0.0	0.00000		0.00000			
		0.00033		0.00100		
0.1	0.00033		0.00100		0.00200	
		0.00234		0.00300		0.00001
0.2	0.00267		0.00400		0.00201	
		0.00633		0.00501		
0.3	0.00900		0.00901			

Using the tabulated data, we find that

$$\Delta y_3 = 0.00901 + \tfrac{1}{2} \cdot 0.00501 + \tfrac{5}{12} \cdot 0.00201 + \tfrac{3}{8} \cdot 0.00001 = 0.01236,$$
$$y_4 = y_3 + \Delta y_3 = 0.02136,$$

and we can complete the next diagonal. The results of computations for values of x between 0.0 and 0.6 are shown in Table 7.

We will now compare these results with the results obtained above with other methods. The various analytic methods we discussed in Section 1 lead to the approximate solution

$$y(x) \approx \frac{x^3}{3} + \frac{x^7}{63},$$

whose error, as we have seen, is small. When $x = 0.6$ we have

$$\frac{x^3}{3} + \frac{x^7}{63} = 0.07244,$$

which is within 3×10^{-5} of the result of Table 7. The Runge-Kutta formula, as we have seen (Paragraph 3), yields a value of 0.072448, in which all digits are exact.

Table 7

x	y	Δy	η	$\Delta \eta$	$\Delta^2 \eta$	$\Delta^3 \eta$
0.0	0.00000		0.00000			
		0.00033		0.00100		
0.1	0.00033		0.00100		0.00200	
		0.00234		0.00300		0.00001
0.2	0.00267		0.00400		0.00201	
		0.00633		0.00501		0.00002
0.3	0.00900		0.00901		0.00203	
		0.01236		0.00704		0.00005
0.4	0.02136		0.01605		0.00208	
		0.02043		0.00912		
0.5	0.04179		0.02517			
		0.03062				
0.6	0.07241					

2.5 The Adams interpolation formula. We return to Formula (1.61), and, for the function $f(x, y(x))$, we substitute the polynomial that interpolates it in the segment $x_{n-k} \leqslant x \leqslant x_{n+1}$. This leads us to the approximation formula

$$y_{n+1} = y_n + h \sum_{j=-1}^{+k} c_{kj} f(x_{n-j}, y_{n-j}), \qquad (1.69)$$

where

$$c_{kj} = \frac{(-1)^{j+1}}{(j+1)!(k-j)!} \int_0^1 \frac{(t-1)t(t+1) \cdots (t+k)}{t+j} \, dt. \qquad (1.70)$$

Table 8. Values of c_{kj}

k \ j	-1	0	1	2
0	$\frac{1}{2}$	$\frac{1}{2}$		
1	$\frac{1}{12}$	$\frac{2}{3}$	$-\frac{1}{12}$	
2	$\frac{3}{8}$	$\frac{19}{24}$	$-\frac{5}{24}$	$\frac{1}{24}$

Formula (1.69) is called the *Adams interpolation formula*. In contrast to Formula (1.64) it does not give y_{n+1}, immediately since y_{n+1} is contained in the right-hand side, in the term with index $j = -1$. Formula (1.69) yields an equation in the unknown y_{n+1}; and this equation can be solved by iteration if

$$h < \frac{1}{|c_{k,-1}| M_1}, \qquad M_1 = \sup \left| \frac{\partial f}{\partial y} \right|. \qquad (1.71)$$

Thus, the Adams interpolation formula is more cumbersome than the extrapolation formula, but more accurate.

Table 8 shows several values of the coefficients c_{kj},

If the differences of the function $f(x, y(x))$, are introduced, Formula (1.69) can be reduced to the form

$$\Delta y_n = \eta_{n+1} + c_1 \Delta \eta_n + c_2 \Delta^2 \eta_{n-1} + \cdots + c_{k+1} \Delta^{k+1} \eta_{n-k}, \qquad (1.72)$$

where

$$c_j = \frac{1}{l!} \int_{-1}^0 t(t+1) \cdots (t+j-1) \, dt \qquad (1.73)$$

$$(j = 1, 2, \ldots, k+1);$$

all of the coefficients c_j are negative. Table 9 shows the first several coefficients c_j.

Below is a computation scheme for use of the Adams interpolation formula. To simplify the notation, in Formula (1.72) we set $k = 2$, which leads to the following special form of the Adams interpolation formula:

$$\Delta y_n = \eta_{n+1} - \tfrac{1}{2}\Delta\eta_n - \tfrac{1}{12}\Delta^2\eta_{n-1} - \tfrac{1}{24}\Delta^3\eta_{n-2}. \tag{1.74}$$

We assume that we know y_1, y_2, and y_3; in the general case, $y_1, y_2, \ldots, y_k$, and y_{k+1} must be known for some value of k if Formula (1.72) is used. The values of y_1, y_2, and y_3 can be used to compose a table of the same type as Table 4 of Paragraph 4. The problem consists in computing the next lower diagonal entries η_4, $\Delta\eta_3$, $\Delta^2\eta_2$, $\Delta^3\eta_1$; then, setting $n = 3$ in Formula (1.74), we compute Δy_3, and then $y_4 = y_3 + \Delta y_3$.

Table 9.   Values of c_j

j	1	2	3	4	5	6	7
$-c_j$	$\dfrac{1}{2}$	$\dfrac{1}{12}$	$\dfrac{1}{24}$	$\dfrac{19}{720}$	$\dfrac{3}{160}$	$\dfrac{863}{60,480}$	$\dfrac{275}{2016}$

The desired diagonal is then constructed with an iteration method. We take $\Delta^3\eta_1^{(0)} = \Delta^3\eta_0$ for the initial approximation. Then we successively find

$$\Delta^2\eta_2^{(0)} = \Delta^2\eta_1 + \Delta^3\eta_1^{(0)}, \qquad \Delta\eta_3^{(0)} = \Delta\eta_2 + \Delta^2\eta_2^{(0)}, \qquad \eta_4^{(0)} = \eta_3 + \Delta\eta_3^{(0)},$$

and use Formula (1.74) to compute

$$\Delta y_3^{(0)} = \eta_4^{(0)} - \tfrac{1}{2}\Delta\eta_3^{(0)} - \tfrac{1}{12}\Delta^2\eta_2^{(0)} - \tfrac{1}{24}\Delta^3\eta_3^{(0)}$$

and, finally,

$$y_4^{(0)} = y_3 + \Delta y_3^{(0)}.$$

Knowing $y_4^{(0)}$, we compute the next approximation for the same diagonal by means of the formulas

$$\eta_4^{(1)} = hf(x_4, y_4^{(0)}),$$

$$\Delta\eta_3^{(1)} = \eta_4^{(1)} - \eta_3, \quad \Delta^2\eta_2^{(1)} = \Delta\eta_3^{(1)} - \Delta\eta_2, \quad \Delta^3\eta_1^{(1)} = \Delta^2\eta_2^{(1)} - \Delta^2\eta_1,$$

and then use Formula (1.74) to compute $\Delta y_3^{(1)}$, Now $y_4^{(1)} = y_3 + \Delta y_3^{(1)}$. The value of $y_4^{(1)}$ that we have found is used to compute $\eta_4^{(2)} = hf(x_4, y_4^{(1)})$, etc. The process repeats until $\eta_4^{(m-1)}$ and $\eta_4^{(m)}$ coincide.

EXAMPLE 10:   We again consider Example 9 of Paragraph 4. The starting point is Table 6 (see p. 28).
Setting $\Delta^3\eta_1^{(0)} = 0.00001$, we find that

$$\Delta^2\eta_2^{(0)} = 0.00202; \qquad \Delta\eta_3^{(0)} = 0.00703; \quad \eta_4^{(0)} = 0.01604;$$

$$\Delta y_3^{(0)} = 0.01604 - \tfrac{1}{2}0.00703 - \tfrac{1}{12}\cdot 0.00202 - \tfrac{1}{24}\cdot 0.00001 = 0.01235;$$

$$y_4^{(0)} = 0.00900 + 0.01235 = 0.02135.$$

We now compute the first approximation. We have

$$\eta_4^{(1)} = 0.1(x_4^2 + y_4^{(0)2}) = 0.01605,$$

$$\Delta\eta_3^{(1)} = 0.01605 - 0.00901 = 0.00704,$$

$$\Delta^2\eta_2^{(1)} = 0.00704 - 0.00501 = 0.00203,$$

$$\Delta^3\eta_1^{(1)} = 0.00203 - 0.00201 = 0.00002.$$

Now

$$\Delta y_3^{(1)} = 0.01605 - \tfrac{1}{2} \cdot 0.00704 - \tfrac{1}{12} \cdot 0.00203 - \tfrac{1}{24} \cdot 0.00002 = 0.01236,$$

$$y_4^{(1)} = 0.00900 + 0.01236 = 0.02136.$$

When we compute $\eta_4^{(2)} = 0.1(0.4^2 + y_4^{(1)2})$, we obtain the previous value of 0.01605; as a result, we can set $y_4 = y_4^{(1)2} = 0.02136$. We can now add values of y_4, Δy_3, η_4, ..., $\Delta^3\eta_1$, ... to our table and compute y_5. We should note that the y_4 we have obtained coincides with the one given by the relatively exact formula

$$y(x) \approx \frac{x^3}{3} + \frac{x^7}{63}$$

The Runge-Kutta method yields (see Paragraph 3) $y_4 = 0.021359$.

2.6 Other difference methods. It is possible to derive extrapolation formulas different from the Adams formula by starting, for example, from the formula

$$y_{n+1} = y_{n-s} + \int_{x_{n-s}}^{x_{n+1}} f(x, y(x))\, dx, \tag{1.61'}$$

in which s is some natural number; the integral in (1.61') is then replaced by an approximate value obtained with some quadrature formula with pivot points at the points $x_{n-s}, x_{n-s+1}, \ldots, x_n, x_{n+1}$; in particular, it is possible to replace the function $f(x, y(x))$ by its interpolation polynomial for the segment $x_{n-k} \leqslant x \leqslant x_{n+1}$. When $s = 1$, we obtain the so-called *Nyström extrapolation formula* [30]:

$$y_{n+1} = y_{n-1} + 2\eta_n + \tfrac{1}{3}\nabla^2\eta_n + \tfrac{1}{3}\nabla^3\eta_n + \tfrac{29}{30}\nabla^4\eta_n + \tfrac{14}{45}\nabla^5\eta_n + \ldots, \tag{1.75}$$

where ∇ is the backward difference, so that, for example,

$$\nabla\eta_n = \eta_n - \eta_{n-1}, \quad \nabla^2\eta_n = \eta_n - 2\eta_{n-1} + \eta_{n-2},$$

etc.

It is also possible to construct interpolation formulas that are frequently more accurate than the Adams interpolation formula, although they require more complex iterations. This can be done by replacing the function $f(x, y(x))$ in Formula (1.61) or (1.61') by a polynomial that interpolates it in the segment $[x_{n-k}, x_{n+p}]$, where $p > 1$. Commonly used are the so-called *Cowell-type* formulas:

$$\Delta y_n = \frac{\eta_{n+1} + \eta_n}{2} + a_1 \frac{\Delta^2\eta_n + \Delta^2\eta_{n-1}}{2} + a_2 \frac{\Delta^4\eta_{n-1} + \Delta^4\eta_{n-2}}{2} + \cdots$$

$$\cdots + a_k \frac{\Delta^{2^k}\eta_{n-k+1} + \Delta^{2^k}\eta_{n-k}}{2}, \quad (1.76)$$

$$a_j = \frac{1}{(2j)!}\int_0^1 (t + j - 1)(t + j - 2) \cdots t(t - 1) \cdots (t - j)\, dt.$$

The first values of the coefficients a_j are

$$a_1 = -\tfrac{1}{12}, \quad a_2 = \tfrac{11}{720}, \quad a_3 = \tfrac{191}{60480}.$$

When $k = 2$ Formula (1.76) takes the form

$$\Delta y_n = \frac{\eta_{n+1} + \eta_n}{2} - \frac{1}{12}\frac{\Delta^2\eta_n + \Delta^2\eta_{n-1}}{2} + \frac{11}{720}\frac{\Delta^4\eta_{n-1} + \Delta^4\eta_{n-2}}{2}. \quad (1.77)$$

We will now briefly discuss computation with Formula (1.77). In the general case, Formula (1.76) is used analogously. Assume that we know $y_1, y_2, y_3,$ and y_4 [in the general case of Formula (1.76), we know the values of $y_1, y_2, \ldots, y_{2k}$]. Our immediate purpose is to compute y_5. We compose the table

Table 10

x	y	Δy	η	$\Delta\eta$	$\Delta^2\eta$	$\Delta^3\eta$	$\Delta^4\eta$
x_0	y_0		η_0				
		Δy_0		$\Delta\eta_0$			
x_1	y_1		η_1		$\Delta^2\eta_0$		
		Δy_1		$\Delta\eta_1$		$\Delta^3\eta_0$	
x_2	y_2		η_2		$\Delta^2\eta_1$		$\Delta^4\eta_0$
		Δy_2		$\Delta\eta_2$		$\Delta^3\eta_1$	
x_3	y_3		η_3		$\Delta^2\eta_2$		$\Delta^4\eta_1$
		Δy_3		$\Delta\eta_3$		$\Delta^3\eta_2$	
x_4	y_4		η_4		$\Delta^2\eta_3$		$\Delta^4\eta_2$
				$\Delta\eta_4$		$\Delta^3\eta_3$	
x_4			η_5		$\Delta^2\eta_4$		$\Delta^4\eta_3$
				$\Delta\eta_5$		$\Delta^3\eta_4$	
x_6			η_6		$\Delta^2\eta_5$		
				$\Delta\eta_6$			
x_7			η_7				

The quantities located under the stepped line in Table 10 are unknown and depend on the still not computed values of y_5, y_6, and y_7. When we set $n = 4$ in Formula (1.77), we find that

$$\Delta y_4 = \frac{\eta_5 + \eta_4}{2} - \frac{1}{12}\frac{\Delta^2\eta_4 + \Delta^2\eta_3}{2} + \frac{11}{720}\frac{\Delta^4\eta_3 + \Delta^4\eta_2}{2};$$

certain quantities in the right-hand side of the last equation are unknown, and we solve this equation by iteration.

To obtain the initial approximation, we choose certain initial values of the fourth differences. It is simplest to set

$$\Delta^4\eta_1^{(0)} = \Delta^4\eta_2^{(0)} = \Delta^4\eta_3^{(0)} = \Delta^4\eta_0.$$

Now it is easy to compute $\Delta^3\eta_2^{(0)}$, $\Delta^3\eta_3^{(0)}$, and the remaining unknown quantities in Table 10. We set

$$\Delta y_4^{(0)} = \frac{\eta_5^{(0)} + \eta_4}{2} - \frac{1}{12}\frac{\Delta^2\eta_4^{(0)} + \Delta^2\eta_3^{(0)}}{2} + \frac{11}{720}\frac{\Delta^4\eta_3^{(0)} + \Delta^4\eta_2^{(0)}}{2}$$

and $y_5^{(0)} = y_4 + \Delta y_4^{(0)}$. We compute the quantity

$$\eta_5^{(1)} = hf(x_5, y_5^{(0)}).$$

If $\eta_5^{(1)} = \eta_5^{(0)}$, we set $y_5 = y_5^{(0)}$, enter the known quantities in Table 10 in the diagonal under the broken line, and compute y_6. If, however, $\eta_5^{(1)} \neq \eta_5^{(0)}$, we construct the next approximation $y_5^{(1)}$. To do so, we compute the elements in the first diagonal under the broken line:

$$\eta_5^{(1)} = hf(x_5, y_5^{(0)}), \quad \Delta\eta_4^{(1)} = \eta_5^{(1)} - \eta_4, \quad \Delta^2\eta_3^{(1)} = \Delta\eta_4^{(1)} - \Delta\eta_3,$$

$$\Delta^3\eta_2^{(1)} = \Delta^2\eta_3^{(1)} - \Delta^2\eta_2, \quad \Delta^4\eta_1^{(1)} = \Delta^3\eta_2^{(1)} - \Delta^3\eta_1.$$

We now select approximations for $\Delta^4\eta_2^{(1)}$ and $\Delta^4\eta_3^{(1)}$; for example, we can take

$$\Delta^4\eta_2^{(1)} = \Delta^4\eta_3^{(1)} = \Delta^4\eta_1^{(1)}.$$

Now we compute all entries of Table 10 under the broken line and determine the value of

$$\Delta y_4^{(1)} = \frac{\eta_5^{(1)} + \eta_4}{2} - \frac{1}{12}\frac{\Delta^2\eta_4^{(1)} + \Delta^2\eta_3^{(1)}}{2} + \frac{11}{720}\frac{\Delta^4\eta_3^{(1)} + \Delta^4\eta_2^{(1)}}{2}$$

$$y_5^{(1)} = y_4 + \Delta y_4^{(1)}.$$

and $y_5^{(1)} = y_4 + \Delta y_4^{(1)}$. We now compute

$$\eta_5^{(2)} = hf(x_5, y_5^{(1)});$$

if $\eta_5^{(2)} = \eta_5^{(1)}$, we set $y_5 = y_5^{(1)}$ and compute y_6, otherwise, we repeat the process.

2.7 Difference methods for systems and for higher-order equations.   In the case of systems of first-order equations, difference methods lead, in essence, to the same formulas as those for one equation. Thus, for Cauchy Problem (1.12)–(1.13) with the notation

$$\eta_j = hf(x_j, y_j, z_j), \quad \zeta_j = h\varphi(x_j, y_j, z_j), \tag{1.78}$$

we obtain the following approximation formulas:

The Adams extrapolation formula:

$$\left.\begin{aligned} \Delta y_n &= \eta_n + \tfrac{1}{2}\Delta\eta_{n-1} + \tfrac{5}{12}\Delta^2\eta_{n-2} + \tfrac{3}{8}\Delta^3\eta_{n-3} + \dots, \\ \Delta z_n &= \zeta_n + \tfrac{1}{2}\Delta\zeta_{n-1} + \tfrac{5}{12}\Delta^2\zeta_{n-2} + \tfrac{3}{8}\Delta^3\zeta_{n-3} + \dots \end{aligned}\right\} \tag{1.79}$$

The Adams interpolation formula:

$$\left.\begin{aligned} \Delta y_n &= \eta_{n+1} - \tfrac{1}{2}\Delta\eta_n - \tfrac{1}{12}\Delta^2\eta_{n-1} - \tfrac{1}{24}\Delta^3\eta_{n-2} - \dots, \\ \Delta z_n &= \zeta_{n+1} - \tfrac{1}{2}\Delta\zeta_n - \tfrac{1}{12}\Delta^2\zeta_{n-1} - \tfrac{1}{24}\Delta^3\eta_{n-2} - \dots \end{aligned}\right\} \tag{1.80}$$

The Cowell-type interpolation formula:

$$\begin{aligned} \Delta y_n &= \frac{\eta_{n+1} + \eta_n}{2} - \frac{1}{12}\frac{\Delta^2\eta_n + \Delta^2\eta_{n-1}}{2} \\ &\quad + \frac{11}{720}\frac{\Delta^4\eta_{n-1} + \Delta^4\eta_{n-2}}{2} - \dots, \\[2ex] \Delta z_n &= \frac{\zeta_{n+1} + \zeta_n}{2} - \frac{1}{12}\frac{\Delta^2\zeta_n + \Delta^2\zeta_{n-1}}{2} \\ &\quad + \frac{11}{720}\frac{\Delta^4\zeta_{n-1} + \Delta^4\zeta_{n-2}}{2} - \dots \end{aligned} \tag{1.81}$$

In carrying out computations with one or another of Formulas (1.79)–(1.81) we must construct two tables, as in the Adams or Cowell methods, for one equation; in the general case, a system of m first-order equations requires m such tables.

An equation or system of equations of order higher than the first can easily be reduced to a system of first order equations, to which Formulas (1.79)–(1.81) apply. Here we will consider only the Cauchy problem for one differential equation of the form

$$y'' = f(x, y), \quad y|_{x=x_0} = y_0, \quad y'|_{x=x_0} = y'_0. \tag{1.82}$$

For this case there are difference formulas, the so-called *Störmer extrapolation and interpolation formulas*, that require only one table. We set

$$\xi_j = h^2 f(x_j, y_j). \tag{1.83}$$

Table II. Values of a_j

j	2	3	4	5	6
α_j	$\dfrac{1}{12}$	$\dfrac{1}{12}$	$\dfrac{19}{240}$	$\dfrac{3}{40}$	$\dfrac{863}{12,096}$

The Störmer extrapolation formula is of the form

$$\left.\begin{aligned}
\Delta^2 y_{n-1} &= \xi_n + \alpha_2 \Delta^2 \xi_{n-2} + \alpha_3 \Delta^3 \xi_{n-3} + \cdots + \alpha_k \Delta^k \xi_{n-k}, \\
\alpha_j &= \frac{1}{j} \int_{-1}^{1} t(t+1) \cdots (t+j-1)(1-|t|)\, dt.
\end{aligned}\right\} \quad (1.84)$$

Table 11 shows values of the first coefficients α_j.
If we limit the discussion, for example, to $k = 3$, we have

$$\Delta^2 y_{n-1} = \xi_n + \tfrac{1}{12}\Delta^2 \xi_{n-2} + \tfrac{1}{12}\Delta^3 \xi_{n-3}. \quad (1.85)$$

To use formula (1.85) it is first necessary to find a method for computing y_1, y_2, and y_3. Then a table (see Table 12) whose entries are all known can be constructed.

Setting $n = 3$ in Formula (1.85), we compute

$$\Delta^2 y_2 = \xi_3 + \tfrac{1}{12}\Delta^2 \xi_1 + \tfrac{1}{12}\Delta^3 \xi_0.$$

We can now find y_4:

$$y_4 = y_3 + \Delta y_2 + \Delta^2 y_2.$$

We now enter y_4, Δy_3, $\Delta^2 y_2$; ξ_4, $\Delta \xi_3$, $\Delta^2 \xi_2$, and $\Delta^3 \xi_1$ in the lowest diagonal of Table 12. The same method is used to compute y_6, etc.

Table 12

x	y	Δy	$\Delta^2 y$	ξ	$\Delta \xi$	$\Delta^2 \xi$	$\Delta^3 \xi$
x_0	y_0			ξ_0			
		Δy_0			$\Delta \xi_0$		
x_1	y_1		$\Delta^2 y_0$	ξ_1		$\Delta^2 \xi_0$	
		Δy_1			$\Delta \xi_1$		$\Delta^3 \xi_0$
x_2	y_2		$\Delta^2 y_1$	ξ_2		$\Delta^2 \xi_1$	
		Δy_2			$\Delta \xi_2$		
x_3	y_3			ξ_3			
x_4							
$\cdots$	$\cdots$	$\cdots$	$\cdots$	$\cdots$	$\cdots$	$\cdots$	$\cdots$
x_n							
$\cdots$	$\cdots$	$\cdots$	$\cdots$	$\cdots$	$\cdots$	$\cdots$	$\cdots$

Störmer's interpolation formula is of the form

$$\Delta^2 y_{n-1} = \xi_n + \beta_2 \Delta^2 \xi_{n-1} + \beta_3 \Delta^3 \xi_{n-2} + \cdots + \beta_{k+1} \Delta^{k+1} \xi_{n-k},$$

$$\beta_j = \frac{1}{j!} \int_{-2}^{0} t(t+1) \cdots (t+j-1)(1 - |1+t|) \, dt;$$

the first values of β_j are shown in Table 13.

Table 13.   Values of β_j

j	2	3	4	5	6
β_j	$\dfrac{1}{2}$	0	$-\dfrac{1}{240}$	$-\dfrac{1}{240}$	$-\dfrac{221}{60,480}$

If we limit the discussion to $k = 4$, we obtain the formula

$$\Delta^2 y_{n-1} = \xi_n + \tfrac{1}{2}\Delta^2 \xi_{n-1} - \tfrac{1}{240}\Delta^4 \xi_{n-3} - \tfrac{1}{240}\Delta^5 \xi_{n-4}.$$

Computations with Störmer's interpolation formula proceed in the same manner as with the Adams interpolation formula.

Interpolation formulas of Cowell type can be constructed for Problem (1.82).

2.8 Construction of initial tables.   It follows from the discussion of Paragraph 4 that solution of the Cauchy problem by difference methods requires an initial table containing, in addition to y_0 (known from the initial conditions), the first several values of $y_1, y_2, \ldots, y_k$.

Various methods for construction of an initial table have been proposed. On the whole, they can be divided into two groups: explicit and iteration methods.

Examples of Explicit Methods:

(a) Segments of the Taylor series for the solution $y(x)$ (see Section 1.1) are found, and $y_1, y_2, \ldots, y_k$ are found by setting $x = h$, $x = 2h, \ldots$, $x = kh$ in the Taylor series expansion.

(b) The Runge-Kutta method with given x_0 and y_0 is used to successively find the k values $y_1, y_2, \ldots, y_k$ for $x = x_1, x_2, \ldots, x_k$, where $x_j = x_0 + jh$.

For determination of $y_1, y_2, \ldots, y_k$, iteration methods require composition of a system of k equations that, for sufficiently small h, admit solution by iteration methods.

The methods in this group differ from one another only, in essence, in the notation, the sequence of operations in the iterations, and the method of determining the initial approximation for iteration.

The system of equations is found on the following basis: For any integer r and any positive integer $k \geqslant 1$ it is possible to find numbers $A_i^{(k,r)}$ ($i = 0, 1, 2, \ldots, k$), such that for any polynomial $P(x)$ of degree no greater than $k + 1$ in x with arbitrary $h > 0$, we have

$$P(rh) - P(0) = h \sum_{i=0}^{k} A_i^{(k,r)} P'(ih).$$

If the solution $y(x)$ to the Cauchy problem is a polynomial of degree no greater than $k + 1$, we have, by Eq. (1.1),

$$y_r - y = h \sum_{i=0}^{k} A_i^{(k,r)} f(x_i, y_i) \tag{1.86}$$

when $y(x_i)$ is substituted for y_i and $y'(x_i)$ is substituted for $f(x_i, y_i)$,

(a) Setting $r = 1, 2, \ldots, k$, in (1.86), we obtain a system of k equations [60]:

$$y_r = y_0 + h \sum_{i=0}^{k} A_i^{(k,r)} f(x_i, y_i) \quad (r = 1, 2, \ldots, k). \tag{1.87}$$

For sufficiently small h, system (1.87) has a unique solution, for which $y_1, y_2, \ldots, y_k$ differ little from y_0, and this solution can be obtained with an iteration method.

The initial approximation $y_1^{(0)} y_1^{(0)}, \ldots, y_k^{(0)}$ can be obtained, for example, with Euler's method.

Table 14 shows values of $A_i^{(k,r)}$ for $k = 1, 2, 3, 4;\ 0 \leqslant r \leqslant k$.

In the simplest case ($k = 1$) the system degenerates into one equation

$$y_1 = y_0 + \frac{h}{2} [f(x_0, y_0) + f(x_1, y_1)],$$

which coincides with the equation of the trapezoid method.

In case $k = 2$ the system has the form

$$y_1 = y_0 + \frac{h}{12} [5f(x_0, y_0) + 8f(x_1, y_1) - f(x_2, y_2)]$$

$$y_2 = y_0 + \frac{h}{3} [f(x_0, y_0) + 4f(x_1, y_1) + f(x_2, y_2)].$$

Successive approximations are computed with the formulas*

$$y_1^{(m+1)} = y_0 + \frac{h}{12} [5f(x_0, y_0) + 8f(x_1, y_1^{(m)}) - f(x_2, y_2^{(m)})],$$

$$y_2^{(m+1)} = y_0 + \frac{h}{3} [f(x_0, y_0) + 4f(x_1, y_1^{(m+1)}) + f(x_2, y_2^{(m)})].$$

* If it is expected that the number of iterations will be small (1-2 iterations), it is possible, for the sake of economy, to substitute $f(x_1, y_i^{(m)})$ for $f(x_1, y_i^{(m+1)})$ in the right hand side of the second formula.

Table 14. Values of $A_i^{(k,r)}$

$k = 1$

r \ i	0	1
1	$\frac{1}{2}$	$\frac{1}{2}$

$k = 2$

r \ i	0	1	2
1	$\frac{5}{12}$	$\frac{8}{12}$	$-\frac{1}{12}$
2	$\frac{1}{3}$	$\frac{4}{3}$	$\frac{1}{3}$

$k = 3$

r \ i	0	1	2	3
1	$\frac{3}{8}$	$\frac{19}{24}$	$-\frac{5}{24}$	$\frac{1}{24}$
2	$\frac{1}{3}$	$\frac{4}{3}$	$\frac{1}{3}$	0
3	$\frac{3}{8}$	$\frac{9}{8}$	$\frac{9}{8}$	$\frac{3}{8}$

$k = 4$

r \ i	0	1	2	3	4
1	$\frac{251}{720}$	$\frac{323}{360}$	$-\frac{11}{30}$	$\frac{53}{360}$	$-\frac{19}{720}$
2	$\frac{29}{90}$	$\frac{62}{45}$	$\frac{12}{45}$	$-\frac{2}{45}$	$-\frac{1}{90}$
3	$\frac{27}{80}$	$\frac{51}{40}$	$\frac{9}{10}$	$\frac{21}{40}$	$-\frac{3}{80}$
4	$\frac{14}{45}$	$\frac{64}{45}$	$\frac{24}{45}$	$\frac{64}{45}$	$\frac{14}{45}$

(b) System (1.87) can be written in difference form. To do so, we introduce the differences $\Delta y_r = y_{r+1} - y_r$ $(r = 0, 1, 2, \ldots, k - 1)$, as well as $\eta_j = hf(x_j, y_j)$ $(j = 0, 1, 2, \ldots, k)$ and their differences of order up to k. Consider the quantities

$$B_i^{(k,r)} = A_i^{(k,r+1)} - A_i^{(k,r)} \text{(assuming that } A_i^{(k,0)} = 0).$$

Subtraction of two adjacent equations transforms system (1.87) into the form

$$\Delta y_r = \sum_{i=0}^{k} B_i^{(k,r)} \eta_i \qquad (r = 0, 1, 2, \ldots, k - 1).$$

Each equation in this system is transformed in the following manner:

(α) If $i < r$, then η_i is replaced by a linear combination of η_r, $\Delta\eta_{r-1}$, $\Delta^2\eta_{r-2}, \ldots, \Delta^{r-i}\eta_i$.

(β) If $i > r$, then η_i is replaced by a linear combination of the quantities

$$\eta_r, \Delta\eta_{r-1}, \ldots, \Delta^r\eta_0, \Delta^{r+1}\eta_0, \ldots, \Delta^i\eta_0.$$

This substitution leads to the equation

$$\Delta y_r = \eta_r + \sum_{i=1}^{r} D_i^{(r)} \Delta^i \eta_{r-i} + \sum_{i=r+1}^{k} D_i^{(r)} \Delta^i \eta_0. \qquad (1.88)$$

It turns out that the $D_i^{(r)}$ are independent of the choice of k. Table 15 shows values of $D_i^{(r)}$ for $1 \leqslant i \leqslant 5$, $0 \leqslant r \leqslant 4$.

Table 15. Values of $D_i^{(r)}$

r \ i	1	2	3	4	5
0	$\frac{1}{2}$	$-\frac{1}{12}$	$\frac{1}{24}$	$-\frac{19}{720}$	$\frac{3}{160}$
1	$\frac{1}{2}$	$\frac{5}{12}$	$-\frac{1}{24}$	$\frac{11}{720}$	$-\frac{11}{1440}$
2	$\frac{1}{2}$	$\frac{5}{12}$	$\frac{3}{8}$	$-\frac{19}{720}$	$\frac{11}{1440}$
3	$\frac{1}{2}$	$\frac{5}{12}$	$\frac{3}{8}$	$\frac{251}{720}$	$-\frac{3}{160}$
4	$\frac{1}{2}$	$\frac{5}{12}$	$\frac{3}{8}$	$\frac{251}{720}$	$\frac{95}{288}$

Equations of the form (1.88) were proposed by Krylov [31]. For example, system (1.88) with $k = 3$ takes the form

$$\Delta y_0 = \eta_0 + \tfrac{1}{2}\Delta\eta_0 - \tfrac{1}{12}\Delta^2\eta_0 + \tfrac{1}{24}\Delta^3\eta_0,$$

$$\Delta y_1 = \eta_1 + \tfrac{1}{2}\Delta\eta_0 + \tfrac{5}{12}\Delta^2\eta_0 - \tfrac{1}{24}\Delta^3\eta_0,$$

$$\Delta y_2 = \eta_2 + \tfrac{1}{2}\Delta\eta_1 + \tfrac{5}{12}\Delta^2\eta_0 + \tfrac{3}{8}\Delta^3\eta_0.$$

If m iterations have made it possible to obtain $y_1^{(m)}$, $y_2^{(m)}$, and $y_3^{(m)}$, the following approximations $y_1^{(m+1)}$, $y_2^{(m+1)}$, and $y_3^{(m+1)}$, can be obtained in the following manner: The known $y_1^{(m)}$, $y_2^{(m)}$, and $y_3^{(m)}$ are used to compute $\eta_1^{(m)}$, $\eta_2^{(m)}$, and $\eta_3^{(m)}$; these values and the known value η_0 are used to find the differences in Formula (1.88). This makes it possible to compute $\Delta y_r^{(m+1)}(r = 0, 1, 2)$ and then to find the quantities

$$y_1^{(m+1)} = y_0 + \Delta y_0^{(m+1)}, \quad y_2^{(m+1)} = y_1^{(m+1)} + \Delta y_1^{(m+1)},$$

$$y_3^{(m+1)} = y_2^{(m+1)} + \Delta y_2^{(m+1)},$$

which concludes one iteration. The iteration process is repeated until the difference $|y_r^{(m+1)} - y_r^{(m)}|$ is sufficiently small.

The initial approximation $y_1^{(0)}$, $y_2^{(0)}$, and $y_3^{(0)}$ for the iteration can be obtained with Euler's method.

The following method, proposed by Krylov [31], is recommended for obtaining the most accurate initial approximation:

(1) Set $\Delta y_0^{(1)} = \eta_0$.
(2) Find $y_1^{(1)} = y_0 + \eta_0$ (Euler's formula).
(3) Compute $\eta_1^{(1)} = hf(x_1, y_1^{(1)})$.
(4) Compute the difference $\Delta \eta_0^{(1)} = \eta_1^{(1)} - \eta_0$.
(5) Find the increments $\Delta y_0^{(2)}$ and $\Delta y_1^{(2)}$ with the formulas

$$\Delta y_0^{(2)} = \eta_0 + \tfrac{1}{2}\Delta\eta_0^{(1)}, \qquad \Delta y_1^{(2)} = \eta_1^{(1)} + \tfrac{1}{2}\Delta\eta_0^{(1)}.$$

(6) Find $y_1^{(2)}$ and $y_2^{(2)}$: $y_1^{(2)} = y_0 + \Delta y_0^{(2)}$, $y_2^{(2)} = y_2^{(2)} + \Delta y_1^{(2)}$.
(7) Compute $\eta_1^{(2)} = hf(x_1, y_1^{(2)})$ and $n_2^{(2)} = hf(x_2, y_2^{(2)})$.
(8) Use η_0, $\eta_1^{(2)}$ and $\eta_2^{(2)}$ to find the differences

$$\Delta\eta_0^{(2)} = \eta_1^{(2)} - \eta_0, \qquad \Delta\eta_1^{(2)} = \eta_2^{(2)} - \eta_1^{(2)}, \qquad \Delta^2\eta_0^{(2)} = \Delta\eta_1^{(2)} - \Delta\eta_0^{(2)}.$$

(9) Find the increments $\Delta y_0^{(3)}$, $\Delta y_1^{(3)}$, and $\Delta y_2^{(3)}$ with the formulas

$$\Delta y_0^{(3)} = \eta_0 + \tfrac{1}{2}\Delta\eta_0^{(2)} - \tfrac{1}{12}\Delta^2\eta_0^{(2)},$$

$$\Delta y_1^{(3)} = \eta_1^{(2)} + \tfrac{1}{2}\Delta\eta_0^{(2)} + \tfrac{5}{12}\Delta^2\eta_0^{(2)},$$

$$\Delta y_2^{(3)} = \eta_2^{(2)} + \tfrac{1}{2}\Delta\eta_1^{(2)} + \tfrac{5}{12}\Delta^2\eta_0^{(2)}.$$

(10) Find $y_1^{(3)}$, $y_2^{(3)}$, and $y_3^{(3)}$:

$$y_1^{(3)} = y_0 + \Delta y_0^{(3)}, \; y_2^{(3)} = y_1^{(3)} + \Delta y_1^{(3)}, \; y_3^{(3)} = y_2^{(3)} + \Delta y_2^{(3)}.$$

The quantities $y_1^{(3)}$, $y_2^{(3)}$, and $y_3^{(3)}$ are taken for the initial approximation for iteration for system (1.88) ($k = 3$).

Remark. If $f(x, y)$ is given as a complex analytic expression, it is natural to estimate the quantity of work required for numerical solution of the Cauchy problem in terms of the number of times $f(x, y)$ is computed during the solution, and to neglect the other auxiliary computations (construction of differences, multiplication by the coefficients $D_i^{(r)}$, etc.). Determination of the initial approximation with Euler's method requires (for $k = 3$) three computations of $f(x, y)$, while Krylov's method requires four. Since, as a rule, a more accurate initial approximation reduces the number of necessary iterations (necessary for achieving the desired accuracy) and each iteration with system (1.88) requires four evaluations of $f(x, y)$, it is clear that it is more desirable to use Krylov's method to find the initial approximation.

2.9 Concerning the stability of difference methods. We again consider Cauchy Problem (1.1)–(1.2). Application of any difference method is associated with errors introduced by the following circumstances: inaccuracy of assumptions at the basis of the approximate formulas; inaccuracy of the intermediate operations and resulting round-off errors; inaccuracy in determination of the initial values of y_1, y_2, ..., y_k; and errors in the iterations used when interpolation formulas are applied. Since the values of y_n are determined recursively, it is not impossible for the error in the determination of y_n to accumulate and exceed admissible limits as n increases.

Neglecting round-off errors, we will assume that both the error of approximate difference formulas under consideration and the error in the initial values of y_1, y_2, ..., y_k are sufficiently small. If the error in the determination of y_n remains bounded as n increases, the difference formula under consideration is said to be stable; if, however, the error increases infinitely as $n \rightarrow \infty$, the difference formula is said to be unstable.

We will now derive a stability criterion for difference formulas. We assume that the difference formula has the form

$$\sum_{j=0}^{k} \alpha_j y_{n+j} - \sum_{j=0}^{k} \beta_j \eta_{n+j} = 0 \qquad (1.89)$$

where α_j and β_j are real numbers, $\alpha_k \neq 0$. Note that all of the difference formulas given above are of the form (1.89). Consider the polynomials

$$\left. \begin{aligned} \rho(z) &= \alpha_k z^k + \alpha_{k-1} z^{k-1} + \cdots + \alpha_0, \\ \sigma(z) &= \beta_k z^k + \beta_{k-1} z^{k-1} + \cdots + \beta_0. \end{aligned} \right\} \qquad (1.90)$$

We assume that the polynomials $\rho(z)$ and $\sigma(z)$ have no common roots, for otherwise we would be able to simplify Formula (1.89) and decrease the degree k. The requirement that the approximate solution (under the assumption that is is computed without error) uniformly converge to the exact solution as $h \rightarrow 0$ imposes two further conditions on polynomials (1.89):

$$\rho(1) = \sum_{j=0}^{k} \alpha_j = 0, \quad \rho'(1) = \sigma(1). \qquad (1.91)$$

It is also possible to obtain Eqs. (1.91) by starting from the requirement that Formula (1.89) be exact when $y(x)$ is a polynomial of degree one and, consequently, $f(x, y) = $ const.

Under the above conditions, difference formula (1.89) is stable if and only if all roots of the polynomial $\rho(z)$ are located inside or on the boundary of the disk $|z| \leqslant 1$ of the complex z-plane, where the roots located on the boundary (i.e., the roots of modulus one) must be simple.

All of the difference formulas given in Sections 2.4–2.7 are stable.

The formula

$$y_{n+2} + 4y_{n+1} - 5y_n = 4\eta_{n+1} + 2\eta_n \qquad (1.92)$$

is unstable. In this case

$$\rho(z) = z^2 + 4z - 5. \quad \sigma(z) = 4z + 2;$$

the polynomials $\rho(z)$ and $\sigma(z)$ have no common roots and $\rho(1) = 0$, $\rho'(1) = \sigma(1) = 6$. The roots of the polynomial $\rho(z)$ are 1 and -5; the second root has modulus larger than one, and Formula (1.92) is therefore unstable. In order to verify this, we will use Formula (1.92) to solve the Cauchy problem

$$y' = y, \quad y\big|_{x=0} = 1,$$

whose exact solution is $y = e^x$. Set $h = 0.1$.

To compute with Formula (1.92) we must find $y_1 = y(0.1)$. For y_1 we take the value $y(0.1) = e^{0.1}$ computed to six exact decimal places: $y_1 = 1.105171$. Computation yields $y_{10} = y(1) = -0.284254$: the error, which at $n = 1$ is less than 10^{-6}, is now

$$|y(1) - y_{10}| = e + 0.284254 = 3.002536.$$

The stability of difference formulas of the form

$$y_{n+1} - \sum_{j=0}^{k} A_j y_{n-j} - h^2 \sum_{j=-1}^{k} B_j f(x_{n-j}, y_{n-j}) = 0 \qquad (1.93)$$

has been investigated for second-order equations of the form $y'' = f(x, y)$ with the initial conditions

$$y\big|_{x=x_0} = y_0, \quad y'\big|_{x=x_0} = y_0'.$$

The coefficients of Formula (1.93) are subject to the requirement that they be exact for the differential equation $y'' = 0$; this implies that

$$\sum_{j=0}^{k} A_j = 1, \qquad \sum_{j=0}^{k} j A_j = -1. \qquad (1.94)$$

Difference formula (1.93) is stable if and only if the roots of the polynomial

$$z^{k+1} - \sum_{j=0}^{k} A_j z^{k-j} = 0 \qquad (1.95)$$

satisfy the same condition that was formulated above for the polynomial $\rho(z)$: Either the roots have modulus less than one or have modulus equal to one and are simple.

2.10 The error of the Adams formulas.   We will limit the discussion to the Adams formulas, for they are the most commonly used; concerning the errors of other difference formulas, see [2] and [73].

The Adams formulas, both the extrapolation and interpolation formulas, can be written in a single form:

$$y_{n+1} = y_n + h \sum_{j=-1}^{k} \beta_j f(x_{n-j}, y_{n-j}); \qquad (1.96)$$

for the extrapolation formula, $\beta_{-1} = 0$, while for the interpolation formula,

$\beta_{-1} > 0$. We shall assume that the initial values $y_1, y_2, \ldots, y_k$ are each given with an error no greater than some given ε. The values of $y_{k+1}, y_{k+2}, \ldots$ are determined with Eq. (1.96) with some error due to rounding off, the error in the initial values $y_1, y_2, \ldots, y_k$ and, finally, the error of the Adams formula itself. Assume that we have actually calculated some $\tilde{y}_n$; it clearly must satisfy an equation of the form

$$\tilde{y}_{n+1} = \tilde{y}_n + h \sum_{j=-1}^{k} \beta_j f(x_{n-j}, y_{n-j}) + \Gamma_n, \tag{1.97}$$

where Γ_n is the round-off error in Eq. (1.96) and $\tilde{y}_j = y_j (j = 0, 1, 2, \ldots, k)$. On the other hand, if $y(x)$ is the exact solution of the Cauchy problem, then $y(x_n)$ does not satisfy approximate Equation (1.96) exactly; by introducing the corresponding correction, which we will denote by R_n, we can assume that $y(x_n)$ exactly satisfies the equation

$$y(x_{n+1}) = y(x_n) + h \sum_{j=-1}^{k} \beta_j f(x_{n-j}, y(x_{n-j})) + R_n. \tag{1.98}$$

Notation:
$$\varepsilon_n = y(x_n) - \tilde{y}_n. \tag{1.99}$$

The problem consists in estimating $|\varepsilon_n|$.

Let K denote the Lipschitz constant of the function $f(x, y)$; we can set

$$K = \max \left| \frac{\partial f}{\partial y} \right|.$$

Assume that we know the upper limits of $|\Gamma_n|$ and $|R_n|$, i.e., we know constants Γ and R such that $|\Gamma_n| \leqslant \Gamma$ and $|R_n| \leqslant R$. It is known that if the solution $y(x)$ of Problem (1.1)–(1.2) has the necessary number of continuous derivatives we can set
$$R = ch^{r+2} \max |y^{(r+2)}(x)|,$$

where c is constant and $r = k$ for the Adams extrapolation formula, while $r = k + 1$ for the interpolation formula. We also set

$$\sigma = \sum_{j=-1}^{k} |\beta_j| \tag{1.100}$$

and choose h so small that $h\beta_{-1}K < 1$; for the Adams extrapolation formula, the last condition is clearly satisfied for any h. Consider the equation

$$(1 - h\beta_{-1} K)z^{k+1} - (1 + h\beta K)z^k - hK \sum_{j=1}^{k} |\beta_j| z^{k-j} = 0. \tag{1.101}$$

It turns out that it has a root $z_1 > 1$, and the desired estimate can be expressed in terms of this root:

$$|\varepsilon_n| \leqslant \varepsilon z_1^n + \frac{R + \Gamma}{hK\sigma} (z_1^n - 1). \tag{1.102}$$

It can be shown (see [73]) that for small h we have the approximate equation

$$z_1^n \approx e^{K\sigma(x_n - x_0)}$$

and, consequently, ε_n remains bounded as n increases.

Estimate (1.102) is usually rather crude. A recurrence formula provides a more accurate estimate of the error. Let δ_n be the upper bound of $|\varepsilon_n|$ and assume that $\delta_1, \delta_2, \ldots, \delta_k$ are known. Then $\delta_n, n > k$, can be found with the recurrence relation

$$(1 - h\beta_{-1}K)\,\delta_{n+1} = (1 + h\beta_0 K)\,\delta_n + hK\sum_{j=1}^{k}|\beta_j|\,\delta_{n-j} + R + \Gamma. \quad (1.103)$$

2.11 Comparison of numerical methods. The fundamental advantage of the Runge-Kutta method in comparison with difference methods consists in the fact that the step h_n can be chosen arbitrarily at any point in the computation. This circumstance is used for monitoring the computation and selection of a step that will provide a particular computational accuracy [41]. It is not necessary to construct an initial table for the initial computations with the Runge-Kutta method, which is also an advantage of this method.

To pass from x_n to x_{n+1} by the Runge-Kutta method, four computations of $f(x, y)$ (for the fundamental method) are required; at the same time, any extrapolation difference method requires only one computation of $f(x, y)$ for the same purpose, and this is an unfavorable aspect of the Runge-Kutta method.

This disadvantage of the Runge-Kutta method becomes less noticeable when it is compared with interpolation difference methods that, as a rule, require no less than double computation for transition from x_n to x_{n+1}.

It appears that, with the appearance of high-speed digital computers, the esteem of the Runge-Kutta method has risen, and at the present time a tendency toward more widespread use of the Runge-Kutta method at computer centers has been observed.

BIBLIOGRAPHIC NOTES

Both analytic and numerical approximate methods for solution of the Cauchy problem for ordinary differential equations are discussed in [2, 31, 89]; numerical methods are also discussed in [30, 57, 73, 84]; see also [22].

Certain conclusions about application of Chaplygin's method to different problems in the theories of differential and integral equations, as well as bibliographic comments, may be found in [52]. A more detailed discussion of Chaplygin's method can be found in [2, 16, 31, 106].

A number of interesting conclusions about the method of the small parameter may be found in [31].

Section 1.6 considers certain results of Lozinskiy [50], appropriately simplified for application to one first-order equation. For further developments of this author's work, see [47–49, 51].

The article [5] presents a proof of Euler's method for the case in which $f(x, y)$ in differential Equation (1.1) experiences a finite jump to certain lines in the (x, y) plane but satisfies the Lipschitz condition between these lines. Similar results were obtained in [5] for first-order equations.

A large number of finite difference formulas is given in [59] and [60]; in a number of cases, additional formulas for checking or refining results provided by the fundamental formulas are given. The notion of stability of difference methods was developed by Dalhquist in [114], which contains stability criteria and an example of an unstable difference formula; this same article also contains other results associated with the notion of stability. The fundamental results of [114] were discussed in detail in [2], and more briefly in [73].

The stability of difference formulas for equations of the form $y'' = f(x, y)$ was investigated by Krylov in [32].

The error of the Adams method was investigated in [124]; an estimate of the error of more general difference formulas of the form

$$y_{n+1} = \sum_{j=1}^{k} \alpha_j y_{n-j} + h \sum_{j=0}^{k} \beta_j f_{n-j}$$

was given in [107]. An estimate for the error of formulas of the same form was given in [1] for the case in which it is assumed that functions $Y_1(x)$ and $Y_2(x)$, satisfying the inequalities $Y_1(x) \leqslant y(x) \leqslant Y_2(x)$, $Y_1(x) \leqslant \bar{y}_m(x) \leqslant Y_2(x)$, are known, where $y(x)$ is the exact solution of Cauchy Problem (1.1)–(1.2), $\bar{y}_m(x)$ is the exact solution of the Cauchy problem for Eq. (1.1) with the initial condition $y|_{x=x_m} = y_m$ and y_m is the quantity given by the difference formula. The error of extrapolation formulas was discussed in [51].

Chapter Two

GRID METHODS

I. ELLIPTIC EQUATIONS

1.1 Grid equations. In this chapter we will consider grid methods for approximate solution of fundamental problems in mathematical physics.

Let Ω be a finite or infinite region in n-dimensional Euclidean space E_n, and let Γ be the boundary of Ω. Moreover, let Lu be some (as a rule, linear) differential operator defined on a function $u(X) = u(x_1, \ldots, x_n)$ where $X = (x_1, \ldots, x_n)$ is a point in E_n. The problem is to find a function $u(X)$ satisfying the differential equation

$$Lu = f(X) \tag{2.1}$$

at each point in Ω, and one or more boundary conditions

$$l_i u \big|_{\Gamma_i} = \varphi_i(X) \qquad (i = 1, 2, \ldots, s), \tag{2.2}$$

where the Γ_i are parts of the boundary Γ and $l_i u$ are differential operators. In Eqs. (2.1) and (2.2) the functions $f(X)$ and $\varphi_i(X)$ are defined in Ω and on Γ_i, respectively. If Ω and the operators L and l_i are given, they define an entire class of problems, for each of which the functions $f(X)$ and $\varphi_i(X)$ are given and it is required to use them to determine $u(X)$.

Various methods, some of which are called grid methods, have been proposed for approximate solution of Problem (2.1)–(2.2).

Grid methods include those in which we attempt to find a table of approximate values of the desired solution on some set of points $X_k \in \Omega + \Gamma (k = 1, 2, \ldots)$, called a *grid*, where the individual points X_k are called *mesh points*. Sometimes, in addition to the mesh points $X_k \in \Omega + \Gamma$ auxiliary mesh points outside Ω are selected. We will call the mesh points $X_k \in \Omega + \Gamma$ *fundamental*. The equations used to determine the desired values of the approximate solution are called *grid equations*. The method used to choose the grid and to obtain the grid equations distinguishes one grid method from another.

We will assume that each grid method prescribes an infinite set of grids Ω_h, depending on one or more positive parameters characterizing the density of the mesh points. In what follows, we will denote this parameter or group of parameters by h. The smaller h (the parameters comprising h), the smaller the grid Ω_h. It is assumed that in the set $\{\Omega_h\}$ it is possible to find a sequence such that $h \to 0$. The values of h for which a corresponding grid Ω_h exists are said to be *admissible*.

As an example, we will consider the frequently used *rectangular* grid. Let Ω be a region in the (x, y) plane. In this plane we draw two families of lines parallel to the coordinate axes: $x = ih_1$, $y = jh_2$, where h_1 and h_2 are arbitrary positive numbers, $i, j = 0, \pm 1, \pm 2, \ldots$. These lines partition the entire plane into rectangles with sides h_1 and h_2; the vertices of these rectangles are called the *mesh points* of the rectangular grid. By Ω_h we denote the set of mesh points of the rectangular grid inside or on the boundary of Ω. It may happen that no constraints are imposed on h_1 and h_2, at which time all positive h_1 and h_2 will be admissible $h(h_1, h_2)$. It may happen that the region Ω is bounded and the grid method requires the presence of no less than a particular number of mesh points in Ω; and then all $h(h_1, h_2)$, with h_1 and h_2 bounded from above will be admissible. Or it may occur that the only admissible $h(h_1, h_2)$, are those satisfying the conditions $h_1 = a/N_1$, $h_2 = b/N_2$, where a and b are positive numbers, while N_1 and N_2 are positive integers; this occurs when Ω is a rectangle with sides a and b, and it is desired that Ω be completely coverable by elementary rectangular grids.

In this section we will assume that Ω is finite and the grid Ω_h for each admissible h consists of a finite number N_h of mesh points.

In what follows, u_h will denote the table of approximate values of the desired solution. We will call this table the *grid function*, while we call the individual numbers in this table the *values of the grid function at mesh points*.

To determine the grid function for a grid method, a system of grid equations is prescribed, and the solution of this system provides the numbers forming u_h. The general form of this system is

$$R_h u_h = f_h, \tag{2.3}$$

$$r_{ih} u_h = \varphi_{ih} \qquad (i = 1, 2, \ldots, s), \tag{2.4}$$

where it is assumed that Eqs. (2.3) are the grid analog of differential Equation (2.1), while Eqs. (2.4) are the grid analog of boundary conditions (2.2). We will call system (2.3)–(2.4) the *grid equations for Problem* (2.1)–(2.2).

The method of *substituting finite-difference quotients for derivatives* is frequently used when a rectangular grid is used to obtain grid Equations (2.3).

Below we will present an example of this technique.

It is natural to impose the following requirements on system (2.3)–(2.4).

(1) *Solvability of System* (2.3)–(2.4).   We assume that problem (2.1)–(2.2) has a unique solution in some function class U. For each admissible h system (2.3)–(2.4) must have a unique solution $\{u_h(X_k^h)\}$, where X_k^h is the mesh point with index k in the grid Ω_h.

(2) *Convergence to Exact Solutions.*   The grid solution $u_h(X_k^h)$ must, in some sense, approach the exact solution $u(X)$ as $h \to 0$.

To describe this requirement, we introduce the following spaces and norms (see [13] and [104]):

(a) the function space U containing the exact solution $u(X)$ of Problem (2.1)–(2.2); in this space we introduce some norm $\|u\|_U$;

(b) by U_h we will mean the space whose elements are the pairs consisting of the numbers N_h and the corresponding grid solutions of system (2.3)–(2.4); in the space U_h we introduce a norm $\|u_h\|_{U_h}$ (some norm in the N_h-dimensional vector space U_h).

Consistency of Norms. We will assume that the norms $\|u\|_U$ and $\|u_h\|_{U_h}$ are consistent in the following sense: Since the values of each function $u(X) \in U$, are known at the fundamental mesh points in the grid Ω_h, we can treat each such function as an element of the space U_h; *for any function* $u(X) \in U$ we must have

$$\lim_{h \to 0} \|u(X)\|_{u_h} = \|u(X)\|_U. \qquad (2.5)$$

We will call the quantity $\|u_h - u(X)\|_{U_h}$ the *error* of the approximate solution u_h relative to the exact solution $u(X)$.

We will say that u_h *converges* to the exact solution $u(X)$, if

$$\lim_{h \to 0} \|u_h - u(X)\|_{u_h} = 0. \qquad (2.6)$$

Error Estimates. It is of value to obtain formulas making it possible to estimate the error $\|u_h - u(X)\|_{U_h}$ from above. This problem usually reduces to finding a positive function $\omega(h)$ of h and the parameters characterizing the exact solution (the parameters of Ω, the boundary conditions, the moduli of the derivatives of the exact solution, etc.) that approaches zero as $h \to 0$, and is such that

$$\|u_h - u(X)\|_{U_h} \leqslant \omega(h). \qquad (2.7)$$

Formula (2.7) not only permits us to investigate the convergence of (2.6), but indicates the rate at which the error decreases as $h \to 0$. When it is possible to find such a function $\omega(h)$, we will say that *an error estimate has been found.*

In concluding these general comments, we will give an example of the problem of writing grid equations for the case in which Problem (2.1)–(2.2) is the Dirichlet problem for an elliptic equation in two independent variables.

In writing these equations, we will use the above-noted method of substituting finite-difference ratios for derivatives.

Let Ω be a finite region in the (x, y) plane that is bounded by a simple, sufficiently piecewise-smooth contour Γ. In addition, let a, b, c, d, g, and f be sufficiently smooth functions in Ω, where $a > 0$, $b > 0$, and consider the equation

$$Lu \equiv a\frac{\partial^2 u}{\partial x^2} + b\frac{\partial^2 u}{\partial y^2} + c\frac{\partial u}{\partial x} + d\frac{\partial u}{\partial y} - gu = f. \qquad (2.8)$$

Assume that a function φ has been given on the contour Γ. The Dirichlet problem is: Find a solution $u(x, y)$ of Eq. (2.8) that becomes φ on Γ, i.e., find a solution satisfying the condition

$$lu|_\Gamma \equiv u(x, y)|_\Gamma = \varphi. \tag{2.9}$$

Notation: (i, j) is the mesh point with coordinates (ih_1, jh_2) where i and j are integers; $(u)_{i,j}$ is the value of the function u at the mesh points (i, j); $u_{i,j}$ is the value of the grid function u_h at the mesh point (i, j).

We set

$$\left.\left(\frac{\partial u}{\partial x}\right)\right|_{i,j} \approx \frac{(u)_{i+1,j} - (u)_{i-1,j}}{2h_1}, \quad \left.\left(\frac{\partial u}{\partial y}\right)\right|_{i,j} \approx \frac{(u)_{i,j+1} - (u)_{i,j-1}}{2h_2},$$

$$\left.\left(\frac{\partial^2 u}{\partial x^2}\right)\right|_{i,j} \approx \frac{(u)_{i+1,j} - 2(u)_{i,j} + (u)_{i-1,j}}{h_1^2}.$$

$$\left.\left(\frac{\partial^2 u}{\partial y^2}\right)\right|_{i,j} \approx \frac{(u)_{i,j+1} - 2(u)_{i,j} + u_{i,j-1}}{h_2^2}. \tag{2.10}$$

We will call the set of five mesh points (i, j), $(i + 1, j)$, $(i, j + 1)$, $(i - 1, j)$, and $(i, j - 1)$ the *five-pointed star* with center at (i, j) [we will frequently omit "five-pointed"], and we will use the following system for labeling the mesh points in a star (Fig. 1).

We denote the set of all mesh points in Ω or on Γ by Ω_h. We will say that a mesh point (i, j) is an *interior* point if all mesh points of the star with center at (i, j) also belong to Ω_h and the line segments connecting the center with the remaining mesh points of the star belong to Ω. Substituting $(a)_{i,j}, (b)_{i,j}, \ldots$ for $a, b, \ldots$ in (2.8), and substituting expressions obtained from the right-hand sides of (2.10) by substituting $u_{i,j}, u_{i+1,j}, \ldots$, for $(u)_{i,j}, (u)_{i+1,j}, \ldots$ for the derivatives of $u(x, y)$ we obtain the following relation for each interior

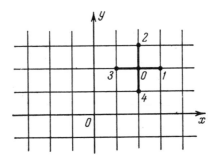

Fig. I

mesh point:

$$R_h u_h \equiv (a)_{i,j} \frac{u_{i+1,j} - 2u_{i,j} + u_{i-1,j}}{h_1^2}$$

$$+ (b)_{i,j} \frac{u_{i,j+1} - 2u_{i,j} + u_{i,j-1}}{h_2^2} + (c)_{i,j} \frac{u_{i+1,j} - u_{i-1,j}}{2h_1} \qquad (2.11)$$

$$+ (d)_{i,j} \frac{u_{i,j+1} - u_{i,j-1}}{2h_2} - (g)_{i,j} u_{i,j} = (f)_{i,j};$$

we will take this expression for the grid analog of Eq. (2.8) at the interior mesh point (i, j). There are as many such equations as interior mesh points in Ω_h.

We will say that a mesh point (i, j) is a *boundary* point if at least one mesh point of the star with center at (i, j) does not belong to Ω_h or at least one segment connecting the center with a mesh point of the star intersects Γ. We will now discuss several methods of replacing Eq. (2.9) by grid equations.

(1) *Simple Shift.* Let the mesh point (i, j) be a boundary point, and let $Q_{i,j} \in \Gamma$ be the boundary point either closest to (i, j) or closest to a boundary point in the direction of the coordinate axes. We set

$$r_h u_h \equiv u_{i,j} = \varphi(Q_{i,j}), \qquad (2.12)$$

as a result of which the values of u_h at the boundary mesh points are known immediately.

(2) *Accounting for Boundary Conditions by Linear Interpolation* (Collatz [30]). Let (i, j) be a boundary mesh point. Then at least one of the segments connecting (i, j) with the remaining nodes of the star with center at (i, j), will intersect Γ. For definiteness, we assume that this is the segment to the mesh point $(i + 1, j)$ (Fig. 2), and we assume that $Q \in \Gamma$ is the intersection point closest to (i, j). It is also assumed that every segment connecting Q with $(i - 1, j)$ belongs to Ω. If the desired function $u(x, y)$ is linear on this segment, we have

$$\frac{(u)_{i,j} - (u)_{i-1,j}}{h_1} = \frac{u(Q) - (u)_{i,j}}{\delta},$$

where δ is the distance from Q to (i, j). Setting $u(Q) = \varphi(Q)$, we obtain the equation

$$\left(1 + \frac{\delta}{h_1}\right) u_{i,j} - \frac{\delta}{h_1} u_{i-1,j} = \varphi(Q),$$

for the grid function u_h; in place of this equation, we can use the more general equation

$$r_h u_h \equiv \left(1 + \frac{\delta}{h}\right) u_{i,j} - \frac{\delta}{h} u_{i',j'} = \varphi(Q), \qquad (2.13)$$

where h denotes either h_1 or h_2, depending on which axis is parallel to the segment connecting Q with (i, j), and (i', j') is the mesh point at the end of the segment under consideration. With each boundary mesh point we associate one equation (2.13). Thus, the system obtained by combining all of Eqs.

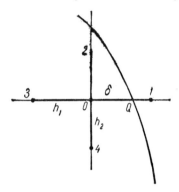

Fig. 2

(2.11) and (2.13) contains as many equations as the number of mesh points in Ω_h, and has as many unknowns.

(3) *Writing Equations at Boundary Mesh Points (Mikeladze [58])*. For simplicity, we assume that $a \equiv b \equiv 1$, $c \equiv d \equiv g \equiv 0$, i.e., that the operator L is the Laplacian, and Eq. (2.8) is Poisson's equation:

$$Lu \equiv \Delta u \equiv \frac{\partial^2 u}{\partial x^2} + \frac{\partial^2 u}{\partial y^2} = f. \qquad (2.14)$$

Then (2.11) takes the form

$$R_h u_h \equiv \frac{u_{i+1,j} - 2u_{i,j} + u_{i-1,j}}{h_1^2} + \frac{u_{i,j+1} - 2u_{i,j} + u_{i,j-1}}{h_2^2} = (f)_{i,j} \quad (2.15)$$

and for a square grid ($h_1 = h_2 = h$) becomes

$$\Delta_h u_h \equiv \frac{u_{i+1,j} + u_{i,j+1} + u_{i-1,j} + u_{i,j-1} - 4u_{i,j}}{h^2} = (f)_{i,j}. \qquad (2.16)$$

Consider a star with center at some boundary mesh point not on Γ. The boundary Γ intersects at least one of the rays leaving the center for other mesh points of the star. Assume that δ_1, δ_2, δ_3, and δ_4 are the distances from the center of the star in the direction of the ray either to the closest mesh point or to a boundary point; for example, δ_2 may be equal to h_2, or less than h_2. Now, let Q_1, Q_2, Q_3, and Q_4 be the corrresponding points on the rays, e.g., Q_2 may be the second mesh point of the star or a point of the boundary Γ. The values of $u(Q_1)$, $(u)_{i,j}$, and $u(Q_3)$ are used to compose an interpolation polynomial, and its second derivative is taken for the approximate value $(\partial^2 u/\partial x^2)_{i,j}$. We thus obtain

$$\left(\frac{\partial^2 u}{\partial x^2}\right)_{i,j} \approx 2\left(\frac{u(Q_1)}{\delta_1(\delta_1 + \delta_3)} + \frac{u(Q_3)}{\delta_3(\delta_1 + \delta_3)} - \frac{(u)_{i,j}}{\delta_1\delta_3}\right).$$

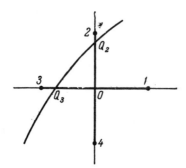

Fig. 3

We find a similar approximate value for $(\partial^2 u/\partial y^2)_{i,j}$, add these approximate values and set the sum equal to $(f)_{i,j}$, thus obtaining a grid equation for (2.14) at a boundary mesh point. We transform the equation thus obtained in the following manner: Some of the points Q_1, Q_2, Q_3, and Q_4 lie on Γ, so the value of $u(X)$ at these points is known and coincides with $\varphi(X)$; we carry the terms corresponding to these points to the right-hand side, and separate the equation thus obtained into the sum of coefficients with translated values. If, for simplicity, we assume that the grid is square, and that the points Q_2 and Q_3 lie on Γ for some boundary mesh point (Fig. 3), we find that, if we set $\delta_2/h \equiv \delta_2'$, $\delta_3/h \equiv \delta_3'$,

$$r_h u_h \equiv \frac{(\delta_2' + \delta_3')(1 + \delta_2')(1 + \delta_3')}{A} u_{i,j}$$

$$- \frac{\delta_2'\delta_3'(1 + \delta_2')}{A} u_{i+1,j} - \frac{\delta_2'\delta_3'(1 + \delta_3')}{A} u_{i,j-1}$$

$$= \frac{\delta_3'(1 + \delta_3')}{A} \varphi(Q_2) + \frac{\delta_2'(1 + \delta_2')}{A} \varphi(Q_3) - \frac{\delta_2'\delta_3'(1 + \delta_2')(1 + \delta_3')}{2A} h^2(f)_{i,j},$$

$$(2.17)$$

where

$$A = \delta_2'(1 + \delta_2') + \delta_3'(1 + \delta_3').$$

If a boundary mesh point lies on Γ and coincides with $Q \in \Gamma$, then we set

$$r_h u_h \equiv u_{i,j} = \varphi(Q). \tag{2.18}$$

The number of equations in system (2.11), (2.17), (2.18) coincides with the number of mesh points in Ω_h.

We assume that Ω_h is such that each interior mesh point can be connected to at least one boundary mesh point by a broken line whose vertices (except for the end) are interior mesh points with each succeeding mesh point belonging to the star with center at the preceding mesh point.

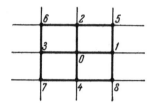

Fig. 4

Theorem 1. Assume that the functions a, b, c, d, and g satisfy the following conditions:

(1) there exists an $M > 0$, such that for all $(x, y) \in \Omega$

$$|c| < Ma, \quad |d| < Mb; \tag{2.19}$$

(2) $$g \geqslant 0. \tag{2.20}$$

Then the linear systems (2.11), (2.12) and (2.11), (2.13) have unique solutions for all h_1 and h_2, satisfying the inequalities

$$h_1 < \frac{2}{M}, \quad h_2 < \frac{2}{M}. \tag{2.21}$$

Remark 1. An equation analogous to (2.17) can be written at a boundary mesh point for Eq. (2.8). Under the conditions of Theorem 1, system (2.11)—the analog of (2.17)—has a unique solution.

Remark 2. In place of the five-pointed star used above, a nine-pointed star can be used (Fig. 4). If the term $2e(x, y)(\partial^2 u/\partial x\,\partial y)$ is added to Eq. (2.8) (where it is assumed that $e^2 < ab$ is the ellipticity of the transformed equation), the corresponding grid equation obtained from (2.11) by addition of the term

$$2(e)_{i,j} \frac{1}{2h_1} \left(\frac{u_{i+1,j+1} - u_{i+1,j-1}}{2h_2} - \frac{u_{i-1,j+1} - u_{i-1,j-1}}{2h_2} \right)$$

$$= (e)_{i,j} \frac{u_{i+1,j+1} - u_{i-1,j+1} + u_{i-1,j-1} - u_{i+1,j-1}}{2h_1 h_2}$$

to the left-hand side is the grid analog $2\left(e\,\dfrac{\partial^2 u}{\partial x\,\partial y}\right)_{i,j}$. For boundary mesh points
(in the sense of the new notion of a star), we use Eq. (2.12) (simple shift). It has
still not been proved whether the new linear system (2.11)–(2.12) is solvable.

1.2 Approximation of an exact problem by a grid problem.   (a) *Definitions.*
Let U be a class of functions containing the exact solution $u(X)$ of Problem
(2.1)–(2.2). The left-hand side of Eq. (2.1) is the operator Lu, mapping the
class U into some class F. For example, if L is the Laplacian and U is the class
of m-times ($m \geqslant 2$) continuously differentiable functions in Ω, then F is the
class of functions $m - 2$ times continuously differentiable in Ω. The left-hand
side of some of boundary conditions (2.2), e.g., $l_i u|_{\Gamma_i}$, is the operator mapping
U into some class Φ_i of functions defined on part Γ_i of the boundary Γ. For
example, if U is the class of m-times ($m \geqslant 1$) continuously differentiable
functions in the closed region $\Omega + \Gamma$ and Γ_1 is a sufficiently smooth boundary
component, while a $l_1 u|_{\Gamma_1} = \dfrac{\partial u}{\partial v}\Big|_{\Gamma_1}$ is the normal derivative of the function
$u(X)$ at the points of Γ_1, then $l_1 u|_{\Gamma_1}$ maps U into the class of functions that
are $m - 1$-times continuously differentiable and defined on Γ_1. Thus, the
operators $Lu, l_1 u|_{\Gamma_1}, \ldots, l_s u|_{\Gamma_s}$ map U into classes $\Gamma, \Phi_1, \Phi_2, \ldots, \Phi_s$ of
functions, respectively, defined in $\Omega, \Gamma_1, \Gamma_2, \ldots, \Gamma_s$.

Assume that each of these classes has a norm, which we will denote by
$\|f\|_F, \|\varphi_1\|_{\Phi_1}, \ldots, \|\varphi_s\|_{\Phi_s}$, respectively. The classes $\Gamma, \Phi_1, \ldots, \Phi_s$ are not
assumed to be closed under the norms that have been introduced; it is only
assumed that Problem (2.1)–(2.2) is well-posed (that there is a continuous
relationship between the solution $u(X)$ and the functions $f, \varphi_1, \varphi_2, \ldots, \varphi_s$)
[77, 98].

We now introduce the grid analogs of the classes $F, \Phi_1, \ldots, \Phi_s$, and the corresponding norms. Assume that each equation of system (2.3)–(2.4) has been
written so that the left-hand side is a function of the values of the desired
solution u_h at certain mesh points and is independent of $f, \varphi_1, \ldots, \varphi_s$, while
the right-hand side depends only on the functions $f, \varphi_1, \ldots, \varphi_s$; namely,
it is some functional over the group of functions $f, \varphi_1, \ldots, \varphi_s$.

Let N_h^0 be the number of equations in system (2.3), and let N_h^i be the
number of equations in the ith group of system (2.4) ($i = 1, 2, \ldots, s$). The
grid function u_h can be treated as a vector in the N_h-dimensional space U_h,
where N_h is the number of mesh points in Ω_h. Then the set of left-hand sides
of system (2.3) can be treated as an operator mapping U_h into the N_h^0-dimen-
sional space F_h, while the set of left sides of the ith group of system (2.4) can be
treated as an operator mapping U_h into the N_h^i-dimensional space Φ_{ih}. The
set of functionals over the group $f, \varphi_1, \ldots, \varphi_s$ in the right-hand sides of
system (2.3) can be treated as an operator mapping the product $F \times \Phi_1 \times$
$\cdots \times \Phi_s$ into F_h and we will denote this operator by Π_h^0. Similarly, by Π_h^i we

will denote the operator that maps $F \times \Phi_1 \times \cdots \times \Phi_s$ into Φ_{ih} and is transformed by the functionals into the right-hand sides of the ith group of system (2.4).

System (2.3)–(2.4) takes the form

$$R_h u_h = \Pi_h^0 (f, \varphi_1, \ldots, \varphi_s), \tag{2.22}$$

$$r_{ih} u_h = \Pi_h^i (f, \varphi_1 \ldots, \varphi_s) \quad (i = 1, 2, \ldots, s). \tag{2.23}$$

$$F_h, \Phi_{1h}, \ldots, \Phi_{sh}$$

In the vector spaces $F_h, \Phi_{1h}, \ldots, \Phi_{sh}$ we introduce norms, which we denote by $\|f_h\|_{F_h}, \|\varphi_{1h}\|_{\Phi_{1h}}, \ldots, \|\varphi_{sh}\|_{\Phi_{sh}}$.

We will say that the norms $\|f_h\|_{F_h}, \|\varphi_{1h}\|_{\Phi_{1h}}, \ldots, \|\varphi_{sh}\|_{\Phi_{sh}}$ are *consistent* with the norms $\|f\|_F, \|\varphi_1\|_{\Phi_1}, \ldots, \|\varphi_s\|_{\Phi_s}$, if we have

$$\left. \begin{aligned} \lim_{h \to 0} \|\Pi_h^0 (f, \varphi_1, \ldots, \varphi_s)\|_{F_h} &= \|f\|_F, \\ \lim_{h \to 0} \|\Pi_h^i (f, \varphi_1, \ldots, \varphi_s)\|_{\Phi_{ih}} &= \|\varphi_i\|_{\Phi_i} \quad (i = 1, 2, \ldots, s) \end{aligned} \right\} \tag{2.24}$$

for any set of functions $(f, \varphi_1, \ldots, \varphi_s) \in F \times \Phi_1 \times \cdots \times \Phi_s$.

Remark 1. Π usually does not depend on $\varphi_1, \ldots, \varphi_s$; for example, Eq. (2.17) shows that Π_h^1 depends not only on φ, but on f as well.

Remark 2. If we take the maximum modulus (of the functions comprising a vector) for the norm in all of the function classes and vector spaces we have defined, Eqs. (2.11), (2.12), (2.13), (2.17) and (2.18) can be written so that condition (2.24) for norm consistency is satisfied.

Definition. We will say that Eqs. (2.22)–(2.23) *approximate* Eqs. (2.1)–(2.2) in a class U, if for all $u \in U$ we have

$$\lim_{h \to 0} \|R_h u - \Pi_h^0 (Lu, l_1 u, \ldots, l_s u)\|_{F_h} = 0, \tag{2.25}$$

$$\lim_{h \to 0} \|r_{ih} u - \Pi_h^i (Lu, l_1 u, \ldots, l_s u)\|_{\Phi_{ih}} = 0 \tag{2.26}$$

$$(i = 1, 2, \ldots, s).$$

Let $\alpha(h)[\alpha_i(h)]$ be some positive function of the parameters comprising h that approaches zero as $h \to 0$.

We will say that an approximation of Eq. (2.1) [(2.2)] by Eq. (2.22) [(2.23)] is *estimated* by a function $\alpha(h)[a_i(h)]$, if for any function $u \in U$ there exists a positive number $M[M_i]$ such that for each admissible h we have the inequality

$$\|R_h u - \Pi_h^0 (Lu, l_1 u, \ldots, l_s u)\|_{F_h} \leqslant M\alpha(h) \tag{2.27}$$

$$[\|r_{ih} u - \Pi_h^i (Lu, l_1 u, \ldots, l_s u)\|_{\Phi_{ih}} \leqslant M_i \alpha_i(h)]. \tag{2.28}$$

Remark.   If h is the only parameter and $\alpha(h) = h^\rho$ (ρ is a positive number), we will say that the *order of approximation* of Eq. (2.1) by Eq. (2.22) is *equal to ρ*.

For the norms in the following examples, we will take the maximum modulus of the functions in the function spaces (uniform norm), while in the vector spaces we will mean the maximum modulus of the vector components.

EXAMPLE 1:   For system (2.11), the components of the vector $R_h u_h$ are the values of the left-hand side of (2.11) for each interior mesh point, while the components of the vector Π_h^0 are the values of $f(X)$ at these points.

In what follows, C^k will denote the class of functions whose derivatives of up to order k, inclusive, are continuous in the closed region $\Omega + \Gamma$. Let $U = C^4$ and let (i, j) be an interior mesh point (in the sense of a five-pointed star) of a rectangular grid Ω_h. Using the Taylor series, we write the values of $u(x, y)$ at the mesh points in terms of $u(x, y)$ and its derivatives at the center of the star. We have, for example,

$$(u)_{i+1,j} \equiv u((i + 1)h_1, jh_2) = (u)_{i,j} + \left(\frac{\partial u}{\partial x}\right)_{i,j} h_1$$

$$+ \frac{1}{2}\left(\frac{\partial^2 u}{\partial x^2}\right)_{i,j} h_1^2 + \frac{1}{6}\left(\frac{\widetilde{\partial^3 u}}{\partial x^3}\right)h_1^3 = (u)_{i,j} + \left(\frac{\partial u}{\partial x}\right)_{i,j} h_1$$

$$+ \frac{1}{2}\left(\frac{\partial^2 u}{\partial x^2}\right)_{i,j} h_1^2 + \frac{1}{6}\left(\frac{\partial^3 u}{\partial x^3}\right)_{i,j} h_1^3 + \frac{1}{24}\left(\frac{\widetilde{\partial^4 u}}{\partial x^4}\right)h_1^4,$$

where $(\widetilde{\partial^3 u}/\partial x^3)$ and $(\widetilde{\partial^4 u}/\partial x^4)$ are the values of the derivatives at points on the segment connecting the mesh points (i, j) and $(i + 1, j)$. Similar expressions are obtained for $(u)_{i-1,j}$ by substituting h_1 for h_1 and $\approx$ for $\sim$.

It thus follows that

$$\frac{(u)_{i+1,j} - 2(u)_{i,j} + (u)_{i-1,j}}{h_1^2} = \left(\frac{\partial^2 u}{\partial x^2}\right)_{i,j} + \frac{h_1^2}{24}\left[\left(\frac{\widetilde{\partial^4 u}}{\partial x^4}\right) + \left(\frac{\widetilde{\widetilde{\partial^4 u}}}{\partial x^4}\right)\right],$$

$$\frac{(u)_{i+1,j} - (u)_{i-1,j}}{2h_1} = \left(\frac{\partial u}{\partial x}\right)_{i,j} + \frac{h_1^2}{12}\left(\left[\frac{\widetilde{\partial^3 u}}{\partial x^3} + \frac{\widetilde{\widetilde{\partial^3 u}}}{\partial x^3}\right]\right),$$

and there are analogous expressions for $h_2^{-2}[(u)_{i,j+1} - 2(u)_{i,j} + (u)_{i,j-1}]$ and $(2h_2)^{-1}[(u)_{i,j+1} - (u)_{i,j-1}]$ (which are obtained by substitution of h_2 for h_1 and differentiation by y) for differentiation by x.

We multiply the four equations thus obtained by $(a)_{i,j}$, $(c)_{i,j}$, $(b)_{i,j}$, and $(d)_{i,j}$, add $-(g)_{i,j}(u)_{i,j}$ to both sides, and thus obtain the left-hand side of Eq. (2.11), i.e., $(R_h u)_{i,j}$, while on the right we obtain the sum of the values of $(Lu)_{i,j} = (\Pi_h^0 (Lu))_{i,j}$ and terms containing the factors h_1 and h_2.

We denote the largest of the norms of the kth derivatives of the function $u(x, y)$ by $M^{(k)}$, while we let A denote the largest of the norms of the co-efficients a, b, c, and d of Eq. (2.8), which leads us to the inequality

$$|(R_h u)_{i,j} - (\Pi_h^0 (Lu))_{i,j}| = |(R_h u)_{i,j} - (Lu)_{i,j}|$$
$$\leqslant A\left(\frac{2M^{(4)}}{24} + \frac{2M^{(3)}}{12}\right)(h_1^2 + h_2^2),$$

i.e.,

$$\|R_h u - \Pi_h^0(Lu)\| \leqslant M(h_1^2 + h_2^2), \qquad (2.29)$$

where

$$M = A\left(\frac{M^{(4)}}{12} + \frac{M^{(3)}}{6}\right).$$

Inequality (2.29) indicates that the approximation of Eq. (2.8) by Eq. (2.11) is estimated by the function $\alpha(h) = h_1^2 + h_2^2$.

Remark 1. If U is the class C^2, we can only say that

$$\lim_{h \to 0} \|R_h u - \Pi_h^0 (Lu)\| = 0, \qquad (2.30)$$

i.e., we can say only that an approximation exists.

Remark 2. Consider the following boundary-value problem for an ordinary second-order differential equation: On the segment $0 \leqslant x \leqslant 1$ find a function $u(x)$, satisfying the equation

$$Lu \equiv u''(x) + c(x)u' - g(x)u = f(x) \qquad (2.31)$$

and the boundary conditions

$$u(0) = \alpha, \quad u(1) = \beta \qquad (2.32)$$

where $c(x)$, $g(x)$, and $f(x)$ are given functions, while α, and β are given constants.

To solve this problem approximately by the grid method, we introduce mesh points x_k on the segment $[0, 1]$ with step h: $x_k = x_0 + kh$. When $x_0 = 0$, $h = 1/N$ (N is a positive integer), the two mesh points x_0 and x_N coincide with the ends of the segment $[0, 1]$. Generally, this does not occur. We will call a mesh point x_k interior if the mesh points x_{k-1} and x_{k+1} belong to the segment $[0, 1]$, and for interior mesh points we have the equation

$$(R_h u_h)_k \equiv \frac{u_{k+1} - 2u_k + u_{k-1}}{h^2} + c(x_k)\frac{u_{k+1} - u_{k-1}}{2h} - g(x_k)u_k = f(x_k).$$
$$(2.33)$$

As in Example 1, we can say that if $u(x) \in C^4$, then Eq. (2.33) approximates Eq. (2.31), and the approximation is estimated by the function h^2, i.e., the order of the approximation is 2.

EXAMPLE 2:   For simplicity, we assume that the grid is square. If a mesh point (i, j) is a boundary point, the closest point $Q_{i,j} \in \Gamma$ is $\delta < h$ distant from the mesh point (i, j). For $u(x, y) \in C^1$ we therefore have

$$|(u)_{i,j} - u(Q_{i,j})| \leqslant M^{(1)}\delta < M^{(1)}h. \tag{2.34}$$

This means that the order of approximation of Eq. (2.9) by Eq. (2.12) is 1. This conclusion is also true for C_k, where $k \geqslant 1$, since C^k is part of the class C^l when $k > l$.

Let (i, j) be a boundary mesh point. Assuming that $u \in C^2$ and using Taylor's formula to write the values of $u((i - 1)h, jh)$ and $u(ih + \delta, jh)$ in terms of $u(x, y)$ and the derivatives at (i, j), we obtain

$$|(r_h u)_{i,j} - [\Pi_h^1 (l, u)]_{i,j}| = \left\| \left[\left(1 + \frac{\delta}{h} \right)(u)_{i,j} - \frac{\delta}{h}(u)_{i-1,j} \right] - u(ih + \delta, jh) \right\|$$

$$\leqslant \frac{\delta}{2} \left| h \left(\widetilde{\frac{\partial^2 u}{\partial x^2}} \right) + \delta \left(\widetilde{\frac{\partial^2 u}{\partial x^2}} \right) \right| \leqslant M^{(2)}h^2,$$

for Eq. (2.13), i.e., the order of approximation of Eq. (2.9) by Eq. (2.13) is 2. It is easy to see that the order of approximation of Eq. (2.9) [for Eq. (2.15)] by Eq. (2.17) is 3.

Remark.   If a grid such that $x_0 = 0$, $x_N = 1$ has been chosen for Problem (2.31)–(2.32), the grid analogs, of boundary conditions (2.32) are

$$u_0 = \alpha, \quad u_N = \beta, \tag{2.36}$$

and the order of approximation of Eqs. (2.32) by Eqs. (2.36) is ∞ (there is no error). If, for some reason, the grid is selected so that at least one of the ends $x = 0$ or $x = 1$ is not a mesh point, the grid analogs of (2.32) can be constructed by simple shift, linear interpolation, or Mikeladze's method. The conclusions concerning the order of approximation are the same as for the two-dimensional problem.

(b) *Selection of Grid Equations Approximating Linear Differential Equations.* Let Lu be a linear differential operator of order p, with coefficients defined in some region Ω of the (x, y) plane. In addition, assume that some grid Ω_h has been selected in this region. We will call a set of several mesh points $X_1, \ldots, X_k$ and some point X_0 a *star* with center at X_0 (X_0 may coincide with one of the mesh points of the star). Let $c_1, \ldots, c_k$ be chosen so that the expression

$$c_1 u(X_1) + \cdots + c_k u(X_k)$$

coincides with $Lu(X)$ at X_0 for all integral rational functions of some degree $q > p$ relative to x and y. It is then natural to assume that the equation

$$R_h u_h \equiv c_1 u_h(X_1) + \cdots + c_k u_h(X_k) = f(X_0) \tag{2.37}$$

is the grid analog of differential Equation (2.1) at X_0. For a function $u(X)$ that is not an integral rational function of degree q, the difference

$$R_h u - (Lu)_{X_0} \equiv c_1 u(X_1) + \cdots + c_k u(X_k) - (Lu)_{X_0},$$

is generally nonzero.

Let h denote the smallest distance between mesh points of a star. It can be shown that (under the assumption that $c_1, \ldots, c_k$ are uniquely determined) for $u(X) \in C^{q+1}$

$$|R_h u - (Lu)_{X_0}| \leqslant A M^{(q+1)} h^{q-p+1}, \tag{2.38}$$

where A is a positive number that depends only on the coefficients of the operator L and the shape of the star (but not on its dimensions).

Now, assume that the mesh of the grid Ω_h is made finer, so that the star is compressed toward the center under a similarity transformation. Then, if Π_h^0, means $f(X_0)$ inequality (2.38) indicates that the order of approximation of Eq. (2.1) by Eq. (2.37) is $q - p + 1$.

Assume that $a_{\alpha_1, \alpha_2}(x, y)$ is the coefficient of $\partial^{\alpha_1 + \alpha_2} u / \partial x^{\alpha_1} \partial x^{\alpha_2}$ in the notation of the operator Lu. Then we have the linear system

$$\sum_{j=1}^{k} c_j (x_j - x_0)^{\alpha_1} (y_j - y_0)^{\alpha_2} = \begin{cases} \alpha_1! \alpha_2! a_{\alpha_1, \alpha_2}(x_0, y_0), & 0 \leqslant \alpha_1 + \alpha_2 \leqslant p, \\ 0, & p + 1 \leqslant \alpha_1 + \alpha_2 \leqslant q, \end{cases} \tag{2.39}$$

for determination of the coefficients $c_1, \ldots, c_k$ where $(x_j,$ and $y_j)$ are the coordinates of the point $X_j (j = 0, 1, \ldots, k)$.

The system we have obtained does not have a solution for all stars, operators L or numbers q. If the star and the operator L have been chosen, it is desirable to state the problem of finding the largest value of q for which system (2.39) has a solution.

For the case of one-dimensional operators [e.g., for operator (2.31)], system (2.39) is always solvable [30].

As we have already noted, the method of substituting finite-difference ratios for derivatives is frequently used to compose the grid equations for the case of rectangular grids. If the grid is not rectangular, it is possible to use the method of "selection of coefficients" to obtain Eq. (2.37).

In the examples given below, the Laplacian $\Delta u \equiv \dfrac{\partial^2 u}{\partial x^2} + \dfrac{\partial^2 u}{\partial y^2}$ is used as the linear operator L.

EXAMPLE 3.1: On the plane we construct a triangular grid, for which, through the point $(ih, 0)$ of the Ox axis $(i = 0)$, ± 1, ± 2, $\ldots$) we draw two families of lines at angles of $60°$ and $120°$ to the Ox axis, and a family of lines that are parallel to the Ox axis and pass through the points at which the lines in the first two families intersect. The plane is thus covered by a set of equilateral triangles whose vertices are the mesh points of a so-called triangular grid.

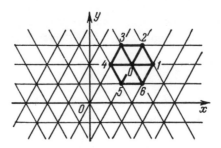

Fig. 5

By a star we will mean the set of seven mesh points containing the center and vertices of the regular hexagon composed of six elementary triangles of the grid (Fig. 5). We label the mesh points $0, 1, 2, 3, 4, 5, 6$ (0 is the center) and write

$$\tilde{\Delta}_h u \equiv \frac{u_1 + u_2 + u_3 + u_4 + u_5 + u_6 - 6u_0}{\dfrac{3h^2}{2}},$$

where u_j is the value of $u(x, y)$ at the mesh point with index j.

We have the formula

$$|\tilde{\Delta}_h u - (\Delta u)_0| \leqslant \tfrac{1}{4} M^{(4)} h^2, \tag{2.40}$$

and, consequently, the order of approximation of the equation $\Delta u = f$ by the equation $\tilde{\Delta}_h u_h = (f)_0$ in the class C^4 is 2 [25, 30].

EXAMPLE 3.2: We cover the plane with regular hexagons with side h, and we take the vertices to be the mesh points of a *hexagonal* grid. By a star we will mean the set of four mesh points indicated in Fig. 6 (Fig. 6 shows two stars with mesh points oriented differently relative to the coordinate axes). We write

$$\tilde{\tilde{\Delta}}_h u \equiv \frac{4(u_1 + u_2 + u_3 - 3u_0)}{3h^2}.$$

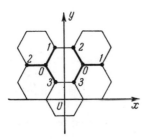

Fig. 6

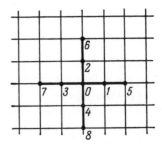

Fig. 7

It has been shown that

$$|\tilde{\Delta}_h u - (\Delta u)_0| \leqslant 1.36 M^{(3)} h,$$

i.e., the order of approximation of the equation $\Delta u = f$ by the equation $\tilde{\Delta}_h u_h = (f)_0$ in the class C^3 is 1 [25, 30].

EXAMPLE 4: *Improvement of approximation by expansion of stars.* For a square grid and a five-pointed star, the approximation order in the class C^4 of Eq. (2.14) by Eq. (2.16) is 2 and $q = 3$. If we use a nine-pointed star of the form shown in Fig. 4, it turns out that the coefficients $c_1, \ldots, c_8$ cannot be chosen so that $q \geqslant 4$. If we take a nine-pointed star of the form shown in Fig. 7, we will have

$$|\Delta_h' u - (\Delta u)_0| \leqslant \tfrac{4}{15} M^{(6)} h^4,$$

if we set

$$\Delta_h' u_h \equiv \frac{16(u_1 + u_2 + u_3 + u_4) - (u_5 + u_6 + u_7 + u_8) - 60 u_0}{12 h^2},$$

i.e., now the order of approximation of Eq. (2.14) by the equation $\Delta_h' u_h = (f)_0$ in the class C^6 is 4 (and now $q = 5$).

Concerning grid approximations of the Laplacian, see [2, 25, 30, 54, 75, 116].

(c) *Improvement of Approximation by Selection of the Operator* Π_h^0. *Multipoint equations.* In the examples given above, the operator associated the value of the right-hand side $f(X)$ at the center of the star with each star. An attempt can be made to improve the approximation by defining Π_h^0 as a linear combination of the values of $f(X)$ at the mesh points of a star. Let Lu, Ω, Ω_h, and the star be defined as in (b). Moreover, assume that the numbers $c_1', \ldots, c_k', d_1, \ldots, d_k$ have been chosen so that

$$c_1' u(X_1) + \cdots + c_k' u(X_k) - [d_1(Lu)_{X_1} + \cdots + d_k(Lu)_{X_k}] = 0 \qquad (2.41)$$

for all integral rational functions of some degree $q_1 > p$ relative to (x, y). It is then natural to assume

$$R_h' u_h \equiv c_1' u_h(X_1) + \cdots + c_k' u_h(X_k) = d_1 f(X_1) + \cdots + d_k f(X_k) \qquad (2.42)$$

as the grid analog of differential Equation (2.1). Assuming that the center of the star is the mesh point X_1, and that it has been possible to choose $c_1, \ldots,$ c_k so that $R_h u_h$ in (2.37) coincides with $(Lu)_{X_1}$ for all integral rational functions of degree q, and setting $c_1' = c_1, \ldots, c_k' = c_k$, $d_1 = 1$, $d_2 = d_3 = \cdots = d_k = 0$, we can see that Eq. (2.41) holds for all integral rational functions of degree q. It is therefore not impossible for there to exist a set of numbers $c_1', \ldots, d_k$, such that Eq. (2.41) holds for all integral rational functions of degree $q_1 > q$.

The coefficients $c'_1, \ldots, d_k$ can be determined with the system of linear homogeneous equations

$$\sum_{j=1}^{k} c'_j (x_j - x_1)^{\alpha_1} (y_j - y_1)^{\alpha_2}$$

$$- \sum_{j=1}^{k} d_j \left(\sum_{\nu=0}^{p} \sum_{\substack{\beta_1+\beta_2=\nu \\ \beta_1 \leqslant \alpha_1, \beta_2 \leqslant \alpha_2}} \alpha_{\beta_1,\beta_2}(x_j, y_j) \frac{\alpha_1!}{(\alpha_1 - \beta_1)!} \frac{\alpha_2!}{(\alpha_2 - \beta_2)!} \right.$$

$$\left. \times (x_j - x_1)^{\alpha_1-\beta_1}(y_j - y_1)^{\alpha_2-\beta_2} \right) = 0,$$

$$0 \leqslant \alpha_1, 0 \leqslant \alpha_2, \alpha_1 + \alpha_2 \leqslant q_1, \tag{2.43}$$

whose solution requires satisfaction of the condition

$$\sum_{j=1}^{k} |d_j| = 1. \tag{2.44}$$

If system (2.43)–(2.44) has a unique solution, then we have the inequality

$$|R'_h u - \Pi_h^0(Lu)| < CM^{(q_1+1)} h^{q_1-p+1} \tag{2.45}$$

for any $u(x, y) \in C^{q_1+1}$.

Equations of the form (2.42) are called *multipoint* grid equations. As inequality (2.45) implies, the order of approximation of Eq. (2.1) by such equations is $q_1 - p + 1$.

Remark. Let $\{\Omega_h\}$ be a sequence of grids with $h \to 0$. Assume that N_h^0 stars have been constructed for each admissible h and that an equation of the form (2.42) has been written for each star. Then Π_h^0 is an operator mapping the function $f \in F$ into a N_h^0 dimensional vector. If F is the class C^0, (2.44) is satisfied, and for each star the d_j have the same signs, and the norms $\|f_h\|_{F_h}$ and $\|f\|_F$ are consistent.

EXAMPLE 5: It has already been noted (Example 4) that for the star of Fig. 4 it is impossible to choose coefficients $c_0, c_1, \ldots, c_s$, providing a better approximation than a five-pointed star. The numbers

$$c'_0 = -\frac{40}{12h^2}, \quad c'_1 = c'_2 = c'_3 = c'_4 = \frac{2}{3h^2},$$

$$c'_5 = c'_6 = c'_7 = c'_8 = \frac{1}{6h^2}, \quad d_0 = \frac{2}{3},$$

$$d_1 = d_2 = d_3 = d_4 = \frac{1}{12}, \quad d_5 = d_6 = d_7 = d_8 = 0$$

satisfy system (2.43)–(2.44) for $L = \Delta (a_{00} = a_{10} = a_{01} = a_{11} = 0, a_{20} = a_{02} = 1, p = 2, q_1 = 5)$, and the grid equation

$$\bar{\Delta}_h u \equiv \frac{4(u_1 + u_2 + u_3 + u_4) + (u_5 + u_6 + u_7 + u_8) - 20u_0}{6h^2}$$

$$= \frac{2}{3}(f) + \frac{1}{12}((f)_1 + (f)_2 + (f)_3 + (f)_4) \qquad (2.46)$$

therefore approximates Eq. (2.14); it can be shown that for $u(x, y) \in C^6$, we have the inequality

$$\left| \bar{\Delta}_h u - \left\{ \frac{2}{3}(\Delta u)_0 + \frac{1}{12}[(\Delta u)_1 + (\Delta u)_2 + (\Delta u)_3 + (\Delta u)_4] \right\} \right| \leqslant \frac{h^4}{45} M^{(6)}.$$

The book [30] contains tables of multipoint formulas for the Laplace and biharmonic operators for square and triangular grids, as well as for the one-dimensional operators u', u'', u''', and u^{IV}.

EXAMPLE 6: *Improvement of approximation by choosing* Π_h^0 *depending on the derivatives of the functions* $f(X)$. For a nine-pointed star (see Fig. 4) and $u \in C^8$, it is easy to use Taylor's formula to show that

$$u_1 + u_2 + u_3 + u_4 - 4u_0 = h^2 \left[(\Delta u)_0 + \frac{2h^2}{4!} \left(\frac{\partial^4 u}{\partial x^4} + \frac{\partial^4 u}{\partial y^4} \right)_0 \right.$$

$$+ \frac{2h^4}{6!} \left(\frac{\partial^6 u}{\partial x^6} + \frac{\partial^6 u}{\partial y^6} \right)_0 + \frac{h^6}{8!} \left(\frac{\widetilde{\partial^8 u}}{\partial x^8} + \frac{\widetilde{\partial^8 u}}{\partial x^8} + \frac{\widetilde{\partial^8 u}}{\partial y^8} + \frac{\widetilde{\partial^8 u}}{\partial y^8} \right) \right],$$

$$u_5 + u_6 + u_7 + u_8 - 4u_0 = h^2 \left[2(\Delta u) + \frac{4h^2}{4!} \left(\frac{\partial^4 u}{\partial x^4} + 6 \frac{\partial^4 u}{\partial x^2 \partial y^2} + \frac{\partial^4 u}{\partial y^4} \right)_0 \right.$$

$$+ \frac{4h^4}{6!} \left(\frac{\partial^6 u}{\partial x^6} + 15 \frac{\partial^6 u}{\partial x^4 \partial y^2} + 15 \frac{\partial^6 u}{\partial x^2 \partial y^4} + \frac{\partial^6 u}{\partial y^6} \right)_0$$

$$+ \frac{h^6}{8!} \left(\frac{\widetilde{\partial^8 u}}{\partial x^8} + \frac{\widetilde{\partial^8 u}}{\partial x^8} + \frac{\widetilde{\partial^8 u}}{\partial x^8} + \cdots \right) \right],$$

where the unwritten terms contain eighth derivatives of the function $u(x, y)$ at certain intermediate points of the rays connecting the center of the star with the mesh points 5, 6, 7 and 8. If the first of these equations is multiplied by 4 and added to the second, division by $6h^2$ yields

$$\bar{\Delta}_h u \equiv \frac{4(u_1 + u_2 + u_3 + u_4) + (u_5 + u_6 + u_7 + u_8) - 20u_0}{6h^2}$$

$$= (\Delta u)_0 + \frac{h^2}{12}(\Delta^2 u)_0 + \frac{h^4}{360} \left[(\Delta^3 u)_0 + 2 \left(\frac{\partial^4 \Delta u}{\partial x^2 \partial y^2} \right)_0 \right]$$

$$+ \frac{h^6}{6 \cdot 8!} \left[4 \left(\frac{\widetilde{\partial^8 u}}{\partial x^8} + \cdots \right) + \left(\frac{\widetilde{\partial^8 u}}{\partial x^8} + \cdots \right) \right],$$

where

$$\Delta^2 u \equiv \Delta(\Delta u) \equiv \frac{\partial^4 u}{\partial x^4} + 2\frac{\partial^4 u}{\partial x^2 \partial y^2} + \frac{\partial^4 u}{\partial y^4},$$

$$\Delta^3 u \equiv \Delta(\Delta^2 u) \equiv \frac{\partial^2 u}{\partial x^6} + 3\frac{\partial^6 u}{\partial x^4 \partial y^2} + 3\frac{\partial^6 u}{\partial x^2 \partial y^4} + \frac{\partial^6 u}{\partial y^6}.$$

If we set

$$(\Pi_h^0(f))_0 \equiv (f)_0 + \frac{h^2}{12}(\Delta f)_0 + \frac{h^4}{360}\left[(\Delta^2 f)_0 + 2\left(\frac{\partial^4 f}{\partial x^2 \partial y^2}\right)_0\right],$$

then the order of approximation of Eq. (2.14) by the equation

$$\bar{\Delta}_h u_h = \Pi_h^0(f) \qquad (2.47)$$

in the class C^3 in six and is estimated by the quantity $520h^6/3 \cdot 8! M^{(8)}$ [30].

Remark 1. The left-hand sides of Eqs. (2.46) and (2.47) coincide.

Remark 2. If we set $(\Pi_h^0(f))_0 = (f)_0 + \dfrac{h^2}{16}(\Delta f)_0$, in Example 3 (triangular grid), we can, for $u \in C_6$ replace estimate (2.40) by the estimate [25]

$$|\tilde{\Delta}_h u - \Pi_h^0(\Delta u)| \leqslant \frac{7h^4}{270} M^{(6)}.$$

EXAMPLE 7: *The Biharmonic Poisson equation.* This is the name given to the differential equation

$$\Delta^2 u \equiv \frac{\partial^4 u}{\partial x^4} + 2\frac{\partial^4 u}{\partial x^2 \partial y^2} + \frac{\partial^4 u}{\partial y^4} = f(x, y). \qquad (24.8)$$

To obtain a grid equation approximating Eq. (2.48), we can proceed in the following manner. Each mesh point (i, j) of a square grid is assumed to be the center of the thirteen-pointed star composed of all mesh points of five-pointed stars having centers at all mesh points of the five-pointed star with center at (i, j) [see Fig. 8 for the mesh-point indexing].

If we set $\Delta_h^2 = \Delta_h(\Delta_h)$, we find that

$$\Delta_h^2 u_h = \Delta_h(\Delta_h u_h) = \frac{1}{h^2}\left[\frac{u_9 + u_5 + u_0 + u_8 - 4u_1}{h^2}\right.$$

$$+ \frac{u_5 + u_{10} + u_6 + u_0 - 4u_2}{h^2} + \frac{u_0 + u_6 + u_{11} + u_7 - 4u_3}{h^2}$$

$$\left. + \frac{u_8 + u_0 + u_7 + u_{12} - 4u_4}{h^2} - 4\frac{u_1 + u_2 + u_3 + u_4 - 4u_0}{h^2}\right]$$

$$= \frac{1}{h^4}[20u_0 - 8(u_1 + u_2 + u_3 + u_4) + 2(u_5 + u_6 + u_7 + u_8)$$

$$+ (u_9 + u_{10} + u_{11} + u_{12})].$$

Let Ω_h be the set of all mesh points of the square grid that lie inside or on the boundary Γ of the region Ω, for which Eq. (2.48) is being solved. For each interior (in the sense of the thirteen-pointed star) mesh point $(i, j) \in \Omega_h$ we write the equation

$$(\Delta_h^2 u)_{i,j} = (f)_{i,j}. \qquad (2.49)$$

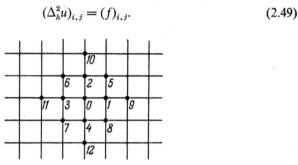

Fig. 8

In the class C^6 the order of approximation of Eq. (2.48) by Eq. (2.49) is 2 (it is estimated by $\frac{10}{9} h^2 M^{(6)}$) [25].

1.3 Problems concerning solvability, convergence, and error estimates. (a) *Solvability of Grid Equations.*

A. The grid analog of the principle of the maximum. The following property (*principle of the maximum*) is known for certain elliptic operators [61]: If a function $v(X)$ is such that $Lv \geqslant 0$ in Ω, then $v(X)$ can have no positive relative maximum in Ω.

For a number of grid operators appearing in approximation of elliptic differential equations, there is a property that may be called the *grid analog of the principle of the maximum*.

We label all mesh points of a grid Ω_h with numbers from 1 to N_h; we will call this indexing a general indexing. We assume that each mesh point $X_j \in \Omega_h$ (with general index j) is the center of some star and belongs to this star. Note that we have not eliminated the possibility that a star consisting of one mesh point, the center. For any star, we will say that a mesh point different from the center is *adjacent* to the center. Let k_j be the number of adjacent mesh points of X_j; we label the mesh points adjacent to X_j with numbers from 1 to k_j and call this labeling, internal. By $j(i)$ we denote the general index of the mesh point with internal index i in the star with center at X_j.

Assume that each equation in the grid system is of the form

$$(R_h u_h)_j \equiv A_j^{(1)} u_h(X_{j(1)} + \cdots + A_j^{(k_j)} u_h(X_{j(k_j)}) - A_j^{(0)} u_h(X_j) = F_j \quad (2.50)$$

$$(j = 1, 2, \ldots, N_h),$$

where the coefficients $A_j^{(i)}$ satisfy the conditions

$$\left.\begin{array}{l} A_j^{(i)} > 0 \quad (i = 0, 1, \ldots, k_j), \\ \sum_{i=1}^{k} A_j^{(i)} \leqslant A_j^{(0)} \ (j = 1, 2, \ldots, N_h). \end{array}\right\} \qquad (2.51)$$

If the mesh points X_j are such that $\sum_{i=1}^{kj} A_j^{(i)} = A_j^{(0)}$, we will say that X_j is a *mesh point of the first kind*; if $\sum_{i=1}^{kj} A_j^{(i)} < A_j^{(0)}$, we will say that X_j is a *mesh point of the second kind*.

We assume that:

1. there is at least one mesh point of the second kind:
2. if there are mesh points of the first kind, each of them can be connected by a broken line to at least one mesh point of the second kind so that all vertices of the broken line (except the end) are mesh points of the first kind and each succeeding mesh point is adjacent to the preceding point (belongs to the star with center at the preceding mesh point).

Lemma 1. If a grid function v_h is such that

$$(R_h v_h)_j \geqslant 0 \quad (j = 1, 2, \ldots, N_h),$$

then

$$v_h(X_j) \leqslant 0 \quad (j = 1, 2, \ldots, N_h).$$

Lemma 1'. If a grid function v_h is such that

$$(R_h v_h)_j \leqslant 0 \quad (j = 1, 2, \ldots, N_h),$$

then

$$v_h(X_j) \geqslant 0 \quad (j = 1, 2, \ldots, N_h).$$

Lemmas 1 and 1' give us the following:

Corollary. If $(R_h v_h)_j = 0$ $(j = 1, 2, \ldots, N_h)$ then $v_h(X_j) = 0$ $(j = 1, 2, \ldots, N_h)$,

This means that the homogeneous system corresponding to system (2.50) has only the trivial solution; it is known that this implies that the determinant of this system is therefore nonzero and it has a unique solution. We therefore have

Theorem 2. System (2.50) is solvable and has a unique solution (if the above-noted conditions concerning the coefficients and mesh points of the first and second kinds are satisfied).

EXAMPLE 8: System (2.11)–(2.12) has a unique solution. Indeed, each equation of system (2.11) can be written in the form

$$(R_h u_h)_{i,j} \equiv A_{i,j}^{(1)} u_{i+1,j} + A_{i,j}^{(2)} u_{i,j+1} + A_{i,j}^{(3)} u_{i-1,j}$$
$$+ A_{i,j}^{(4)} u_{i,j-1} - A_{i,j}^{(0)} u_{i,j} = (f)_{i,j}, \tag{2.52}$$

where, in virtue of (2.19), (2.20) and (2.21) of Theorem 1 (we assume that these conditions are satisfied), the coefficients $A_{i,j}^{(k)} (k = 0, 1, 2, 3, 4)$ satisfy the inequalities

$$A_{i,j}^{(k)} > 0 \quad (k = 0, 1, 2, 3, 4), \quad \sum_{k=1}^{4} A_{i,j}^{(k)} \leqslant A_{i,j}^{(0)}.$$

Equations (2.12) can be rewritten as follows: $-u_{i,j} = -\varphi(Q_{i,j})$, so here $A_{i,j}^{(0)} = -1$, and the star consists of one center. The boundary mesh points are mesh points of the second kind. Moreover, it follows from the assumptions of Theorem 1 concerning the grid Ω_h that there exists a broken line connecting mesh points of the first kind (if there are any) with mesh points of the second kind.

EXAMPLE 9: System (2.11)–(2.13) has a unique solution. Equation (2.13) can be rewritten in the form

$$\frac{\delta}{h} u_{i',j'} - \left(1 + \frac{\delta}{h}\right) u_{i,j} = -\varphi(Q_{i,j}),$$

and if $\delta \neq 0$, the star with center at (i, j) consists of two mesh points: (i', j') and (i, j). Since $\delta/h < 1 + (\delta/h)$, the boundary mesh point is a mesh point of the second kind, and the rest follows as in Example 8.

EXAMPLE 10: Grid equations (2.16), (2.17) and (2.18) have unique solutions.

Remark. Assume that in Eq. (2.31) the coefficients $c(x)$ and $g(x)$ satisfy the conditions $|c(x)| < M$, $g(x) \geqslant 0$. Then, for $h < 2/M$, the system of grid Equations (2.33) for the interior mesh points and (2.36) for the boundary mesh points satisfies the principle of the maximum and has a unique solution. The same can be said if the boundary conditions (2.32) are taken into account by linear interpolation or with Mikeladze's method.

EXAMPLE 11: For approximate solution of the Dirichlet problem for the equation $\Delta u - gu = f (g \geqslant 0$ in $\Omega)$ use a triangular grid (see Paragraph 2, Example 3.1) with side h. For an interior mesh point (in the sense of the seven-pointed star of Fig. 5) we have

$$\frac{2}{3h^2} (u_1 + u_2 + u_3 + u_4 + u_5 + u_6) - \left(\frac{4}{h^2} + (g)_0\right) u_0 = (f)_0, \tag{2.53}$$

and, therefore, an interior mesh point is a mesh point of the first kind if $(g)_0 = 0$, and a mesh point of the second kind if $(g)_0 > 0$.

At each boundary mesh point, the value of u_h is found by simple shift. The system of linear equations thus obtained has a unique solution.

A similar conclusion may be drawn for systems obtained by using a hexagonal grid (see Paragraph 2, Example 3.2).

Remark. The system consisting of the equation

$$\frac{2}{3h^2}(u_1 + u_2 + u_3 + u_4 + u_5 + u_6) - \frac{4}{h^2} u_0 = \left(f + \frac{h^2}{16}\Delta f\right)_0$$

and (2.12), which approximate the Dirichlet problem for $\Delta u = f$ (see Paragraph 2, Remark 2 on Example 6) has a unique solution.

EXAMPLE 12:   We will use a rectangular grid and a nine-pointed star (see Fig. 4) to find an approximate solution for the Dirichlet problem for the equation $\Delta u - gu = f$ $(g \geqslant 0)$. For each star with mesh points all belonging to Ω_h (in the sense of this star, for each interior mesh point), we write the multipoint equation (see Paragraph 2, Example 5)

$$\frac{4(u_1 + u_2 + u_3 + u_4) + (u_5 + u_6 + u_7 + u_8) - 20u_0}{6h^2}$$

$$= \tfrac{2}{3}((f)_0 + (g)_0 u_0) + \tfrac{1}{12}[(f)_1 + (g)_1 u_1 + \cdots],$$

obtained from (2.46) by substituting $f + gu$ for f. Thus,

$$\frac{2}{3h^2}\left[\left(1 - \frac{h^2}{8}(g)_1\right)u + \left(1 - \frac{h^2}{8}(g)_2\right)u_2 + \left(1 - \frac{h^2}{8}(g)_3\right)u_3\right.$$

$$\left. + \left(1 - \frac{h^2}{8}(g)_4\right)u_4\right] + \frac{1}{6h^2}(u_5 + u_6 + u_7 + u_8) \qquad (2.54)$$

$$- \left(\frac{10}{3h^2} + \frac{2}{3}(g)_0\right)u_0 = \frac{2}{3}(f)_0 + \frac{1}{12}[(f)_1 + (f)_2 + (f)_3 + (f)_4].$$

For $h^2 < 8/\max g$ the coefficients of $u_1, u_2, \ldots, u_8$ are positive, and because g is nonnegative, their sum is no larger than the coefficient of u_0, for

$$\frac{2}{3h^2}\left[4 - \frac{h^2}{8}((g)_1 + (g)_2 + (g)_3 + (g)_4)\right] + \frac{4}{6h^2}$$

$$= \frac{10}{3h^2} - \frac{1}{12}((g) + (g)_2 + (g)_3 + (g)_4) \leqslant \frac{10}{3h_2} \leqslant \frac{10}{3h^2} + \frac{2}{3}(g).$$

Thus, any interior mesh point is a mesh point of the first kind if $g \equiv 0$, but may be a mesh point of the second kind if $g \geqslant 0$. If u_h is assigned a value at the boundary mesh points by simple shift, the system of all of the equations has a unique solution.

Remark 1. Equation (2.47) can be used to solve the Poisson equation. System (2.47), (2.12) has a unique solution, since the left-hand sides of (2.46) and (2.47) are the same.

Remark 2. If boundary equations of the type (2.13) are written for Examples 11 and 12, the systems obtained will also have unique solutions.

EXAMPLE 13: Consider the following mixed problem: Find a solution $u(x, y)$ of Eq. (2.8) under the condition that $u(x, y)$ is given on some part of Γ_1 of the boundary Γ, while at each point $Q \in \Gamma - \Gamma_1 = \Gamma_2$ we are given the value $\psi(Q)$ of the derivative of $u(x, y)$ in the direction $l(Q)$, forming, with the interior normal, an acute angle $\alpha(Q)$ no larger than some fixed angle α_0.

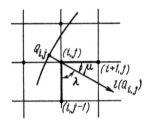

Fig. 9

To find the grid equations for a square grid, we write Eq. (2.11) for the interior mesh points (in the sense of a five-pointed star); at the boundary mesh points for which the closest boundary points lie on Γ_1, we write Eq. (2.12) (simple shift). Let (i, j) be a boundary mesh point for which the closest boundary point $Q_{i,j}$ lies in Γ_2 and consider the five-pointed star with center at (i, j). We assume that among the mesh points belonging to the stars in Ω_h, there are two such that the rays from (i, j) to these mesh points form acute angles μ and λ with $l(Q_{i,j})$; for definiteness assume that these mesh points are $(i + 1, j)$ and $(i, j - 1)$ (Fig. 9). For this boundary mesh point we write

$$\frac{\partial u}{\partial l(Q_{i,j})} \approx \frac{u_{i+1,j} - u_{i,j}}{h} \cos \mu + \frac{u_{i,j-1} - u_{i,j}}{h} \cos \lambda = \psi(Q_{i,j})$$

or

$$\frac{\cos \mu}{h} u_{i+1,j} + \frac{\cos \lambda}{h} u_{i,j-1} - \frac{\cos \mu + \cos \lambda}{h} u_{i,j} = \psi(Q_{i,j}), \qquad (2.55)$$

i.e., we have an equation of the form (2.50) with (i, j) a mesh point of the first kind.

If all of the boundary mesh points for which the closest boundary points belong to Γ_2, have the above property (acute angles between $l(Q)$ and rays from the mesh point), an equation of the form (2.55) can be written for each.

The system composed of Eqs. (2.11), (2.12) and (2.55) has a unique solution if there is at least one mesh point for which Eq. (2.12) has been written, or if the set of interior mesh points contains at least one mesh point of the second kind (which is possible only when $g \not\equiv 0$).

We will now derive another grid analog of $\partial u/\partial l$. Let the ray passing through the boundary mesh point (i, j) in the direction $l(Q_{i,j})$ enter one of the grid squares with vertex at the mesh point (i, j), and intersect the side opposite (i, j) at some point Q between the mesh points (i', j') and (i'', j'') closest to it. If $u(x, y)$ is linear on the segment between (i', j') and (i'', j''), we have

$$u(Q) = \left(1 - \frac{h'}{h}\right)(u)_{i',j'} + \frac{h'}{h}(u)_{i'',j''},$$

where h' is the distance from Q to (i', j') (Fig. 10).

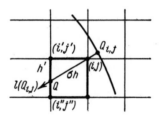

Fig. 10

Letting $\sigma h \, (1 \leqslant \sigma \leqslant \sqrt{2})$ denote the distance between (i, j) and Q, we take the expression

$$\frac{\left(1 - \dfrac{h'}{h}\right) u_{i',j'} + \dfrac{h'}{h} u_{i'',j''} - u_{i,j}}{\sigma h} \tag{2.56}$$

for the grid analog of $\partial u/\partial l$ [110]. The boundary mesh point whose equation is obtained by substitution of (2.56) for the left-hand side of Eq. (2.55) is a mesh point of the first kind.

Remark 1. For elliptic equation (2.8), the method of substituting finite-difference ratios for derivatives leads to grid system (2.11) which approximates Eq. (2.8) and forms, together with (2.12) or (2.13), a system that has a unique solution (because it satisfies the principle of the maximum).

If we consider an elliptic equation of the more general form

$$a \frac{\partial^2 u}{\partial x^2} + 2e \frac{\partial^2 u}{\partial x \, \partial y} + b \frac{\partial^2 u}{\partial y^2} + c \frac{\partial u}{\partial x} + d \frac{\partial u}{\partial y} - gu = f, \tag{2.57}$$

$$(e^2 < ab)$$

substitution of finite-difference ratios for derivatives in the case $e \not\equiv 0$ leads to a system that, generally speaking, does not satisfy the principle of the maximum. It was shown in [125] that for each elliptic equation (2.57) (under certain general assumptions about the coefficients a, b, and e) there exists a star (for a square grid) and an equation of the form (2.50) [with coefficients satisfying condition (2.51)] approximating Eq. (2.57).

Remark 2. When the conditions

$$(\alpha) \quad |e(x, y)| < \min \, (a(x, y), b(x, y)),$$

$$(\beta) \quad |c(x, y)| < M(a(x, y) - |e(x, y)|),$$

$$|d(x, y)| < M(b(x, y) - |e(x, y)|),$$

$$(\gamma) \quad g(x, y) \geqslant 0,$$

are satisfied, it is possible to find a grid equation for Eq. (2.57) that has star part of a nine-pointed star, satisfies condition (2.51), and has order of approximation 2. This equation is

$$(a)_0 \frac{u_1 - 2u_0 + u_3}{h^2} + (b)_0 \frac{u_2 - 2u_0 + u_4}{h^2}$$

$$+ 2(e)_0 \frac{u_5 + u_7 + 2u_0 - (u_1 + u_2 + u_3 + u_4)}{2h^2}$$

$$+ (c)_0 \frac{u_1 - u_3}{2h} + (d)_0 \frac{u_2 - u_4}{2h} - (g)_0 u_0 = (f)_0, \qquad (2.58)$$

if $(e)_0 \geqslant 0$; and

$$(a)_0 \frac{u_1 - 2u_0 + u_2}{h^2} + (b)_0 \frac{u_2 - 2u_0 + u_4}{h^2}$$

$$+ 2(e)_0 \frac{u_1 + u_2 + u_3 + u_4 - (u_6 + u_8 + 2u_0)}{2h^2}$$

$$+ (c)_0 \frac{u_1 - u_3}{2h} + (d)_0 \frac{u_2 - u_4}{2h} - (g)_0 u_0 = (f)_0, \qquad (2.59)$$

if $(e)_0 < 0$.

In virtue of conditions (α), (β), (γ) the coefficients for $u_1, \ldots, u_8$ are nonnegative when $h < 2/M$, while the coefficient of u_0 is negative and its modulus is no less than the sum of all of the other coefficients. When $(e)_0 > 0$, the star consists of the mesh points 0, 1, 2, 3, 4, 5, and 7; when $(e)_0 < 0$ the mesh points are 0, 1, 2, 3, 4, 6, and 8; when $(e)_0 = 0$, the mesh points are 0, 1, 2, 3, and 4.

B. *The grid analog of a self-adjoint elliptic differential equation.* It is known ([63], see also Chapter Three, Section 3, Paragraph 4 of the present book) that the solution of the Dirichlet problem for the self-adjoint elliptic differential equation

$$Lu \equiv \sum_{i=1}^{n} \sum_{j=1}^{n} \frac{\partial}{\partial x_i}\left(a_{ij}\frac{\partial u}{\partial x_j}\right) - gu = f \qquad (2.60)$$

where the $(a_{ij}(X))$ are the coefficients of a positive definite quadratic form, $g(X) \geqslant 0$ minimizes the functional

$$F[u] \equiv \int_{\Omega}\left[\sum_{i=1}^{n}\sum_{j=1}^{n}a_{ij}\frac{\partial u}{\partial x_i}\frac{\partial u}{\partial x_j} + gu^2 + 2fu\right]d\Omega \qquad (2.61)$$

over the class of functions that transform into the given function $\varphi(X)$; on Γ conversely, any function $u(X)$, that minimizes functional (2.61) over the functions transforming into φ on Γ is a solution of the Dirichlet problem for Eq. (2.60). This fact may be used as a basis for deriving grid analogs of the Dirichlet problem for Eqs. (2.60). To construct a system of such equations, the analog of functional (2.61) is constructed by substituting difference ratios for $\partial u/\partial x_i$, and an integral sum for the integral.

This grid analog of $F_h[u_h]$ is a quadratic function (the sum of a quadratic and a linear form) of u_h, a quadratic form of which is positive.

This quadratic function is bounded from below for grid functions taking given fixed values at certain mesh points (for example, values are assigned at the boundary mesh points by simple shift). Then the equations satisfied by the remaining values of the grid function are obtained by setting the derivatives of $F_h[u_h]$ with respect to each $u_h(X_j)$, equal to zero, where X_j is a mesh point where u_h is not fixed. The system of grid equations thus obtained has a unique solution.

EXAMPLE 14:   We consider the problem

$$\frac{\partial}{\partial x}\left(a\frac{\partial u}{\partial x} + e\frac{\partial u}{\partial y}\right) + \frac{\partial}{\partial y}\left(e\frac{\partial u}{\partial x} + b\frac{\partial u}{\partial y}\right) - gu = f, \left.\right\} \qquad (2.62)$$

$$u|_{\Gamma} = \varphi,$$

where the functions $a(x, y)$, $b(x, y)$, and $e(x, y)$ are such that $a > 0$, $b > 0$, $ab - e^2 > 0$. For definiteness, we take

$$F_h[u_h] \equiv h^2 \sum_{(i,j)\in\Omega_n}\left\{(a)_{i,j}\left(\frac{u_{i+1,j} - u_{i,j}}{h}\right)^2 + 2(e)_{i,j}\left(\frac{u_{i+1,j} - u_{i,j}}{h}\frac{u_{i,j+1} - u_{i,j}}{h}\right)\right.$$

$$+ (b)_{i,j}\left(\frac{u_{i,j+1} - u_{i,j}}{h}\right)^2 + (g)_{i,j}u_{i,j}^2 + 2(f)_{i,j}u_{i,j}\right\}, \qquad (2.63)$$

for the grid analog of $F_h[u_h]$, where it is understood that the finite-difference ratios $(u_{i+1,j} - u_{i,j})/h$ and $(u_{i,j+1} - u_{i,j})/h$ are replaced by zeros for those (i, j) for which the mesh point $(i + 1, j)$ or $(i, j + 1)$ does not belong to Ω_h. We separate all of the mesh points in Ω_h into interior and boundary (in the sense of a five-pointed star) mesh points. For the boundary mesh points we write (2.12) [simple shift], while for each interior mesh point (i, j) we obtain an equation of the form

$$A_{i,j}^{(1)}u_{i+1,j} + A_{i,j}^{(2)}u_{i,j+1} + A_{i,j}^{(3)}u_{i-1,j} + A_{i,j}^{(4)}u_{i,j-1}$$
$$+ A_{i,j}^{(6)}u_{i-1,j+1} + A_{i,j}^{(8)}u_{i+1,j-1} - R_{i,j}^{(0)}u_{i,j} = (f)_{i,j}, \quad (2.64)$$

where the coefficients $A_{i,j}^{(k)}$ are given by the formulas

$$A_{i,j}^{(1)} = \frac{(a)_{i,j} + (e)_{i,j}}{h^2}, \qquad A_{i,j}^{(2)} = \frac{(b)_{i,j} + (e)_{i,j}}{h^2},$$

$$A_{i,j}^{(3)} = \frac{(a)_{i-1,j} + (e)_{i-1,j}}{h^2}, \qquad A_{i,j}^{(4)} = \frac{(b)_{i,j-1} + (e)_{i,j-1}}{h^2},$$

$$A_{i,j}^{(6)} = -\frac{(e)_{i-1,j}}{h^2}, \qquad A_{i,j}^{(8)} = -\frac{(e)_{i,j-1}}{h^2},$$

$$A_{i,j}^{(0)} = \frac{1}{h^2}[(a)_{i,j} + (b)_{i,j} + 2(e)_{i,j} + (a)_{i-1,j} + (b)_{i,j-1}] + (g)_{i,j},$$

where $A_{i,j}^{(6)}[A_{i,j}^{(8)}]$ is replaced by a zero if the mesh point $(i - 1, j + 1)$ $[(i + 1, j - 1)]$ does not belong to Ω_h.

The system of grid equations (2.64) and (2.12) has a unique solution (if $ab - e^2 > 0$). In addition, the matrix of this system is symmetric and negative definite.

Notation:

$$u_{hx} = \frac{u_{i+1,j} - u_{i,j}}{h}, \quad u_{h\bar{x}} = \frac{u_{i,j} - u_{i-1,j}}{h},$$

$$u_{hy} = \frac{u_{i,j+1} - u_{i,j}}{h}, \quad u_{h\bar{y}} = \frac{u_{i,j} - u_{i,j-1}}{h}.$$

Now Eq. (2.64) takes the form

$$(au_{hx} + eu_{hy})_{\bar{x}} + (eu_{hx} + bu_{hy})_{\bar{y}} = f. \quad (2.65)$$

Equation (2.65) can be treated as an equation obtained from (2.62) by substitution of difference ratios for derivatives.

If $a \equiv b \equiv 1$, $e \equiv g \equiv 0$ (the Poisson equation), then (2.64) coincides with (2.16).

EXAMPLE 15: *Almost Self-Adjoint Equations.*   A general elliptic equation of the form

$$a \frac{\partial^2 u}{\partial x^2} + 2e \frac{\partial^2 u}{\partial x \, \partial y} + b \frac{\partial^2 u}{\partial y^2} + c* \frac{\partial u}{\partial x} + d* \frac{\partial u}{\partial y} - gu = f$$

can, when the coefficients a, b, and e are sufficiently smooth, be written in the form

$$\frac{\partial}{\partial x}\left(a \frac{\partial u}{\partial x} + e \frac{\partial u}{\partial y}\right) + \frac{\partial}{\partial y}\left(e \frac{\partial u}{\partial x} + b \frac{\partial u}{\partial y}\right) + c \frac{\partial u}{\partial x} + d \frac{\partial u}{\partial y} - gu = f,$$

(2.66)

where

$$c = c_* - \frac{\partial a}{\partial x} - \frac{\partial e}{\partial y}, \qquad d = d_* - \frac{\partial e}{\partial x} - \frac{\partial b}{\partial y}.$$

We assume that the coefficients a, b, and e satisfy the following condition: There exists a positive $\alpha > 0$, such that for all $(x, y) \in \Omega$ the smallest eigenvalue of the matrix $\left\| \begin{matrix} a & e \\ e & b \end{matrix} \right\|$ is no less than α (this assumption implies that $\alpha > 0$, $b > 0$, $ab - e^2 > 0$ for $(x, y) \in \Omega$). We will say that Eq. (2.66) is almost self-adjoint if for any sufficiently small positive ε we have

$$g(x, y) - \frac{1}{4\alpha - \varepsilon} (c^2(x, y) + d^2(x, y)) \geqslant 0.$$

Assume that the Dirichlet problem has been stated for Eq. (2.66). We write Eq. (2.12) for the boundary mesh points (in the sense of a five-pointed star) for a square grid Ω_h, and for each interior mesh point (i, j) we write an equation obtained from (2.65) by adding, to the left-hand side, terms

$$(c)_{i,j} \frac{u_{i+1,j} - u_{i,j}}{h} + (d)_{i,j} \frac{u_{i,j+1} - u_{i,j}}{h},$$

approximating $c \dfrac{\partial u}{\partial k} + d \dfrac{\partial u}{\partial y}$ [we will denote these equations by (2.65′)]. If Eq. (2.66) is almost self-adjoint then grid system (2.12), (2.65′) has a unique solution [35].

EXAMPLE 16: Multiplication of Eq. (2.31) by

$$p(x) \equiv e^{\int_0^x c(\xi) \, d\xi}$$

leads to the so-called self-adjoint form

$$\left. \begin{matrix} L_1 u \equiv \dfrac{d}{dx}\left[p(x) \dfrac{du}{dx}\right] - q(x)u = f_1(x) \\[2mm] q(x) = p(x)g(x), \quad f_1(x) = p(x)f(x), \end{matrix} \right\}$$

(2.67)

which is a special case of Eq. (2.60) for $n = 1$ if $p(x)$ is substituted for a_{11}, $q(x)$ is substituted for $g(x)$ and $f_1(x)$ is substituted for $f(x)$. In this case functional (2.61) takes the form

$$F_1[u] \equiv \int_0^1 [p(x)(u')^2 + q(x)u^2 + 2f_1(x)u] \, dx, \qquad (2.68)$$

and it remains to note the equivalence of the problem of minimizing the functional $F_1[u]$ and problem (2.67), (2.32) [the one-dimensional Dirichlet problem].

For the grid $x_k = kh(k = 0, 1, \ldots, N; \; h = 1/N)$ we introduce a grid analog of functional (2.68) in the form

$$F_{1h}[u_h] \equiv h \sum_{k=0}^{N-1} \left[p\left(x_k + \frac{h}{2}\right) \left(\frac{u_{k+1} - u_k}{h}\right)^2 + q(x_k)u_k^2 + 2f(x_k)u_k \right].$$

As in Example 14, we obtain the following system of $N - 1$ linear equations in $u_1, \ldots, u_{N-1}$

$$p\left(x_k + \frac{h}{2}\right) = p_{k+1/2}, \quad p\left(x_k - \frac{h}{2}\right) = p_{k-1/2}, \quad q(x_k) = q_k, \quad f_1(x_k) = f_{1k}:$$

$$\frac{p_{k+1/2}\dfrac{u_{k+1} - u_k}{h} - p_{k-1/2}\dfrac{u_k - u_{k-1}}{h}}{h} - q_k u_k = f_{1k} \qquad (2.69)$$

$$(k = 1, 2, \ldots, N - 1; \quad u_0 = \alpha, \quad u_N = \beta).$$

System (2.69) has a unique solution and its matrix is symmetric and negative definite. Grid system (2.69) satisfies the principle of the maximum.

EXAMPLE 17: Let Ω_h be a square grid in Ω, and let Ω_h^0 be the set of interior (in the sense of a five-pointed star) mesh points. We set

$$E_h[u_h] \equiv h^2 \sum_{(i,j)\in\Omega_h}^{0} \left[\left(\frac{u_{i+1,j} + u_{i,j+1} + u_{i-1,j} + u_{i,j-1} - 4u_{i,j}}{h^2}\right)^2 \right.$$
$$\left. - 2(f)_{i,j}u_{i,j} \right].$$

Assume that we know u_h at the mesh points that are not interior in the sense of a thirteen-pointed star (see Paragraph 2, Example 7). Then $E_h[u_h]$ is a quadratic function (the sum of quadratic and linear forms) of u_h at the interior (in the sense of a thirteen-pointed star) mesh points, and a quadratic form of this function is positive definite. $E_h[u_h]$ is bounded below and achieves a minimum at certain values of u_h at interior mesh points. These values of $u_{i,j}$, that minimize E_h, satisfy the equations [see (2.49)]

$$(\Delta_h^2 u_h)_{i,j} \equiv \frac{1}{h^4} [20u_{i,j} - 8(u_{i+1,j} + u_{i,j+1} + u_{i-1,j} + u_{i,j-1})$$

$$+ 2(u_{i+1,j+1} + u_{i-1,j+1} + u_{i-1,j-1} + u_{i+1,j-1}) \tag{2.49}$$

$$+ (u_{i+2,j} + u_{i,j+2} + u_{i-2,j} + u_{i,j-2})] = (f)_{i,j},$$

of which there are as many as there are interior mesh points. It is assumed in these equations that $u_{i+\xi,j+\eta}$ ($|\xi| + |\eta| \leqslant 2$) is replaced by its known value if the mesh point $(i + \xi, j + \eta)$ is not an interior mesh point. The system of equations thus obtained has a unique solution [34].

If a boundary-value problem has been stated for the biharmonic Poisson equation (2.48) and the grid boundary conditions have been written so as to make it possible to find the values of $u_{i,j}$ at the boundary mesh points (for a thirteen-pointed star), system (2.49), which approximates Eq. (2.48), has a unique solution.

(b) *Validity of Grid Equations.* Assume that some grid method provides the set of grids $\{\Omega\}_h$, $h \to 0$, for approximate solution of Problem (2.1)–(2.2), and assume that Eqs. (2.22) and (2.23) have been obtained for each grid Ω_h. Moreover, assume that norms have been introduced into the vector spaces thus formed.

Definition. Grid problem (2.22)–(2.23) is said to be well posed if for any $\varepsilon > 0$ there exists a $\delta > 0$ such that for any admissible h and all grid functions u_h and $\tilde{u}_h$ the inequalities

$$\| R_h u_h - R_h \tilde{u}_h \|_{F_h} \leqslant \delta, \tag{2.70}$$

$$\| r_{ih} u_h - r_{ih} \tilde{u}_h \|_{\Phi_{ih}} \leqslant \delta \quad (i = 1, 2, \ldots, s) \tag{2.71}$$

imply that

$$\| u_h - \tilde{u}_h \|_{U_h} \leqslant \varepsilon. \tag{2.72}$$

Remark 1. If a grid problem is well posed, no more than one solution $u_h \in U_h$ to Problem (2.22)–(2.23) can exist for each set $(f_h, \varphi_{1h}, \ldots, \varphi_{sh})$.

Remark 2. Let R_h and r_{ih} be linear operators (this is to be expected, if L and l_i are linear operators). If Grid Problem (2.22)–(2.23) has a unique solution for each admissible h, then for each such h there exist positive numbers N_h and N_{ih}, such that for any grid function u_h we have the inequality

$$\| u_h \|_{U_h} \leqslant N_h \| R_h u_h \|_{F_h} + \sum_{i=1}^{s} N_{ih} \| r_{ih} u_h \|_{\Phi_{ih}}. \tag{2.73}$$

For a grid problem to be well posed, it is necessary and sufficient that N_h and N_{ih} be bounded, i.e., it is necessary and sufficient that there exist positive numbers N and N_i (independent of h), such that for any grid function we have the inequality

$$\|u_h\|_{Uh} \leqslant N \|R_h u_h\|_{F_h} + \sum_{i=1}^{s} N_i \|r_{ih} u_h\|_{\Phi ih}. \qquad (2.74)$$

A. *Validity of grid equations satisfying the principle of the maximum.* For each admissible h assume that the set N_h of grid equations satisfying the principle of the maximum is partitioned into $s + 1$ groups with $N_h^0, N_h^1, \ldots,$ N_h^s equations each ($N_h^0 + N_h^1 + \cdots + N_h^s = N_h$).

We will treat the left-hand sides of the ith group as operators R_h^i, mapping N_h-dimensional vectors into N_h^i-dimensional vectors.

We will denote arbitrary individual components of a vector by [ ] between the vector parentheses. By the *norm* we will mean the maximum modulus of the vector components.

Lemma 2.   If there exist $s + 1$ functions

$$v_0(X), v_1(X), \ldots, v_s(X)$$

such that

$$[R_h^i v_j(X)] \leqslant \begin{cases} -1, & j = i, \\ 0, & j \neq i \end{cases} \quad (i, j = 0, 1, \ldots s), \qquad (2.75)$$

then for any grid function u_h we have the inequality

$$\|u_h\| \leqslant \sum_{i=0}^{s} N_i \|R_h^i u_h\|, \qquad (2.76)$$

where

$$N_i = \max_{X \in \Omega} v_i(X),$$

Lemma 2 makes it possible to prove that the grid equations of Examples 8–12 are valid. In each of these examples the system splits into two groups of equations: those for the interior mesh points and those for the boundary mesh points. The equation for each boundary mesh point X_j is such that

$$A_j^{(0)} - \sum_{i=1}^{k_j} A_j^{(i)} = 1.$$

As a result, $v_1(X) \equiv 1$ satisfies the conditions $(R_h v_1)_j = -1$ for each boundary mesh point X_j and $(R_h v_1)_j \leqslant 0$ for each interior mesh point X_j. Assume that the function $v_0(X)$ is positive in Ω and such that for each admissible h and each interior mesh point X_j we have $(R_h v_0)_j \leqslant -1$. For a boundary mesh point X_j we have

$$(R_h v_0)_j = \sum_{i=1}^{k} A_j^{(i)} v_0(X_{j(i)}) - A_j^{(0)} v_0(X_j)$$

$$< \sum_{i=1}^{k_j} A_j^{(i)} v_0(X_{j(i)}) \leqslant \max_{X \in \Omega} v_0(X) \sum_{i=1}^{k_j} A_j^{(i)} = \max_{X \in \Omega} v_0(X)(A_j^{(0)} - 1).$$

If the boundary condition is taken into account by simple shift, $A_i^{(0)} = 1$ and, therefore, we have $(R_h v_0)_j < 0$, i.e., the two functions $v_0(X)$ and $v_1(X) \equiv 1$ satisfy all the conditions of Lemma 2 for $s = 1$.

For grid boundary conditions (2.13) we have $A_j^{(0)} - 1 = \delta/h < 1$; it is not difficult to see that the function $v_0(X) = v_0(X) + \max v_0(X)$ is such that the two functions $v_0(X)$ and $v_1(X) \equiv 1$ satisfy the conditions of Lemma 2 for $s = 1$. A similar conclusion holds for Eq. (2.17).

Thus, if there exists a function $v_0(X)$ that is positive in Ω and such that $(R_h v_0)_j \leqslant -1$ for each interior mesh point, it follows from Lemma 2 that for Examples 8–12 we have

$$\|u_h\| \leqslant N \|R_h u_h\| + \|r_h u_h\|, \tag{2.77}$$

where

(a) $N = \max v_0(X)$ for boundary equation (2.12);

(b) $N = 2 \max v_0(X)$ for boundary equation (2.13) and (2.17).

We will now find several functions $v_0(X)$ for Examples 8–12.

1. If $c = d \equiv 0$, then $v_0(X) = C - [A(x - x_0)^2 + B(y - y_0)^2]$, where A, B and C are positive constants and (x_0, y_0) is an arbitrary point.

The constants A and B can easily be chosen so that $Lv_0 \leqslant -1$ for all points of Ω; then $[R_h v_0] \leqslant -1$, since $R_h v_0 = \Pi_h^0(Lv_0)$ for v_0. The constant C is chosen so large that $v_0(X) \geqslant 0$ in Ω.

For instance, if Ω is located in the ellipse

$$\mu(x, y) \equiv 1 - \frac{(x - x_0)^2}{p^2} - \frac{(y - y_0)^2}{q^2} \geqslant 0,$$

then we set

$$v_0(x, y) = C\mu(x, y),$$

where

$$C \geqslant \frac{1}{2 \min\limits_{(x,y)\in\Omega} \left[\dfrac{a(x, y)}{p^2} + \dfrac{b(x, y)}{q^2} \right]}.$$

In particular, if $a = b \equiv 1$ (the Laplacian) and $p = q = r$, then

$$v_0(x, y) = \tfrac{1}{4}[r^2 - (x - x_0)^2 - (y - y_0)^2].$$

2. For $c^2 + d^2 \not\equiv 0$, we propose the following two forms of the function $v_0(x, y)$ [30, 83]:

If the domain is located in the ellipse $\mu(x, y) \geqslant 0$ and the coefficients a, b, c and d are such that the function

$$\psi(x, y) \equiv \frac{a(x, y)}{p^2} + \frac{b(x, y)}{q^2} - \frac{|c(x, y)|}{p} - \frac{|d(x, y)|}{q}$$

has a positive minimum ψ_0 in Ω, we set [30]

$$v_0(x, y) = \frac{1}{2\psi_0} \mu(x, y).$$

(β) If $p = q = r$, $s = \min (a + b) (s > 0)$, then [83]

$$v_0(x, y) = \frac{3}{2As} (e^{Ar^2} - e^{A[(x-x_0)^2 + (y-y_0)^2]}),$$

where, by condition (2.19), $A = \dfrac{M^2 + 1}{4}$, $M > 0$.

Thus, the grid equations of Examples 8–12 are valid, and grid problem (2.33), (2.36) is well posed.

B. *Validity of almost self-adjoint grid equations.* We let U_h^0 denote the set of grid functions defined on a square grid in the plane and equal to zero at each mesh point that is not an interior mesh point (in the sense of a five-pointed star) for Ω_h. In U_h^0 we introduce the norm

$$\equiv \sqrt{h^2 \sum_{(i,j)\in\Omega h} \left[(u_{i,j})^2 + \left(\frac{u_{i+1,j} - u_{i,j}}{h}\right)^2 + \left(\frac{u_{i,j+1} - u_{i,j}}{h}\right)^2\right]},$$

which is consistent with the norm

$$\|u\|_{U_0} \equiv \sqrt{\int_\Omega [u^2 + |\operatorname{grad} u|^2]\, d\Omega}$$

in the class U^0 of functions $u(x, y)$, that are continuous in Ω, together with their first derivatives. By F_h we denote the set of grid functions defined on the set Ω_h^0 of interior mesh points; in F_h we introduce the norm

$$\|f_h\|_{F_h} \equiv \sqrt{h^2 \sum_{(i,j)\in\Omega_h^0} (f_{i,j})^2},$$

which is consistent with the norm

$$\|f\|_F \equiv \sqrt{\int_\Omega f^2\, d\Omega}$$

in the class F of functions $f(x, y)$, that are continuous in Ω. We denote the left-hand sides of Eqs. (2.65′) by $(R_h u_h)_{i,j}$.

We therefore state that: If Eq. (2.66) is almost self-adjoint, there exists a positive constant N (independent of α, ε, or the dimensions of Ω), such that for any admissible h and any function $u_h \in U_h^0$ we have (see [35]) the inequality

$$\|u_h\|_{U_h^0} \leqslant N\|R_h u_h\|_{F_h}. \tag{2.78}$$

(c) *A Theorem on Convergence and Estimation of Errors* [83].

Theorem 3.   Assume that: (α) Problem (2.1)–(2.2) has a unique solution; (β) Equations (2.22) and (2.23) approximate Eqs. (2.1) and (2.2); (γ) Grid Problem (2.22)–(2.23) has a solution $u_h \in U_h$ for each admissible h; (δ) Grid Problem (2.22)–(2.23) is well posed.

Then, as $h \to 0$, the grid solution converges to the exact solution, i.e.,

$$\lim_{h \to 0} \|u_h - u(X)\|_{Uh} = 0. \qquad\qquad .(2.79)$$

Corollary.   If, moreover, the operators R_h and r_{ih} are linear, we have the inequality

$$\|u_h - u(X)\|_{Uh} \leqslant N \,\|R_h u - \Pi_h^0(Lu, l_1 u, \ldots, l_s u)\|_{Fh}$$

$$+ \sum_{i=1}^{s} N_i \,\|r_{ih} u - \Pi_k^i(Lu, l_1 u, \ldots, l_s u)\|_{\Phi ih}, \quad (2.80)$$

and if the functions $\alpha(h)$ and $\alpha_i(h)$ estimate the approximation [see (2.27) and (2.28)], then

$$\|u_h - u(X)\|_{Uh} \leqslant MN\alpha(h) + \sum_{i=1}^{s} M_i N_i \alpha_i(h). \qquad (2.81)$$

Remark 1.   The functions $\omega(h)$ in inequality (2.7) may be used as the right-hand sides of inequalities (2.80) and (2.81), i.e., in this case an error estimate has been found.

Remark 2.   It may occur that Grid Problem (2.22)–(2.23) is not well posed but the numbers N_h and N_{ih} of inequality (2.73) and the functions $\alpha(h)$ and $\alpha_i(h)$ are such that

$$\omega(h) \equiv MN_h\alpha(h) + \sum_{i=1}^{s} M_i N_{ih}\alpha_i(h) \to 0, \qquad h \to 0.$$

In this case the grid solution also converges to the exact solution and an error estimate has been found.

We will now use Theorem 3 to obtain estimates of the error in the grid solution of the Dirichlet problem. Theorem 3 will also be used in other sections of the chapter.

1.4 Convergence and estimation of the error for the Dirichlet problem.   (a) *Grid Equations Satisfying the Principle of the Maximum.*

Under certain relatively general conditions concerning the smoothness of the contour, the coefficients a, b, c, d, and g, and the given f and φ, Dirichlet Problem (2.8)–(2.9) has a unique solution $u(x, y)$, that is continuous in the closed region $\Omega + \Gamma$ and is such that certain derivatives may prove to be unbounded in the neighborhood of Γ.

If this solution $u(x, y)$ is so smooth that $u \in C^4$, then Grid Problem

(2.11)–(2.12) or (2.11)–(2.13) has approximation estimates (2.29), (2.34), and (2.35), so conditions (α) and (β) of Theorem 3 are satisfied for $U = C^4$. Moreover, these grid problems are also solvable and well posed, i.e., conditions (γ) and (δ) of Theorem 3 are satisfied. As a result, because R_h and r_h are linear, estimate (2.81) can be used here. We will present the results, assuming, for the sake of simplicity, that the grid is square.

(1) *System* (2.11)–(2.12) [*simple shift*]. Using (2.29), (2.34), and (2.81) [N as in (2.77), $N_1 = 1$], we find that

$$\|u_h - u\| \leqslant NMh^2 + M^{(1)}h = h(M^{(1)} + MNh) \leqslant Ch, \qquad (2.82)$$

i.e., the order of the approximation is 1. This is *Gershgorin's estimate* [117].

If all of the boundary mesh points lie on Γ, then the right-hand side of (2.34) can be replaced by a zero and (2.82) can be replaced by

$$\|u_h - u\| \leqslant NMh^2, \qquad (2.83)$$

i.e., the order of the approximation is 2.

(2) *System* (2.11) *and* (2.13) (*allowance for boundary conditions by linear interpolation*). Using (2.29), (2.35), and (2.81), we find that

$$\|u_h - u\| \leqslant NMh^2 + M^{(2)}h^2 = (M^{(2)} + NM)h^2 = Ch^2, \qquad (2.84)$$

i.e., the order of the approximation is 2. This is *Collatz' estimate* [30].

It follows from comparison of (2.82) and (2.84) that given the same and sufficiently fine mesh, system (2.11), (2.13) yields a more accurate solution than (2.11)–(2.12).

Remark. Estimate (2.84) also holds for a grid system with boundary conditions according to Mikeladze [see (2.17)].

(3) Assume that the Dirichlet problem has been stated for Eq. (2.8). To solve it, both hexagonal and triangular grids can be used, as well as a square grid with either Eqs. (2.46) [multipoint] or (2.47) [allowance for the derivatives of the function $f(x, y)$], with boundary conditions taken into account by simple shift.

If for each admissible h some of the boundary mesh points do not lie in Γ, then the estimate $\|u_h - u\|$ contains the term $M^{(1)}h$ and the order of approximation is no greater than 1. If the region Ω and the grid Ω_h are such that for each admissible h the boundary mesh points lie on Γ, then it is possible to hope for a higher order of approximation of u by u_h. In what follows we will assume that all boundary mesh points lie on Γ.

(α) Assume that a hexagonal grid (see Paragraph 2, Example 3.2) is used. If $u \in C^3$, then

$$\|u_h - u\| \leqslant 1.36NM^{(3)}h.$$

(β) Assume that the grid is triangular (see Paragraph 2, Example 3.1). If $u \in C^4$, then [see (2.40)]

$$\|u_h - u\| \leqslant \frac{N M^{(4)}}{4} h^2,$$

i.e., the order of approximation is 2.

If the same grid is used and the right-hand sides of the grid equations are evaluated with the formula

$$\left(f + \frac{h^2}{16} \Delta f \right)$$

then, if we assume that $u \in C^6$ (see Paragraph 2, Example 6, Remark 2, we obtain the estimate

$$\|u_h - u\| \leqslant \frac{7 N M^{(6)}}{270} h^4.$$

(γ) Assume that the grid is square and the region Ω is such that all boundary mesh points (in the sense of the nine-pointed star of Fig. 4) lie on Γ and assume that $u \in C^6$. If Eq. (2.46) is used,

$$\|u_h - u\| \leqslant \frac{N M^{(6)}}{45} h^4.$$

If $u \in C^8$ and Grid Equations (2.47) are used,

$$\|u_h - u\| \leqslant \frac{520 N M^{(8)}}{3 \cdot 8!} h^6.$$

It is clear from our examples that use of Eqs. (2.46) and (2.47) is justified only when all boundary mesh points lie on Γ and it is certain that $u \in C^6$ or $u \in C^8$, respectively.

(4) In (1) and (2) it was assumed that $(x, y) \in C^4$. We will now assume that instead of this being so, we have $u \in C^2$. Then, using (2.30) instead of (2.29), and (2.80) instead of (2.81), we can see that $\|u_h - u\| \to 0$ as $h \to 0$, i.e., the grid solution uniformly converges to the exact solution. In this case the error estimate can be expressed in terms of the modulus of continuity of the second derivatives of the exact solution $u(x, y)$.

(5) If $u(x, y)$ does not belong to C^2, it is not certain that $u_h \to u$ uniformly. If, for a sufficiently fine mesh, Eq. (2.11) is written only for the interior mesh points that are no further from Γ then some quantity ε larger than h, and if for the remaining mesh points of Ω_h the solution u_h is determined by simple shift, then $u_h \to u$ uniformly when $\varepsilon \to 0$ and $h \to 0$ in the appropriate manner (the ratio h/ε depends on the behavior of the second derivatives in the neighborhood of Γ) [77].

(6) In [9] the *interior mesh points* of a square grid were the points whose distance from Γ was no less than $2h$. In the case of the Laplace Equation $((2.14), f \equiv 0)$, Eq. (2.16) $(f \equiv 0)$, was written for these mesh points, while a new method of writing the boundary conditions was used for the boundary mesh points. This paper also gave estimates of the error under the assumption that $u(x, y) \in C^k (k = 1, 2, 3)$.

(7) The following can be said about the error $\|u - u_h\|$ [u is the solution of Problem (2.31)–(2.32), while u_h is the solution to grid system (2.33), (2.36)]:

$$\|u - u_h\| \leqslant Ch^2, \quad \text{if } u \in C^4,$$

$$\|u - u_h\| \to 0, \qquad \text{if } u \in C^2$$

(it is assumed that $|c(x)| < M, g(x) \geqslant 0$).

(b) *Almost Self-Adjoint Grid Equations.*   As we have already noted (see Paragraph 3, Example 15), Grid Equations (2.65′) have a solution if (2.66) is almost self-adjoint. If $u_h \in U_h^0$ (see Paragraph 3,b, B), system (2.65′) is well posed, provided that $u_{i,j} = 0$ at the boundary mesh points [see (2.78)]. By Theorem 3, the grid solution will converge in the norm of U_h^0 to the exact solution if Eqs. (2.65′) approximate (in the norm of F_h, see Paragraph 3,b, B) Eq. (2.66). It can be shown that such an approximation occurs, for example, for $u \in C^2$ (if the coefficients a, b and e have bounded first derivatives) and, consequently, the grid solution converges in the norm of U_h^0 to the exact solution.

Because the estimates possible here are cumbersome, we will limit ourselves to what has been said above.

(c) *Error Estimates in Terms of the Given for a Problem.*   Estimates (2.82), (2.84), and similar ones have the disadvantage that their right-hand sides contain $M^{(k)}$—the norms of the kth derivatives of the exact solution, which, like the exact solution, are unknown. The following techniques have been developed to eliminate this difficulty.

(α) For a given grid Ω_h, the grid equations are solved and u_h is determined. The difference ratios approximating the derivatives for which it is required to determine the maximum modulus are computed for the grid function found. The maximum modulus of the difference ratios of order k is then taken for $M^{(k)}$. This method always works, but it is unreliable.

(β) It is sometimes possible to use general theoretical considerations to estimate $M^{(k)}$ in terms of the f and φ given for a problem. Namely, assertions of the following type hold for elliptic equations: If the coefficients of the equation, the contour Γ, and the given f and φ are sufficiently smooth, the solution of the Dirichlet problem belongs to the class C_k and $M^{(k)}$ is no larger than some function of the quantities characterizing the smoothness of the coefficients, the contour, and the given functions. The estimate of $M^{(k)}$ obtained in this way is, as a rule, extremely high. While this method is theoretically sound, it is of little use and hardly any practical value because the estimate is so large.

(γ) An attempt is made to estimate the error directly in terms of the given data of the problem. This attempt is successful when the region Ω is a rectangle, L is the Laplacian, and the grid equation is of the form (2.16) ($f \equiv 0$). We will give one result of this type [116].

If Ω is the square $0 \leqslant x \leqslant a, 0 \leqslant y \leqslant a$, then

$$\|u_h - u\| \leqslant (1.4A_2 + 0.43A_3a)h^2, \tag{2.85}$$

where the function $\varphi(s)$ given on the boundary is continuous on the contour has continuous derivatives of up to third order along each side of the square, A_2 is the maximum of $|\varphi''|$ at the vertices of the square, and A_3 is the maximum of $|\varphi'''|$ on the sides of the square.

Generally speaking, the exact solution will not belong to C^4 for certain $\varphi(s)$ and then it is impossible to expect estimate (2.83) to hold (it may, perhaps, be possible to obtain an estimate of the form $NM^{(3)}h$). Estimate (2.85) is better than the one obtained with (2.81).

For other estimates of the form (2.85), see [116].

1.5 Iteration methods for solving the grid Dirichlet problem.   The number of equations in system (2.11)–(2.12) or (2.11), (2.13) is N_h—the number of mesh points in the grid Ω_h—and for a square grid it is approximately equal to $|\Omega|/h^2$, where $|\Omega|$ is the area of the region Ω. Besides the fact that the number of equations in the system rapidly increases as $h \to 0$, the number of conditions on the system [90, 104] increases approximately as fast as the number of equations in the system. Thus, application of exact methods for solution of such systems can be assumed to be of little use and iteration methods become preferable.

(a) *Simple Iteration for Grid Systems Satisfying the Principle of the Maximum.*   Consider system (2.50) under the assumptions of

Lemma 1.   If Eq. (2.50) for the mesh point X_j is solved for $u_h(X_j)$, we obtain, instead of system (2.50), a system of equations of the form

$$u_h(X_j) = a_j^{(1)}u_h(X_{j(1)}) + \cdots + a_j^{(k_j)}u_h(X_{j(k_j)}) + b_j$$

$$(j = 1, 2, \ldots, N_h), \tag{2.86}$$

where

$$a_j^{(i)} = \frac{A_j^{(i)}}{A_j^{(0)}}(i = 1, 2, \ldots, k_j), \qquad b_j = -\frac{F_j}{A_j^{(0)}}.$$

It follows from inequalities (2.51), which are satisfied by $A_j^{(i)}$, that

$$a_j^{(i)} > 0, \qquad \sum_{i=1}^{k_j} a_j^{(i)} \leqslant 1, \qquad (2.87)$$

and for at least one index $j = j_0$ (a mesh point of the second kind)

$$\sum_{i=1}^{k_{j_0}} a_{j_0}^{(i)} < 1. \qquad (2.88)$$

If system (2.86) is written in matrix form

$$u_h = A_h u_h + b_h, \qquad (2.89)$$

it follows from the properties (2.87) of the entries of the matrix A_h that all of its eigenvalues have absolute value no larger than 1.

The fact that it is possible to pass from each mesh point of the first kind (see Paragraph 3a) to a mesh point of the second kind through an adjacent mesh point guarantees that the following statement is true: The absolute values of all eigenvalues of the matrix A_h are less than 1. As we know [104], this implies that the iteration process

$$u_h^{(m+1)} = A_h u_h^{(m)} + b_h, \qquad (2.90)$$

converges, where $u_h^{(m)}$ is the mth iteration and $u_h^{(0)}$ is the arbitrary grid function chosen as the initial approximation.

The computation proceeds as follows: An arbitrary grid function $u_h^{(0)}(X_j)$ is chosen and new grid functions $u_h^{(1)}(X_j), u_h^{(2)}(X_j), u_h^{(3)}(X_j), \ldots, u_h^{(m)}(X_j)$, are chosen by means of the formulas

$$u_h^{(m+1)}(X_j) = a_j^{(1)} u_h^{(m)}(X_{j(1)}) + \cdots + a_j^{(k_j)} u_h^{(m)}(X_{j(k_j)}) + b_j \qquad (2.91)$$

$$(j = 1, 2, \ldots, N_h).$$

After several computation cycles with Formulas (2.91), the process is terminated and the result of the last cycle is taken for the approximate value of the grid function $u_h(X_j)$ ($j = 1, 2, \ldots, N_h$).

Assume that $u_h^{(k)}$ has been obtained after k ($k \geqslant 1$) iterations. Below we will show how the quantity $\sigma^{(k)} = \|u_h^{(k)} - u_h^{(k-1)}\|$, can easily be used, with almost no additional computation, to find the error $\varepsilon^{(k)} = \|u_h^{(k)} - u_h\|$, where u_h is the exact solution of grid system (2.86) or, equivalently, (2.50).

Remark 1. For each mesh point X_j consider the quantity $\eta_j \equiv \sum_{i=1}^{k_j} a_j^{(i)}$. Then we have $0 \leqslant \eta_j \leqslant 1$ for all mesh points, while for mesh points of the second kind we have $\eta_j < 1$. There are l mesh points of the second kind, which we index with numbers from 1 to l so that $\eta_j \leqslant \eta_{j+1}$. The mesh points of the first kind (if there are any) are labeled as follows: Each mesh point must have a mesh point already labeled adjacent to it, and this labeling process continues until all of the mesh points of the grid are exhausted (this process must terminate, since any mesh point of the first kind can be connected through an adjacent mesh point to a mesh point of the second kind, which is already labeled). The Seidel iteration process [104] for system (2.86) will converge when this indexing is used. In comparison with formulas (2.91), the difference in the computation lies in the fact that $u_h^{(m+1)}(X_{j(i)})$, is substituted for $u_h^{(m)}(X_{j(i)})$ when $j(i) < j$.

Remark 2. In paragraph 3, Examples 8–12 provided examples of grid systems approximating the Dirichlet problem for the Laplace equation [Examples 10, 11, 12] and for the general elliptic equation (2.8) [Examples 8, 9]. These grid systems satisfy the principle of the maximum, and their approximate solutions can be found by iteration. If the coefficient $g(x, y)$ is identically equal to zero, all of the interior mesh points are mesh points of the first kind and, for the Seidel iteration process to converge, it is sufficient to label the boundary mesh points (mesh points of the second kind) first, and then, in the order given above, label the remaining interior mesh points.

EXAMPLE 18: We will use a square grid to find an approximate solution to the Dirichlet problem for the Poisson equation. We write Eq. (2.16) for the interior mesh points (in the sense of a five-pointed star), and allow for boundary conditions by means of simple shift. Then the iteration process proceeds as follows. An arbitrary $u_h^{(0)}$ is chosen for the interior mesh points and the computation proceeds according to the formula

$$u_{i,j}^{(m+1)} = \frac{1}{4}\left(u_{i+1,j}^{(m)} + u_{i,j+1}^{(m)} + u_{i-1,j}^{(m)} + u_{i,j-1}^{(m)}\right) - \frac{h^2}{4}(f)_{i,j} \qquad (2.92)$$

when $f \equiv 0$ (the Laplace equation), computation of subsequent approximations with Formula (2.92) is called *Liebmann's method* (or *the averaging method*). If, instead of a square grid, a triangular grid is used, we have

$$u_0^{(m+1)} = \frac{1}{6}\left(u_1^{(m)} + u_2^{(m)} + u_3^{(m)} + u_4^{(m)} + u_5^{(m)} + u_6^{(m)}\right) - \frac{h^2}{4}(f)_0,$$

instead of (2.92), where 0, 1, 2, 3, 4, 5, and 6 are the indices of the center and mesh points of a seven pointed star.

For a hexagonal grid we have

$$u^{(m+1)} = \frac{1}{3}\left(u_1^{(m)} + u_2^{(m)} + u_3^{(m)}\right) - \frac{h^2}{4}(f)_0.$$

Remark 3. For examples 8–12, let A_0 denote the largest of the coefficients $A_j^{(0)}$ for the interior mesh points X_j. For Examples 8 and 9 [system (2.11)] A_0 is no larger than

$$\frac{2\max(a + b)}{h^2} + \max g;$$

for Example 11,

$$A_0 \leqslant \frac{4}{h^2} + \max g$$

(for triangular and hexagonal grids); for Example 12,

$$A_0 \leqslant \frac{10}{3h^2} + \max g$$

(multipoint equation). If the boundary conditions are accounted for by simple shift,

$$\varepsilon_{(k)} \equiv \|u_h^{(k)} - u_h\| \leqslant NA_0 \sigma^{(k)} \equiv NA_0 \| u_h^{(k)} - u_h^{(k-1)}\|, \qquad (2.93)$$

where N is the number of inequalities (2.77); if the boundary conditions are taken into account by linear interpolation,

$$\varepsilon^{(k)} \leqslant (NA_0 + \tfrac{1}{2}) \sigma^{(k)}, \qquad (2.94)$$

and we can therefore determine the error occurring when the kth iteration is taken as the approximation solution of the grid system.

Remark 4. Lyusternik [53] proposed a method for accelerating the iteration process with formula (2.92) by suppressing certain components of the error $u_h^{(m)} - u_h$ (the two components that, differing only in sign, correspond to the largest (in absolute value) eigenvalue of the grid operator

$$S_h u_h \equiv \tfrac{1}{4}(u_{i+1,j} + u_{i,j+1} + u_{i-1,j} + u_{i,j-1}),$$

which is defined on the grid functions equal to zero at the boundary mesh points). Assume that $u_h^{(m)}$, $u_h^{(m+2)}$, and $u_h^{(m+4)}$ have been found. Then, (α) these three vectors are used to compute the ratio

$$\left\{ \sum_{(i,j)\in\Omega_h^0} [u_{i,j}^{(m)} - u_{i,j}^{(m+4)}] \right\} : \left\{ \sum_{(i,j)\in\Omega_h^0} [u_{i,j}^{(m)} - u_{i,j}^{(m+2)}] \right\},$$

which is then set equal to $1 + \lambda^2$, so λ^2 can be found; (β)

$$u_h \approx u_h^{(m)} - \frac{1}{1 - \lambda^2} (u_h^{(m)} - u_h^{(m+2)})$$

must be taken for the corrected value of u_h.

In [53, 75] there are examples in which, for $m = 7$, it was possible to obtain u_h behaving as if 26 iterations had been executed, so this method makes it possible to save 15 iterations ($26 - (7 + 4) = 15$).

(b) *Selection of Factors.* Let R_h denote the $N_h + N_h$ matrix corresponding to grid system (2.50), which satisfies the principle of the maximum; in matrix form, system (2.50) is

$$R_h u_h = F_h. \qquad (2.95)$$

The real part of each eigenvalue of the matrix R_h is negative. It thus follows that there exists a positive factor $\alpha > 0$, for which the eigenvalues of the matrix $E + \alpha R_h$ (E is the identity matrix of order N_h) have modulus less than 1. If such a factor has been found, the system

$$u_h = (E + \alpha R_h)u_h - \alpha F_h, \tag{2.96}$$

is equivalent to system (2.95), and the iteration process

$$u_h^{(m+1)} = (E + \alpha R_h)u_h^{(m)} - \alpha F_h \tag{2.97}$$

converges.

Since all of the grid systems in Examples 8–12 satisfy the principle of the maximum, each of them can be transformed into the form (2.96) and convergence of the iteration can be ensured by proper selection of the factor α. In the general case, selection of this factor for system (2.11)–(2.12) or (2.11), (2.13) is a rather difficult problem, and we will therefore limit the discussion to Examples 11 and 12 and system (2.16), (2.12).

In these examples, the boundary conditions are taken into account by simple shift. In each equation written for an interior mesh point with adjacent boundary mesh points, we place the terms corresponding to boundary mesh points in the right-hand side. The remaining system of equations also satisfies the principle of the maximum (since, if they are mesh points of the first kind in the initial system, interior mesh points of the first kind become mesh points of the second kind in the transformed system). As a result, the real parts of the eigenvalues of the matrix are negative. Since the matrices in these examples are also symmetric, the eigenvalues are real and, consequently, negative. We should note that the same can be said about the matrix corresponding to system (2.64), which is the grid analog of a self-adjoint elliptic equation.

We write this system in the form

$$A_h u_h = F_h,$$

where the matrix A_h is symmetric and negative definite. For a system of this type, the authors of [90, 116] proposed an iteration process of the form

$$u_h^{(m+1)} = u_h^{(m)} + \alpha_m (A_h u_h^{(m)} - F_h),$$

where the iteration process can be appreciably accelerated by choosing an appropriate sequence $\{\alpha_m\}$. Different methods (steepest descent, Chebyshev polynomials, under and over relaxation, etc.) have been proposed as different algorithms for selection of the sequence $\{\alpha_m\}$ [90, 104, 116]. The results of experimental application of these methods for Eq. (2.16) with Ω a rectangle are given in [90, 116].

The so-called Monte Carlo method has been used for solution of grid systems; see "Methods of Statistical Testing (the Monte Carlo Method)," Yu. A. Shreider, Elsevier Publishing Co., 1964.

1.6 Numerical examples. We will conclude the discussion of the Dirichlet grid problem with two examples of problem solution. In the solutions, the grid is chosen so that the number of unknowns in the system of equations is no larger than 20–100, although present high-speed computers make it appear that it will soon be possible to solve grid systems with a much larger number of unknowns.

EXAMPLE 19: Assume that the region Ω is composed of four squares with sides of length 1 and centers at the points $(0, \frac{1}{2})$, $(0, \frac{3}{2})$, $(-1, \frac{1}{2})$, and $(1, \frac{1}{2})$ of

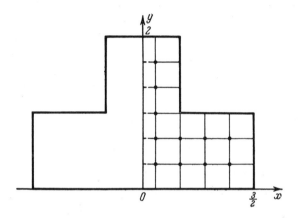

Fig. II

the $u(x, y)$ plane; also assume that the sides are parallel to the coordinate axes (Fig. 11). It is required to find the solution $u(x, y)$ of the Poisson equation

$$\Delta u \equiv \frac{\partial^2 u}{\partial x^2} + \frac{\partial^2 u}{\partial y^2} = -2,$$

that vanishes on the contour Γ of Ω:

$$u \big|_\Gamma = 0.$$

We should note that this problem appears in research on twisting of cylindrical beams whose cross section coincides with the region Ω.

Let l be some line in the (x, y) plane, P any point in the plane, and P' the point symmetric to P about l. We will say that the function $u(x, y)$ is symmetric (antisymmetric) about l, if $u(P) = u(P')$ $(u(P) = -u(P'))$ for an arbitrary point P.

It follows from the symmetry of Ω and the given of the problem that the exact solution $u(x, y)$ is symmetric about the $0y$ axis. It is therefore sufficient to find $u(x, y)$ in the right half only $(x \geqslant 0)$ of Ω. If a square grid with step h is chosen, the region Ω can be partitioned into approximately $4/h^2$ squares, and the number of unknowns (with symmetry taken into account) will be about $2/h^2$. To prevent the computation from becoming too cumbersome, we require that the number of unknowns be no larger than 20, i.e., that $h^2 \geqslant 1/10$. We therefore choose $h = \frac{1}{3}$ and locate the mesh points (k, j) at the points (x_k, y_j), where $x_k = \dfrac{k}{3} - \dfrac{1}{6}$, $y_j = \dfrac{j}{3}$. In this case all of the boundary mesh points (in the sense of a five-pointed star) are on the boundary Γ, while the interior of the right half of Ω has 11 mesh points (see Fig. 11): (1, 1), (1, 2), (1, 3), (1, 4), (1, 5), (2, 1), (2, 2), (3, 1), (3, 2), (4, 1), (4, 2). We let $u_{k,j}$ and $u'_{k,j}$ denote the values of the desired grid function at the mesh point (k, j) and the function symmetric to it about the $0y$ axis. Using simple five-point substitution for the Laplace operator, we obtain, for example,

$$\frac{u_{2,2} + u_{1,3} + u'_{1,2} + u_{1,1} - 4u_{1,2}}{(\frac{1}{3})^2} = -2$$

for the mesh point (1, 2), and, assuming that $u'_{1,2} = u_{1,2}$,

$$u_{1,2} = \tfrac{1}{3}(u_{1,1} + u_{1,3} + u_{2,2}) + \tfrac{2}{27}.$$

Similar equations are obtained for the mesh points (1, 3) and (1, 4). When equations are written for the mesh points not on the line $x = \frac{1}{6}$, the symmetry assumption need not be taken into account. When the equations for the other mesh points, except for (1, 2), (1, 3), and (1, 4), are written, it is necessary to account for the fact that u is equal to 0 at the boundary mesh points. The 11 equations are:

$$u_{1,1} = \tfrac{1}{3}(u_{1,2} + u_{2,1}) + \tfrac{2}{27}, \qquad u_{1,2} = \tfrac{1}{3}(u_{1,1} + u_{1,3} + u_{2,2}) + \tfrac{2}{27},$$

$$u_{1,3} = \tfrac{1}{3}(u_{1,2} + u_{1,4}) + \tfrac{2}{27}, \qquad u_{1,4} = \tfrac{1}{3}(u_{1,3} + u_{1,5}) + \tfrac{2}{27},$$

$$u_{1,5} = \tfrac{1}{3}u_{1,4} + \tfrac{2}{27}, \qquad u_{2,1} = \tfrac{1}{4}(u_{1,1} + u_{2,2} + u_{3,1}) + \tfrac{1}{18},$$

$$u_{2,2} = \tfrac{1}{4}(u_{1,2} + u_{2,1} + u_{3,2}) + \tfrac{1}{18}, \qquad u_{3,1} = \tfrac{1}{4}(u_{2,1} + u_{3,2} + u_{4,1}) + \tfrac{1}{18},$$

$$u_{3,2} = \tfrac{1}{4}(u_{2,2} + u_{3,1} + u_{4,2}) + \tfrac{1}{18}, \qquad u_{4,1} = \tfrac{1}{4}(u_{3,1} + u_{4,2}) + \tfrac{1}{18},$$

$$u_{4,2} = \tfrac{1}{4}(u_{3,2} + u_{4,1}) + \tfrac{1}{18}.$$

Solution of this system yields a crude approximation to the exact solution, and we present the results to four decimal places:

$$u_{1,1} = 0.2602, \qquad u_{1,2} = 0.3265, \qquad u_{1,3} = 0.2513,$$

$$u_{1,4} = 0.2054, \qquad u_{1,5} = 0.1425, \qquad u_{2,1} = 0.2318,$$

$$u_{2,2} = 0.2456, \qquad u_{3,1} = 0.1992, \qquad u_{3,2} = 0.2021,$$

$$u_{4,1} = 0.1407, \qquad u_{4,2} = 0.1412.$$

Assume that it is required to obtain the grid solution for a grid with step twice as small: $h = 1/6$. If the mesh points are placed at the points $x_k = k/6$, $y_j = j/6$, the mesh points of the new grid will coincide with the centers of the squares, the centers of the sides of the squares in the old grid, and the mesh points of the old grid. We index the mesh points as follows: the mesh points on the lines

$$x = 0, \ x = \tfrac{1}{6}, \ x = \tfrac{1}{3}, \ x = \tfrac{1}{2}, \ x = \tfrac{2}{3}, \ x = \tfrac{5}{6}, \ x = 1, \ x = \tfrac{7}{6}, \ x = \tfrac{4}{3}$$

are, respectively, assigned the numbers

$$1\text{--}11, \ 12\text{--}22, \ 23\text{--}33, \ 34\text{--}38, \ 39\text{--}43, \ 44\text{--}48, \ 49\text{--}53, \ 54\text{--}58, \ 59\text{--}63,$$

where on each line $x = \text{const}$ the index increases as y increases. When the equations for mesh points 1–11 are written, it is necessary to allow for the symmetry of the solution. Thus, for example, the equation for mesh point 3 is

$$\frac{2u_{14} + u_2 + u_4 - 4u_3}{(\tfrac{1}{6})^2} = -2 \quad \text{or} \quad u_3 = \frac{u_2 + u_4 + 2u_{14}}{4} + \frac{1}{72}.$$

We will not write out the entire system of 63 linear equations. It was solved by simple iteration, and the solution for the old grid was chosen for the initial approximation $u^{(0)}$. The mesh points 13, 15, 17, 19, 21, 35, 37, 45, 47, 55, 57 coincide with the mesh points of the old grid, and the values of $u^{(0)}$ at these mesh points are taken equal to the values found before. It is not difficult to see that for $u \in C^4$ we have the inequality (see Paragraph 2, Example 6)

$$\left| \frac{u(x + h, y + h) + u(x + h, y - h) + u(x - h, y + h)}{2h^2} \right.$$

$$+ \left. \frac{u(x - h, y - h) - 4u(x, y)}{2h^2} - \Delta u(x, y) \right| \leqslant \frac{2}{3} M^{(4)} h^2,$$

from which it follows that the value of $u(x, y)$ at the center of a nine-pointed star can be approximately computed with the formula

$$u(x, y) \approx \frac{u(x + h, y + h) + u(x + h, y - h) + u(x - h, y + h)}{4}$$

$$+ \frac{u(x - h, y - h)}{4} - \frac{h^2}{2}(\Delta u)_{x,y}.$$

Setting $h = \tfrac{1}{6}$, $(\Delta u)_{x,y} = -2$ and using the known values of $u^{(0)}$ at the mesh points of the old grid, we find $u^{(0)}$ at the mesh points at the centers of the squares in the old grid, i.e., at all remaining mesh points with odd indices. After this, using Formula (2.92), we find the values of $u^{(0)}$ at the mesh points with even indices. The grid function $u^{(0)}$ obtained in this manner was used as the initial approximation for simple iteration. We should note that 80, 120, and 160 iterations were required to prevent $\|u^{(m+1)} - u^{(m)}\|$ from exceeding 10^{-4}, 10^{-5}, and 10^{-6}, respectively, $u^{(m)}$ is the mth iteration, $\|u\|$ denotes maximum modulus). Formula (2.93) ensures that $\|u^{(m+1)} - u_h\|$ is no larger than 10^{-2}, 10^{-3}, and 10^{-4}, respectively, where u_h is the exact solution of the grid system. The results are shown in Table 16 to four decimal places.

Table 16. Values of u_i

1	0.1616	14	0.3257	27	0.2644	40	0.2258	53	0.1172
2	0.2710	15	0.3403	28	0.1891	41	0.2586	54	0.0945
3	0.3324	16	0.3194	29	0.1571	42	0.2363	55	0.1467
4	0.3517	17	0.2792	30	0.1375	43	0.1527	56	0.1637
5	0.3382	18	0.2462	31	0.1195	44	0.1294	57	0.1473
6	0.3067	19	0.2180	32	0.0965	45	0.2068	58	0.0951
7	0.2747	20	0.1885	33	0.0610	46	0.2343	59	0.0602
8	0.2443	21	0.1499	34	0.1482	47	0.2111	60	0.0906
9	0.2110	22	0.0920	35	0.2423	48	0.1341	61	0.1002
10	0.1670	23	0.1551	36	0.2827	49	0.1154	62	0.0909
11	0.1017	24	0.2569	37	0.2670	50	0.1824	63	0.0604
12	0.1599	25	0.3074	38	0.1849	51	0.2050		
13	0.2673	26	0.3087	39	0.1397	52	0.1840		

We obtained the grid functions $u_{1/3}$ and $u_{1/6}$. This made it possible to use the grid function $\tilde{u}_{1/3}$, which is closer to the exact solution $u(x, y)$ than $u_{1/3}$ or $u_{1/6}$. This was done by means of Runge's method, for which a theoretical basis for the case of grid methods was discussed in [83], and examples were given in [75]. In our case, Runge's method reduced to the following procedure: Consider the sequence of grids for which $h = 1/N$ (where N is a positive integer, $N \to \infty$) an all boundary (in the sense of a five-pointed star) mesh points lie on Γ. It turns out that a grid function $h^{-2}(u_h - u)$ approaches some function $v(x, y)$ as $h \to 0$. As a result, $u \approx u_h - h^2 v$ and, in particular,

$$u \approx u_{1/3} - \tfrac{1}{9}v, \quad u \approx u_{1/6} - \tfrac{1}{36}v.$$

Eliminating v, we find that

$$u \approx \tilde{u}_{1/3} \equiv \frac{4u_{1/6} - u_{1/3}}{3}.$$

The function $\tilde{u}_{1/3}$ is defined only as the mesh points of $\Omega_{1/3}$. The values of $\tilde{u}_{1/3}$ are: 0.2697; 0.3449; 0.2885; 0.2222; 0.1523; 0.2458; 0.2742; 0.2094; 0.2140; 0.1487; 0.1493.

In virtue of our smoothness assumptions, we can assume that all derivatives of the exact solution are continuous in $\bar{\Omega}$, i.e., $u \in C_k$ for all k. Since all boundary (in the sense of a nine-pointed star) mesh points lie on Γ, it is meaningful to write the grid equations (2.47) for a nine-pointed star. For mesh point 3, for example, we obtain, after allowing for symmetry,

$$\frac{4(u_2 + u_4 + 2u_{14}) + (2u_{13} + 2u_{15}) - 20u_3}{6(\frac{1}{6})^2} = -2,$$

or

$$u_3 = \frac{4(u_2 + u_4 + 2u_{14}) + 2(u_{13} + u_{15})}{20} + \frac{1}{60}.$$

We will not write out the entire system of 63 equations. The system was solved by simple iteration, with the initial approximation the previously

Table 17. Values of u_i

1	0.1621	14	0.3271	27	0.2664	40	0.2280	53	0.1183
2	0.2719	15	0.3421	28	0.1972	41	0.2617	54	0.0959
3	0.3337	16	0.3225	29	0.1594	42	0.2395	55	0.1487
4	0.3535	17	0.2856	30	0.1390	43	0.1544	56	0.1658
5	0.3417	18	0.2507	31	0.1209	44	0.1306	57	0.1492
6	0.3125	19	0.2211	32	0.0980	45	0.2090	58	0.0965
7	0.2797	20	0.1910	33	0.0626	46	0.2368	59	0.0617
8	0.2480	21	0.1521	34	0.1492	47	0.2132	60	0.0922
9	0.2138	22	0.0936	35	0.2444	48	0.1351	61	0.1016
10	0.1694	23	0.1559	36	0.2861	49	0.1168	62	0.0923
11	0.1032	24	0.2585	37	0.2721	50	0.1845	63	0.0619
12	0.1605	25	0.3096	38	0.1926	51	0.2073		
13	0.2683	26	0.3111	39	0.1409	52	0.1860		

obtained value of $u_{1/2}$. The results are shown in Table 17 to four decimal places.

We denote this grid function by $\tilde{u}_{1/6}$. Its values at the mesh points of $\Omega_{1/3}$ differ little from the values of the grid function $\tilde{u}_{1/3}$. This comparison permits the hope that $\tilde{u}_{1/6}$ approximates $u(x, y)$ to three decimal places.

EXAMPLE 20: In the region $\Omega(x \geqslant 0, y \geqslant 0, x^2 + y^2 \leqslant 4$ [Fig. 12]), find the solution of the differential equation

$$(1 + x^2)\frac{\partial^2 u}{\partial x^2} + 2(1 - xy)\frac{\partial^2 u}{\partial y^2} + (1 + y^2)\frac{\partial^2 u}{\partial y^2}$$

$$= -\left[(x^2 + y^2 + xy) - 2(x^2 y^2) + \frac{3}{4}(x^2 + y^2)^2\right], \quad (2.98)$$

under the boundary condition

$$\left. u \right|_{x=0} = 1 - \frac{y^4}{16}, \quad \left. u \right|_{y=0} = 1 - \frac{x^4}{16}, \left.\right\} \quad (2.98')$$

$$\left. u \right|_{x^2+y^2=4} = 0.$$

Since

$$(1 + x^2)(1 + y^2) - (1 - xy)^2 = x^2 + y^2 + 2xy = (x + y)^2 > 0$$

for $x + y \neq 0$, Eq. (2.98) is elliptic at all points of Ω except $(0, 0)$. Since the condition $|(1 - xy)| < \min((1 + x^2), (1 + y^2))$, is satisfied inside Ω, we can use a square grid and Eqs. (2.58)–(2.59) to solve the problem. We thus obtain a system satisfying the principle of the maximum (provided the equations for the boundary mesh points are appropriately chosen).

The solution $u(x, y)$ of Problem (2.98)–(2.98′) is a function that is symmetric about the line $x = y$. This follows from the fact that when y is substituted for x and x is substituted for y the problem remains the same and the

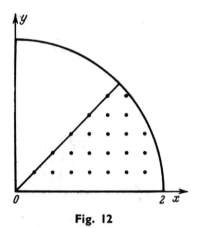

Fig. 12

problem has only one solution. Thus, it is sufficient to attempt to find the solution in the region Ω_1 $(0 \leqslant y \leqslant x, x^2 + y^2 \leqslant 4)$. We take $h = \frac{1}{4}$, $x_k = \frac{k}{4}$, and $y_j = \frac{j}{4}$. Then there will be 23 mesh points inside the region Ω_1 and on the boundary $y = x$, and we index them according to the order in which they appear in the following list: $(\frac{1}{4}, \frac{1}{4})$, $(\frac{1}{2}, \frac{1}{4})$, $(\frac{3}{4}, \frac{1}{4})$, $(1, \frac{1}{4})$, $(\frac{5}{4}, \frac{1}{4})$, $(\frac{3}{2}, \frac{1}{4})$, $(\frac{7}{4}, \frac{1}{4})$, $(\frac{1}{2}, \frac{1}{2})$, $(\frac{3}{4}, \frac{1}{2})$, $(1, \frac{1}{2})$, $(\frac{5}{4}, \frac{1}{2})$, $(\frac{3}{2}, \frac{1}{2})$, $(\frac{7}{4}, \frac{1}{2})$, $(\frac{3}{4}, \frac{3}{4})$, $(1, \frac{3}{4})$, $(\frac{5}{4}, \frac{3}{4})$, $(\frac{3}{2}, \frac{3}{4})$, $(\frac{7}{4}, \frac{3}{4})$, $(1, 1)$, $(\frac{5}{4}, 1)$, $(\frac{3}{2}, 1)$, $(\frac{5}{4}, \frac{5}{4})$, $(\frac{3}{2}, \frac{5}{4})$. There are 9 mesh points on the boundary $y = 0$, and the desired function is known at these mesh points. Mesh points 7, 13, 18, 21, and 23 are boundary mesh points for a five-pointed star, and so a fortiori for a nine-pointed star. The boundary conditions are taken into account by linear interpolation (in the direction of the Ox axis) at these mesh points. For mesh point 18, for example, we have

$$\frac{\delta}{\delta + h} = \frac{\sqrt{4 - (\frac{3}{4})^2} - \frac{7}{4}}{(\sqrt{4 - (\frac{3}{2})^2} - \frac{7}{4}) + \frac{1}{4}} = \frac{\sqrt{55} - 7}{\sqrt{55} - 6}$$

$$= \frac{(\sqrt{55} - 7)(\sqrt{55} + 6)}{55 - 36} = \frac{13 - \sqrt{55}}{19} = 0.2938843,$$

and, therefore, the equation takes the form

$$u_{18} - 0.2938843u_{17} = 0.$$

At the mesh points 1, 2, 3, 4, 5, 6, 8, 9, 10, 11, 12, 14, 15, 16, and 19 we have $1 - xy \geqslant 0$, and we write equations of the form (2.58) for these mesh points. For mesh point 14, for example, the equation takes the form (when the symmetry of the desired function is taken into account)

$$\left(1 + \frac{9}{16}\right)\frac{u_{15} + u_9 - 2u_{14}}{(\frac{1}{4})^2} + \left(1 - \frac{3}{4} \cdot \frac{3}{4}\right)\frac{u_{19} + u_8 + 2u_{14} - (2u_{15} + 2u_9)}{(\frac{1}{4})^2}$$

$$+ \left(1 + \frac{9}{16}\right)\frac{u_9 + u_{15} - 2u_{14}}{(\frac{1}{4})^2}$$

$$= -\left[\left(\frac{9}{16} + \frac{9}{16} + \frac{9}{16}\right) - 2 \cdot \frac{9}{16} \cdot \frac{9}{16} + \frac{3}{4}\left(\frac{9}{16} + \frac{9}{16}\right)^2\right]$$

or, after simplification,

$$7u_8 + 36u_9 - 86u_{14} + 36u_{15} + 7u_{19} = -2.003906.$$

We have $1 - xy < 0$ for mesh points 17, 20, and 22. Equations of the form (2.59) are written for these mesh points. For mesh point 20, for example, the equation takes the form

$$\left(1 + \frac{25}{16}\right)\frac{u_{21} + u_{19} - 2u_{20}}{(\frac{1}{4})^2}$$

$$+ \left(1 - \frac{5}{4} \cdot 1\right)\frac{u_{21} + u_{19} + u_{16} + u_{22} - (u_{20} + u_{17} + 2u_{20})}{(\frac{1}{4})^2}$$

$$+ (1 + 1^2)\frac{u_{16} + u_{22} - 2u_{20}}{(\frac{1}{4})^2}$$

$$= -\left[\left(\frac{25}{16} + 1 + \frac{5}{4} \cdot 1\right) - 2 \cdot \frac{25}{16} \cdot 1 + \frac{3}{4}\left(\frac{25}{16} + 1\right)^2\right]$$

or, after simplification,

$$28u_{16} + 4u_{17} + 37u_{19} - 134u_{20} + 37u_{21} + 28u_{22} = -5.612305.$$

We will not write out the remaining equations of the system. Table 18 shows (to three decimal places) values of u_h—the solution of the grid system—and u—the value of the exact solution $u(x, y) = 1 - \frac{(x^2 + y^2)^2}{16}$ at the mesh points.

Comparison of u_h and u shows that u_h is a very crude approximation of u, and a much finer mesh must be used to obtain greater accuracy.

Table 18.   Values of u_h—the Solution of the Grid System—and u—the Exact Solution

	u_h	u		u_h	u		u_h	u
1	0.986	0.999	9	0.926	0.959	17	0.446	0.506
2	0.977	0.994	10	0.862	0.902	18	0.131	0.179
3	0.955	0.976	11	0.745	0.795	19	0.694	0.750
4	0.902	0.929	12	0.547	0.609	20	0.526	0.590
5	0.797	0.835	13	0.234	0.314	21	0.253	0.340
6	0.607	0.666	14	0.880	0.921	22	0.340	0.390
7	0.294	0.390	15	0.799	0.847	23	0.067	0.092
8	0.958	0.984	16	0.662	0.718			

1.7 Neumann's grid problem. To simplify the exposition we will consider Neumann's problem in the simplest possible statement: In a finite region Ω of the (x, y) plane, find a function $u(x, y)$, satisfying the Poisson equation

$$\Delta u \equiv \frac{\partial^2 u}{\partial x^2} + \frac{\partial^2 u}{\partial y^2} = f(x, y) \tag{2.14}$$

in Ω and the coundary condition

$$\frac{\partial u}{\partial v}\bigg|_{\Gamma} = \varphi(x, y), \tag{2.99}$$

where $\partial u/\partial v$ is the derivative of $u(x, y)$ in the direction of the interior normal to the contour Γ while $f(x, y)$ and $\varphi(x, y)$ are functions given, respectively, in Ω and on Γ.

The special property of this problem lies in the following: (a) the problem does not have a solution for all $f(x, y)$ and $\varphi(x, y)$; (b) if at least one solution $y(x, y)$, exists for given f and φ, then $u(x, y) + C$, where C is an arbitrary constant, is also a solution (and any two solutions differ by a constant).

It is known [94] that Problem (2.14), (2.99) has a solution if and only if (it is assumed that f, φ, and the contour Γ are sufficiently smooth)

$$\int_{\Omega} f \, d\Omega + \int_{\Gamma} \varphi \, d\Gamma = 0. \tag{2.100}$$

It follows from condition (2.100) that the problem is very sensitive to small variations in f and φ: An arbitrary small variation in f or φ, is sufficient to invalidate (2.100) and to prevent the problem from having a solution. A similar circumstance also occurs for the grid equations, to whose consistency we now turn our attention.

If Eq. (2.100) is satisfied, solutions exist, and among them it is possible to select one that satisfies some additional condition such as

$$\int_{\Omega} u(x, y) \, d\Omega = 0 \tag{2.101}$$

or

$$u(x_0, y_0) = 0, \qquad (2.102)$$

where (x_0, y_0) is some point in Ω.

We will consider two approaches to writing the grid equations for Problem (2.14), (2.99).

(a) *Substitution of Finite-Difference Ratios for Derivatives.* Let Ω_h be a square grid. We will denote the set of interior mesh points (in the sense of a five-pointed star) by Ω_h^0, and we will denote the set of boundary mesh points by Ω_h^1. With each $(i, j) \in \Omega_h^0$ we associate the equation

$$(\Delta_h u_h)_{i,j} \equiv \frac{u_{j+1,j} + u_{i,j+1} + u_{i-1,j} + u_{i,j-1} - 4u_{i,j}}{h^2}$$
$$= (\Pi_h^0(f, \varphi))_{i,j}, (i, j) \in \Omega_h^0. \qquad (2.103)$$

With each $(i, j) \in \Omega_h^1$ we associate an equation of the form (see Paragraph 3, Example 13)

$$(r_h u_h)_{i,j} \equiv \frac{u_{i+\xi,j} - u_{i,j}}{h} \cos \mu + \frac{u_{i,j+\eta} - u_{i,j}}{h} \cos \lambda$$
$$= (\Pi_h^{(1)}(f, \varphi))_{i,j}, (i, j) \in \Omega_h^1, \qquad (2.104)$$

where $\xi, \eta = \pm 1$ and the mesh points $(i + \xi, j)$ and $(i, j + \eta)$ belong to Ω_h, while μ and λ are the angles formed by the interior normal to Γ at the point $Q_{ij} \in \Gamma$ closest to (i, j) [and, consequently, the interior normal passing through (i, j)], and the rays from (i, j) to $(i + \xi, j)$, and $(i, j + \eta)$, respectively; it is assumed that $0 \leqslant \mu \leqslant \frac{\pi}{2}, 0 \leqslant \lambda \leqslant \frac{\pi}{2}$ (see Paragraph 3, Example 6).

Under these assumptions, system (2.103)–(2.104) is such that all mesh points $(i, j) \in \Omega_h$ are mesh points of the first kind and the corresponding homogeneous system has the nonzero solution $u_{i,j} \equiv 1, (i, j) \in \Omega_h$. Thus, the determinant of this system is equal to zero and the rank of the coefficient matrix is $N_h - 1$. This last follows because if the system equation corresponding to the mesh point (i_0, j_0), is replaced by the equation $u_{i_0,j_0} = 0$, the mesh point (i_0, j_0) will become a mesh point of the second kind. By Theorem 2, the new system, will have a unique solution which proves our statement about the rank of the matrix. As a result, there exists a unique (with accuracy up to multiplicative factors) system N_h of coefficients such that a linear combination of the left-hand sides of (2.103) and (2.104) is identically equal to zero. We will denote these factors by $h^2\gamma_{i,j}$ for $(i, j) \in \Omega_h^0$, and $h\delta_{i,j}$ for $(i, j) \in \Omega_h^1$.

Now, system (2.103)–(2.104) is consistent if and only if

$$h^2 \sum_{(i,j)\in\Omega_h^0} \gamma_{i,j} (\Pi_h^0(f, \varphi))_{i,j} + h \sum_{(i,j)\in\Omega_h^1} \delta_{i,j} (\Pi_h^1(f, \varphi))_{i,j} = 0. \qquad (2.105)$$

We will call Eq. (2.105) the *grid analog* of Eq. (2.100). For an arbitrary region Ω and selected step h, determination of the numbers $\gamma_{i,j}$ and $\delta_{i,j}$ requires solution of a system of $N_h - 1$ linear equations, which is in itself a difficult problem. For regions whose contours consist of line segments parallel to the coordinate axes (either rectangles or figures composed of rectangles), all of the $\gamma_{i,j}$ and $\delta_{i,j}$ are equal and we can set $\gamma_{i,j} = \delta_{i,j} = 1$. In this case Eq. (2.105) takes the form

$$h^2 \sum_{(i,j)\in\Omega_h^0} (\Pi_h^0(f, \varphi))_{i,j} + h \sum_{(i,j)\in\Omega_h^1} (\Pi_h^1(f, \varphi))_{i,j} = 0. \qquad (2.106)$$

Remark. Terms corresponding to vertices with interior angle $\pi/2$ must be omitted in the second sum.

If (2.100) is satisfied, the region Ω and the contour Γ can be split into disjoint parts that are, respectively, neighborhoods of interior and boundary mesh points. Then we can set

$$(\Pi_h^0)_{i,j} = \frac{1}{h^2} \int_{\Omega_{i,j}} f(x, y) \, d\Omega, \qquad (2.107)$$

$$(\Pi_h^1)_{i,j} = \frac{1}{h} \int_{\Gamma_{i,j}} \varphi \, d\Gamma, \qquad (2.108)$$

where $\Omega_{i,j}$ and $\Gamma_{i,j}$ are selected neighborhoods of the $(i, j) \in \Omega_h^0$ and $(i, j) \in \Omega_h^1$, respectively. When this choice is made, in virtue of (2.100), Eq. (2.106) is satisfied and system (2.103)–(2.104) is consistent.

For the problem to have a unique solution, it is sufficient to give the grid analog of either condition (2.101) or (2.102). Examples of such conditions are

$$h^2 \sum_{(i,j)\in\Omega_h} u_{i,j} = 0 \qquad (2.109)$$

and

$$u_{i_0,j_0} = 0, \qquad (2.110)$$

where (i_0, j_0) is some mesh point closest to the point (x_0, y_0).

EXAMPLE 21: Let Ω be a rectangle with sides a and b parallel to the coordinate axes, where a and b are commensurable numbers; assume, moreover, that h is chosen so that $a = Mh$ and $b = Nh$, where M and N are integers. Let $f \equiv 0$ and set

$$(\Pi_h^0)_{i,j} = 0, \qquad (i, j) \in \Omega_h^0,$$

$$(\Pi_h^1(\varphi))_{i,j} = (\varphi)_{i,j} - \frac{1}{2(M + N - 2)} \sum \varphi_{i',j'},$$

where the sum is taken over all boundary mesh points except the vertices of the rectangle. Then (2.106) is satisfied and the system (2.103)–(2.104) is consistent.

For the rectangle $0 \leqslant x \leqslant 1, 0 \leqslant y \leqslant 1$, the harmonic polynomial

$$U^*(x, y) = (x - \tfrac{1}{2})^2 - (y - \tfrac{1}{2})^2$$

has, on the contour, interior normal derivatives equal to $+1$ on the horizontal sides, and -1 on the vertical sides. It is not difficult to see that the solution of the grid problem for these data is the polynomial

$$u_h(x, y) = (1 - h)^{-1} U^*(x, y),$$

and consequently, the error in the grid solution of Neumann's problem (where the solution is obtained with the method given in this example) decreases no faster than h [118].

EXAMPLE 22: The following method for writing grid equations (for the Laplace equation with a rectangular grid) was proposed in [118]. In addition to the basic mesh points (i, j), $(0 \leqslant i \leqslant M, 0 \leqslant j \leqslant N)$, in the interior or on the boundary of the rectangle, auxiliary mesh points $(-1, j)$, $(M + 1, j)$, $(i, -1)$, and $(i, N + 1)$ are introduced. Grid Equation (2.103) $((\Pi_h^0)_{i,j} = 0)$ is written for each of the basic mesh points (i, j) for the mesh point $(0, j)$, which lies on one of the sides of the rectangle, Eq. (2.99) is replaced by the equation

$$\frac{u_{1,j} - u_{-1,j}}{2h} = (\varphi)_{0,j} - \frac{1}{2(M + N)} \sum \varphi_{i',j'},$$

where the sum is taken over all mesh points of the contour, including the vertices of the rectangle. Boundary conditions for the mesh points on the other sides of the contour are written analogously.

The system obtained in this manner is consistent. If the function φ is continuous and sufficiently smooth on each side of the rectangle, the error of the grid solution is estimated by the function $Ah^2 \ln h$ (under the assumption that both the exact and grid solutions vanish at one of the vertices of the rectangle).

The harmonic polynomial

$$U^*(x, y) = (x - \tfrac{1}{2})^3 - 3(x - \tfrac{1}{2})(y - \tfrac{1}{2})^2 - \tfrac{1}{4}$$

has, on the contour of the square $0 \leqslant x, y \leqslant 1$, a normal derivative φ, such that solution of the grid problem by the method given in this example leads to the function

$$u_h = U^*(x, y) - h^2 x.$$

As a result, the error of the grid solution u_h obtained with the method described above, decreases, generally speaking, no faster than h^2.

Remark 1. We have already noted that the system obtained from (2.103)–(2.104) by substitution of the equation $u_{i_0, j_0} = 0$, for the equation at some mesh point (i_0, j_0) has a unique solution. Let the point $Q(x_0, y_0)$ be a mesh point for each grid in the sequence $\{\Omega_h\}$ ($h \to 0$). By writing system (2.103)–(2.104) for all other mesh points in the grid Ω_h and setting $u_h(Q) = 0$, we obtain a solvable system of equations for each grid.

Let $\{u_h\}$ be the sequence of solutions of the systems obtained in this manner. It can be hoped that u_h approaches the exact solution of Problem (2.14), (2.99), (2.102). This was proved in [10] for the case in which Ω is star-shaped, the boundary Γ is sufficiently smooth, and Eq. (2.104) is replaced by a more accurate grid equation; an estimate of the error was obtained in the same article.

Remark 2. The article [110] considers grid solution of a more general problem: Find the function that satisfies the equation

$$\frac{\partial^2 u}{\partial x^2} + \frac{\partial^2 u}{\partial y^2} + c\frac{\partial u}{\partial x} + d\frac{\partial u}{\partial y} - gu = f \tag{2.111}$$

in Ω, and the boundary condition

$$\left(\frac{\partial u}{\partial \nu} - \kappa u\right)_\Gamma = \varphi(x, y), \tag{2.112}$$

on Γ, where κ is a function defined on Γ. Let $g \geqslant 0$ and $\kappa \geqslant 0$ and either $g \not\equiv 0$ or $\kappa \not\equiv 0$. Then Problem (2.111)–(2.112) cannot have more than one solution. In [110] Eq. (2.112) was replaced by a grid equation of the form [see Paragraph 3, (2.56)]

$$\frac{\left(1 - \dfrac{h'}{h}\right)u_{i',j'} + \dfrac{h'}{h}u_{i'',j''} - u_{i,j}}{\sigma h} - \kappa(Q_{i,j})u_{i,j} = \varphi(Q_{i,j}),$$

while Eq. (2.11) ($a \equiv b \equiv 1$) was substituted for Eq. (2.111). Because $g \not\equiv 0$ or $\kappa \not\equiv 0$ ($g \geqslant 0$, $\kappa \geqslant 0$), the grid system will, for sufficiently small h, contain mesh points of the second kind and satisfy the principle of the maximum; in addition, it will be well posed. The grid solution converges to the exact solution of Problem (2.111)–(2.112).

Remark 3. The one-dimensional analog of Problem (2.111)–(2.112) is as follows: Find the solution of Eq. (2.31) that satisfies the boundary conditions

$$\left(\frac{du}{dx} - \kappa_0 u\right)_{x=0} = \alpha, \quad \left(-\frac{du}{dx} - \kappa_1 u\right)_{x=1} = \beta$$

$$(\kappa_0, \kappa_1 \geqslant 0).$$

If the grid analogs of the last equations for the grid $x_k = kh\left(h = \dfrac{1}{N}\right)$ are chosen so that

$$\frac{u_1 - u_0}{h} - \kappa_0 u_0 = \alpha, \quad -\frac{u_N - u_{N-1}}{h} - \kappa_1 u_N = \beta,$$

these equations, together with (2.33), form a system satisfying the principle of the maximum (it is assumed that $g \not\equiv 0$ when $\kappa_0^2 + \kappa_1^2 = 0$, or $\kappa_0^2 + \kappa_1^2 > 0$). Another grid replacement of the boundary condition (see [25]) leads to a grid system that can be converted fairly easily into a system satisfying the principle of the maximum. The grid problems are well posed in both cases, and the grid solutions converge to the exact solution.

(b) *The Grid Analog of a Variational Problem.* It is known ([33, 63], and Chapter Three, Section 3.4 of the present book) that the solution of Problem (2.14), (2.99) minimizes the functional

$$F[u] \equiv \int_\Omega [|\text{grad } u|^2 + 2fu] \, d\Omega + 2 \int_\Gamma u\varphi \, d\Gamma$$

over the class of sufficiently smooth functions $u(x, y)$.

To construct the grid equations, we must construct the grid analogs of

$$\int_\Omega |\text{grad } u|^2 \, d\Omega, \qquad \int_\Omega fu \, d\Omega, \qquad \int_\Gamma \varphi u \, d\Gamma.$$

We will first consider the grid analogs of $\int_\Omega |\text{grad } u|^2 \, d\Omega$.

(α) Let $(i, j) \in \Omega_h$. If the mesh points $(i + 1, j)$ and $(i, j + 1)$ both belong to Ω_h, then the grid analog of $|\text{grad } u|^2$ is

$$|\text{grad}_h \, u_{i,j}|^2 \equiv \left(\frac{u_{i+1,j} - u_{i,j}}{h} \right)^2 + \left(\frac{u_{i,j+1} - u_{i,j}}{h} \right)^2$$

at the mesh point (i, j); if the mesh point $(i + 1, j)[(i, j + 1)]$ does not belong to Ω_h, the corresponding term in the right-hand side is omitted. Then the grid analog of $\int_\Omega |\text{grad } u|^2 \, d\Omega$ is taken to be

$$h^2 \sum_{(i,j) \in \Omega_h} |\text{grad}_h u_{i,j}|^2 \equiv \sum_1 (u_{i,j} - u_{i',j'})^2,$$

where the sum in the right-hand side is taken over all pairs of adjacent mesh points (i, j) and (i', j') in Ω_h.

(β) In the last sum, we omit the terms corresponding to the pairs of adjacent mesh points (i, j) and (i', j'), when both of these mesh points are boundary points (in the sense of a five-pointed star). We write this sum as

$$\sum_{II} (u_{i,j} - u_{i',j'})^2.$$

If no index I or II is written under the summation sign, we will mean either of them.

We write the grid analogs of the integrals $\int_\Omega fu\,d\Omega$ and $\int_\Gamma \varphi u\,d\Gamma$ in the form

$$h^2 \sum_{(i,j)\in\Omega_h} u_{i,j}(\tilde{\Pi}_h^0(f))_{i,j} \text{ and } h \sum_{(i,j)\in\Omega_h^1} u_{i,j}(\tilde{\Pi}_h^1(\varphi))_{i,j},$$

where $(\tilde{\Pi}_h^0(f))_{i,j}$ and $(\tilde{\Pi}_h^1(\varphi))_{i,j}$ are certain linear functionals of f and φ that depend on f and φ only in some neighborhood of the mesh point (i,j); these functionals should be selected so that the sums written above can reasonably be assumed to be approximate values of the integrals $\int_\Omega fu\,d\Omega$ and $\int_\Gamma \varphi u\,d\Gamma$. Then the grid analog of the functional $F[u]$ takes the form

$$F_h[u_h] \equiv \sum (u_{i,j} - u_{i',j'})^2 + 2h^2 \sum_{(i,j)\in\Omega_h} u_{i,j}(\tilde{\Pi}_h^0(f))_{i,j}$$
$$+ 2h \sum_{(i,j)\in\Omega_h^1} u_{i,j}(\tilde{\Pi}_h^1(\varphi))_{i,j}. \quad (2.113)$$

This functional is bounded above for $\{u_{i,j}\}$, that satisfy either condition (2.109) or (2.110). For definiteness, we use condition (2.109).

In order to obtain the grid equations, we must set each derivative of the sum

$$F_h[u_h] + 2\alpha_h h^2 \sum u_{i,j},$$

with respect to $u_{i,j}$ equal to zero, where the $2\alpha_h$ are Lagrange multipliers. If (i,j) is an interior mesh point, the above method leads to the equation (after division by $2h^2$)

$$(\Delta_h u_h)_{i,j} \equiv \frac{u_{i+1,j} + u_{i,j+1} + u_{i-1,j} + u_{i,j-1} - 4u_{i,j}}{h^2} = (\tilde{\Pi}_h^0(f))_{i,j} + \alpha_h.$$
$$(2.114)$$

If (i,j) is a boundary mesh point, our method leads to the equation (after division by $2h$)

$$(r_h u_h)_{i,j} \equiv \frac{1}{h} [\eta_{1i,j}^1 u_{i+1,j} + \eta_{i,j}^2 u_{i,j+1} + \eta_{i,j}^3 u_{i-1,j} + \eta_{i,j}^4 u_{i,j-1}$$
$$- (\eta_{i,j}^1 + \eta_{i,j}^2 + \eta_{i,j}^3 + \eta_{i,j}^4)u_{i,j}] = (\tilde{\Pi}_h^1(\varphi))_{i,j} + h((\tilde{\Pi}_h^0(f))_{i,j} + a_h).$$
$$(2.115)$$

Here the $\eta_{i,j}^k (k = 1, 2, 3, 4)$ are determined differently, depending on whether we mean $\sum_I$ or $\sum_{II}$ in (2.113); namely, $\eta_{i,j}^k$ is equal to 1 for $\sum_I$ if the kth mesh point of the star with center at (i,j) belongs to Ω_h, and is equal to zero otherwise; $\eta_{i,j}^k$ is equal to 1 for $\sum_{II}$, if the kth mesh point of the star with center at (i,j) is an interior mesh point of Ω_h, and zero otherwise.

Since the sum of the derivatives of $\Sigma (u_{i,j} - u_{i',j'})^2$ with respect to each of the $u_{i,j}$ is identically zero, we have

$$h^2 \Sigma (\Delta_h u_h)_{i,j} + h \Sigma (r_h u_h)_{i,j} = 0$$

for any grid function. Therefore

$$\alpha_h = \frac{1}{N_h h^2} \left[h^2 \sum_{(i,j) \in \Omega_h} (\tilde{\Pi}_h^0(f))_{i,j} + h \sum_{i,j \in \Omega_h^1} (\tilde{\Pi}_h^1(\varphi))_{i,j} \right] \qquad (2.116)$$

When α_h is selected in this way, system (2.114)–(2.115) is consistent and, under condition (2.109), has a unique solution u_h—the approximate solution of Problem (2.14), (2.99) with condition (2.101).

Remark 1. If $a_h \neq 0$, the right-hand sides of each of Eqs. (2.114) and (2.115) also depend on the values of f and φ at points far from (i, j), and not only on the values of f and φ in the neighborhood of (i, j).

For Eqs. (2.114) and (2.115) to have a "local" character, and for the right-hand sides of boundary conditions (2.115) to be independent of f, it is necessary and sufficient that $a_h = 0$ and $(\tilde{\Pi}_h^0(f))_{i,j} = 0 \, (i, j) \in \Omega_h^1$, i.e., it is necessary and sufficient that $\tilde{\Pi}_h^0(f)$ and $\tilde{\Pi}_h^1(\varphi)$ satisfy condition (2.106), which is the grid analog of Eq. (2,100). For this to occur, it is sufficient to use (2.107) and (2.108).

Several examples of $\tilde{\Pi}_h^1(\varphi)$ with "local" properties were considered in [42, 43] for the case $f \equiv 0$. Here the left-hand sides of (2.115) were written for $\sum\limits_{\Pi}$.

Remark 2. The method proposed here for taking boundary conditions into account can be called "simple shift". It is possible to use

$$h \sum_{(i,j) \in \Omega_h^1} \left[\left(1 + \frac{\delta}{h} \right) u_{i,j} - \frac{\delta}{h} u_{i',j'} \right] (\tilde{\Pi}_h^1(\varphi))_{i,j},$$

as the grid analog of $\int_\Gamma \varphi u \, d\Gamma$ and using this expression to account for boundary values by linear interpolation. This method does not change the left-hand sides of (2.114) and (2.115), but it does complicate the right-hand sides somewhat; in this case formula (2.116) remains in force.

(c) *Convergence and Error Estimates.* We will say that a grid function u_h converges to some continuous function $u(x, y)$ in the norm of L_2 if

$$\lim_{h \to 0} \left(h^2 \sum_{(i,j) \in \Omega_h} (u_{i,j} - u(ih, jh))^2 \right) = 0.$$

It was shown [108] that for $\varphi \equiv 0$ and $(\tilde{\Pi}_h^0(f))_{i,j} \equiv f_{i,j}$ the solution of system (2.109), (2.114), (2.115) and its difference ratios

$$\frac{u_{i+1,j} - u_{i,j}}{h}, \frac{u_{i,j+1} - u_{i,j}}{h}$$

converge in the norm of L_2 to the exact solution of problem (2.14), (2.99), (2.101) and its derivatives $\partial u/\partial x$ and $\partial u/\partial y$, respectively.

Several estimates of the error $u_h - u$ and the different differences of this error are given in [44, 45].

1.8 Eigenvalues of elliptic operators.   A number λ is said to be an *eigenvalue* of the self-adjoint elliptic operator

$$Lu \equiv \sum_{i=1}^{n} \sum_{j=1}^{n} \frac{\partial}{\partial x_i} \left(a_{i,j} \frac{\partial u}{\partial x_j} \right) - gu \qquad (2.117)$$

with the boundary condition (Ω is a region in n-dimensional space and Γ is its boundary)

$$u \mid_\Gamma = 0, \qquad (2.118)$$

if there exists a function $u(X)$ that is not identically equal to zero, satisfies condition (2.118) on Γ, and is such that in the region Ω

$$Lu + \lambda u = 0. \qquad (2.119)$$

The function $u(X)$ is called an *eigenfunction* corresponding to the eigenvalue λ. An eigenfunction is said to be *normalized* if

$$I[u, u] \equiv \int_\Omega u^2 \, d\Omega = 1. \qquad (2.120)$$

Let Ω be finite, let the functions $g(X)$ and $a_{i,j}(X)$ be continuous in the closure of Ω, and assume that $a_{i,j}(X)$ satisfies the following condition: There exists a constant $\alpha > 0$ such that for all $X \in \Omega$

$$\sum_{i=1}^{n} \sum_{j=1}^{n} a_{i,j}(X)\xi_i\xi_j \geqslant \alpha \sum_{i=1}^{n} \xi_i^2,$$

where $(\xi_1, \xi_2, \ldots, \xi_n)$ is a set of arbitrary real numbers. Under these conditions, the set of eigenvalues is countable, and if they are indexed in increasing order, $\lambda^{(k)} \to +\infty$ as $k \to \infty$, where $\lambda^{(k)}$ is the eigenvalue with index k.

The eigenvalue problem is the problem of determining the eigenvalues for given Ω and L. More accurately, this problem is solved for very special cases of Ω and L.

The following fact is of fundamental importance for approximate computation of $\lambda^{(k)}$: The eigenvalue $\lambda^{(1)}$ is the greatest lower bound of the functional

$$E[u] \equiv \int_\Omega \left[\sum_{i=1}^{n} \sum_{j=1}^{n} a_{i,j} \frac{\partial u}{\partial x_i} \frac{\partial u}{\partial x_j} + gu^2 \right] d\Omega \qquad (2.121)$$

in the class of functions satisfying conditions (2.118) and (2.120); if $\lambda^{(1)}, \ldots,$ $\lambda^{(k-1)}$ have already been found and $u^{(1)}, \ldots, u^{(k-1)}$ are the corresponding eigenfunctions, $\lambda^{(k)}$ is the greatest lower bound of functional (2.121) in the class of functions satisfying conditions (2.118) and (2.120) and the $k - 1$ orthogonality conditions

$$I[u, u^{(i)}] \equiv \int_\Omega uu^{(i)} \, d\Omega = 0 \qquad (i = 1, 2, \ldots, k - 1). \qquad (2.122)$$

For the sake of simplicity, we assume that Ω is a region in the (x, y) plane and $L = \Delta$ is the Laplacian. In this case $E[u]$ takes the form

$$E[u] = \int_\Omega \left[\left(\frac{\partial u}{\partial x} \right)^2 + \left(\frac{\partial u}{\partial y} \right)^2 \right] \, d\Omega = \int_\Omega |\operatorname{grad} u|^2 \, d\Omega. \qquad (2.123)$$

We will consider the different grid analogs of (2.123), (2.120), and (2.122).

(a) *Finite-Differences.* Consider a square grid in the plane and assume that $u_{i,j} = 0$ for each mesh point (i, j) that is not an interior mesh point of Ω_h (in the sense of a five-pointed star). We then set

$$E_h[u_h] \equiv h^2 \sum_{(i,j)} \left[\left(\frac{u_{i+1,j} - u_{i,j}}{h} \right)^2 + \left(\frac{u_{i,j+1} - u_{i,j}}{h} \right)^2 \right], \qquad (2.124)$$

where summation may be assumed to be over all mesh points in the plane [indeed, only a finite number of terms in the sum are nonzero if $u_{i,j} \neq 0$ for at least one interior mesh point (i, j)];

$$I_h[u_h, v_h] \equiv h^2 \sum_{(i,j) \in \Omega_h^0} u_{i,j} v_{i,j}. \qquad (2.125)$$

The boundary condition (2.118) is taken into account by setting

$$u_{i,j} = 0, \qquad (i, j) \overline{\in} \Omega_h^0. \qquad (2.126)$$

The expressions for $E_h[u_h]$ and $I_h[u_h, u_h]$ are quadratic forms in the variables $u_{i,j}$, $(i, j) \in \Omega_h^0$. It is required to find $u_{i,j}$, for which $E_h[u_h]$ is minimal when $I_h[u_h, u_h] = 1$.

As we know, these values of $u_{i,j}$ constitute the solution of the system of N_h^0 linear homogeneous equations obtained by setting the derivatives of $E_h[u_h] - \lambda_h I[u_h, u_h]$ with respect to each $u_{i,j}$, $(i, j) \in \Omega_h^0$ equal to zero (the λ_h are Lagrange multipliers). This leads to a system of equations of the form

$$u_{i+1,j} + u_{i,j+1} + u_{i-1,j} + u_{i,j-1} - (4 - \lambda_h h^2) u_{i,j} = 0, \qquad (i, j) \in \Omega_h^0, \qquad (2.127)$$

where, by (2.126), some of the first four terms in some of the equations must be set equal to zero.

This system will have a nonzero solution if and only if the determinant of the system is equal to zero. The determinant of this system is a polynomial of degree N_h^0 in λ_h. All roots of this polynomial are real and positive (since they are the eigenvalues of a symmetric positive definite matrix). Let

$$\lambda_h^{(1)} \leqslant \lambda_h^{(2)} \leqslant \cdots \leqslant \lambda_h^{(N_h^0)} \tag{2.128}$$

be the roots of this polynomial. It has been shown [38] that when $h \to 0$ we have

$$\lim_{h \to 1} \lambda_h^{(k)} = \lambda^{(k)}, \tag{2.129}$$

for each fixed k, which permits us to assume that $\lambda_h^{(k)}$ is a valid approximation of $\lambda^{(k)}$.

Remark 1. In this method, boundary condition (2.118) is taken into account by simple shift. Collatz' or Mikeladze's method can also be used for this purpose. One such method for the eigenvalue problem is described in [91], in which, in addition to (2.129), estimates of the error $|\lambda_h^{(k)} - \lambda^{(k)}|$ for $h \to 0$ are also given.

Remark 2. Limit relation (2.129) and estimates for $|\lambda_h^{(k)} - \lambda^{(k)}|$ were obtained in the indicated papers for an operator (2.117) of general form.

(b) *Multilinear Interpolation.* By $\Omega(h)$ we will mean the region composed of all grid squares belonging entirely to Ω, and we will denote the contour of Ω_h by $\Gamma(h)$.

Let u_h be an arbitrary grid function equal to zero at the mesh points on $\Gamma(h)$. With this function u_h we associate a continuous function $\tilde{u}_h(x, y)$, that is defined in Ω as follows:

$$\tilde{u}_h(x, y) = 0 \quad \text{if} \quad (x, y) \in \Omega, \quad \text{but } (x, y) \bar{\in} \Omega(h);$$

$\tilde{u}_h(x, y)$ coincides with u_h at each mesh point (i, j) in $\Omega(h)$; in each square of $\Omega(h)$, $\tilde{u}_h(x, y)$ is multilinear, i.e., linear with respect to each of the arguments separately:

$$\tilde{u}_h(x, y) = \frac{1}{h^2} [u^{(0,0)}(h - x)(h - y) + u^{(1,0)}x(h - y) + u^{(0,1)}(h - x)y + u^{(1,1)}xy],$$

where $u^{(0,0)}$, $u^{(1,0)}$, $u^{(0,1)}$, and $u^{(1,1)}$ are the values of u_h at the vertices of a square with one vertex taken to be the coordinate origin and the other three vertices having the coordinates $(h, 0)$, $(0, h)$, and (h, h).

For the function $\tilde{u}_h(x, y)$ the functionals $E[\tilde{u}_h]$ and $I[\tilde{u}_h, \tilde{u}_h]$ are quadratic forms in the variables $u_{i,j}$((i, j) is a mesh point of $\Omega(h)$). By setting the derivatives of $E[\tilde{u}_h] - \tilde{\lambda}_h I[\tilde{u}_h, \tilde{u}_h]$ with respect to each $u_{i,j}$ equal to zero and arguing as in case (a), we obtain the numbers

$$\tilde{\lambda}_h^{(1)} \leqslant \tilde{\lambda}_h^{(2)} \leqslant \cdots \leqslant \tilde{\lambda}_h^{(N_h^0)},$$

where N_h^0 is the number of mesh points in $\Omega(h)$. It turns out that $\tilde{\lambda}_h^{(k)} \geqslant \lambda^{(k)}$

and $\lambda_h^{(k)} \to \lambda^{(k)}$ as $h \to 0$. Thus, this method yields high approximate values of $\lambda^{(k)}$; as a result, $\bar{\lambda}_h^{(k)}$ provides an upper bound for $\lambda^{(k)}$.

We make each mesh point (i, j) inside $\Omega(h)$ the center of a nine-pointed star (see Fig. 4). Then, with each such mesh point, we associate the equation

$$(u_1 + u_2 + u_3 + u_4 + u_5 + u_6 + u_7 + u_8 - 8u_0)$$

$$+ \frac{h^2\bar{\lambda}_h}{12}[4(u_1 + u_2 + u_3 + u_4) + (u_5 + u_6 + u_7 + u_8) + 16u_0] = 0,$$

$$(2.130)$$

that is,

$$\left(1 + \frac{h^2\bar{\lambda}_h}{3}\right)(u_1 + u_2 + u_3 + u_4) + \left(1 + \frac{h^2\bar{\lambda}_h}{12}\right)(u_5 + u_6 + u_7 + u_8)$$

$$- (8 - \tfrac{4}{3}h^2\bar{\lambda}_h)u_0 = 0,$$

where $u_0, u_1, \ldots, u_8$ are the values of u_h at the center and other mesh points of the star. There are as many equations of the form (2.130) as mesh points (i, j) inside $\Omega(h)$. If a star has mesh points on $\Gamma(h)$, the corresponding u_h must be set equal to zero. The numbers $\bar{\lambda}_h^{(1)}, \ldots, \bar{\lambda}_h^{(N_k{}^0)}$ are the roots of the determinant of the system composed of Eqs. (2.130).

Remark 1. The numbers $\bar{\lambda}_h^{(1)}, \ldots, \bar{\lambda}_h^{(k)}$ are upper bounds for $\lambda^{(1)}, \ldots, \lambda^{(k)}$.

In order to obtain a lower bound for the first eigenvalue $\lambda^{(1)}$, we can proceed as follows. Let $\Omega^*(h)$ denote the region composed of all grid squares that each contain at least one point (x, y), such that there exist $(\alpha, \beta)(0 \leqslant \alpha \leqslant h, 0 \leqslant \beta \leqslant h)$, so that each point $(x + \alpha, y + \beta)$ belongs to Ω. The region $\Omega^*(h)$ contains the entire region Ω. If $\lambda_h^{(1)}$ is found for $\Omega^*(h)$ by means of the method used in Paragraph (a) [we denote this eigenvalue by $\lambda_h^{(1)*}$], then $\lambda_h^{(1)*} < \lambda^{(1)}$.

A method for determining lower bounds $\lambda^{(k)}$ is given in [130].

Remark 2. A number μ is said to be an eigenvalue of self-adjoint elliptic operator (2.117) with the boundary condition

$$\left.\frac{\partial u}{\partial \nu}\right|_\Gamma = 0 \qquad (2.131)$$

(ν is the normal direction [63, 94]) if there exists a function $u(X)$, that is not identically equal to zero, satisfies condition (2.131) on Γ, and satisfies the equation $Lu + \mu u = 0$ in Ω. There exists a sequence of numbers $\mu^{(k)}(\mu^{(k)} \leqslant \mu^{(k+1)})$, $\mu^{(k)} \to \infty$ as $k \to \infty$. By slightly changing the considerations of Paragraph (a), we can obtain a method for approximating $\mu^{(k)}$. Since, if L is the Laplacian Δ, in the sum (2.124) we need retain only those terms $[h^{-1}(u_{i+1,j} - u_{i,j})]^2$ or $[h^{-1}(u_{i,j+1} - u_{i,j})]^2$, for which both of the mesh points

(i, j) and $(i + 1, j)$ or (i, j) and $(i, j + 1)$ belong to Ω_h. Then, for interior mesh points, Eq. (2.127) is replaced by its analog (λ_h is replaced by μ_h), and for boundary mesh points it takes the form

$$\eta_{i,j}^1 u_{i+1,j} + \eta_{i,j}^2 u_{i,j+1} + \eta_{i,j}^3 u_{i-1,j} + \eta_{i,j}^4 u_{i,j-1}$$
$$- (\eta_{i,j}^1 + \eta_{i,j}^2 + \eta_{i,j}^3 + \eta_{i,j}^4 - \mu_h h^2) u_{i,j} = 0,$$

where the $\eta_{i,j}^k$ are the same as in Section 2.6 for $\sum\limits_{\text{I}}$.

A similar remark holds for eigenvalues when the boundary condition is $\left(\dfrac{\partial u}{\partial \nu} + \kappa u \right)_\Gamma = 0.$

(c) *A Remark About the Lower Bounds of* $\lambda^{(k)}$. Let the domain Ω be the rectangle $0 \leqslant x \leqslant a$, $0 \leqslant y \leqslant b$, where a and b are commensurable. Let h be the length of one of the sides, so that $a = Mh$, $b = Nh$, where M and N are integers no smaller than two. The square grid Ω_h is such that the boundary mesh points lie on the contour. There are $(M - 1)(N - 1)$ interior mesh points in the grid, and the $(M - 1)(N - 1)$ numbers

$$\lambda_h^{(m,n)} = \frac{4}{h^2}\left(\sin^2 \frac{m\pi}{2M} + \sin^2 \frac{n\pi}{2N} \right) = \frac{4}{h^2}\left(\sin^2 \frac{m\pi h}{2a} + \sin^2 \frac{n\pi h}{2b} \right)$$

$$(1 \leqslant m \leqslant M - 1, \quad 1 \leqslant n \leqslant N - 1)$$

are the eigenvalues (2.128) of grid problem (2.127). The exact eigenvalues of problem (2.119) $[L = \Delta]$ are the numbers

$$\lambda^{(m,n)} = \left[\left(\frac{m}{a} \right)^2 + \left(\frac{n}{b} \right)^2 \right] \pi^2 \quad (1 \leqslant m < \infty, \quad 1 \leqslant n < \infty).$$

It is not difficult to see that

$$\lambda_h^{(m,n)} = \lambda^{(m,n)} - \frac{\pi^4 \left[\left(\dfrac{m}{a} \right)^4 + \left(\dfrac{n}{b} \right)^4 \right]}{12} h^2 + O(h^4), \qquad (2.132)$$

where $O(h^4)$ denotes an infinitesimal quantity of the same order as h^4.

Formula (2.132) generalizes to a broad class of regions in the following manner:

Assume that Eq. (2.127) has been written for each interior mesh point $(i, j) \in \Omega_h$. For each boundary mesh point (i, j) not on Γ, we use Mikeladze's method (see Section 2.1) to write the equation

$$2\left[\frac{u(Q_1)}{\delta_1(\delta_1 + \delta_3)} + \frac{u(Q_3)}{\delta_3(\delta_1 + \delta_3)} + \frac{u(Q_2)}{\delta_2(\delta_2 + \delta_4)} \right.$$
$$\left. + \frac{u(Q_4)}{\delta_4(\delta_2 + \delta_4)} - u_{i,j}\left(\frac{1}{\delta_1 \delta_3} + \frac{1}{\delta_2 \delta_4} \right) \right] + \lambda_h u_{i,j} = 0, \quad (2.133)$$

in which $u(Q_k)$ is set equal to zero if $Q_k \in \Gamma$ $(k = 1, 2, 3, 4)$. The system obtained by combining Eqs. (2.127) and (2.133) can be written in matrix form as

$$A_h u_h + \lambda_h u_h = 0, \tag{2.134}$$

where, generally speaking, the matrix A_h is not symmetric when Eqs. (2.133) are present. Let $\bar{A}_h = \frac{1}{2}(A_h + A_h^T)$ where A_h^T is the transpose of A_h, and instead of Eq. (2.134), consider the equation

$$\bar{A}_h u_h + \bar{\lambda}_h u_h = 0.$$

The members $\bar{\lambda}_h^{(k)}$ are the roots of the determinant of the matrix $(\bar{A}_h + \bar{\lambda}_h E)$, which is a polynomial of degree N_h', where N_h' is the number of mesh points in Ω_h that are not on Γ. We assume that the roots are indexed so that

$$\bar{\lambda}_h^{(1)} \leqslant \bar{\lambda}_h^{(2)} \leqslant \cdots \leqslant \bar{\lambda}_h^{(N'h)}.$$

It turns out [116] that if Ω is a region with boundary consisting of a finite number of analytic curves that form corner points with interior angle less than π at the junction points, there exist numbers $\gamma^{(k)}$ such that

$$\bar{\lambda}_h^{(k)} = \lambda^{(k)} - \gamma^{(k)} h^2 + o(h^2),$$

where $o(h^2)$ is an infinitesimal of an order of magnitude larger than h^2.

If Ω is also convex, then $\gamma^{(k)} > 0$ and, consequently, for each k there exists an $h(k)$ such that for all $h < h(k)$ we have the inequality

$$\bar{\lambda}_h^{(k)} < \lambda^{(k)},$$

i.e., $\bar{\lambda}_h^{(k)}$ is a lower bound of $\lambda^{(k)}$.

2. HYPERBOLIC AND PARABOLIC EQUATIONS

2.1 The Cauchy problem. Selection of grids and convergence of grid solutions.
(a) *Hyperbolic Equations.* The simplest hyperbolic equation is the equation for the vibrating string (*one-dimensional wave equation*)

$$\Box u \equiv \frac{\partial^2 u}{\partial t^2} - \frac{\partial^2 u}{\partial x^2} = f(x, t), \tag{2.135}$$

where $f(x, t)$ is a given function.

The Cauchy problem for Eq. (2.135) is stated as follows. In the half-plane $-\infty < x < \infty$, $t > 0$, find the solution of Eq. (2.135) that, on the boundary $t = 0$, satisfies the initial conditions

$$l_1 u \big|_{t=0} \equiv u \big|_{t=0} = \varphi(x), \tag{2.136}$$

$$l_2 u \bigg|_{t=0} = \frac{\partial u}{\partial t} \bigg|_{t=0} = g(x), \tag{2.137}$$

where $\varphi(x)$ and $g(x)$ are given functions. The solution of Problem (2.135), (2.136), (2.137) is given by the formula (D'Alembert's solution) [98]

$$u(x_0, t_0) = \frac{\varphi(x_0 - t_0) + \varphi(x_0 + t_0)}{2} + \frac{1}{2}\int_{x_0-t_0}^{x_0+t_0} g(x)\, dx$$

$$+ \frac{1}{2}\iint_{D(x_0, t_0)} f(x, t)\, dx\, dt, \quad (2.138)$$

where $D(x_0, t_0)$ is the triangle (in the Oxt plane) bounded by the axis $t = 0$ and the lines ("characteristics") $x + t = x_0 + t_0$, $x - t = x_0 - t_0$ that pass through (x_0, t_0). It follows from (2.138) that $u(x, t)$ is determined by the values of φ and g at the points on the base of the triangle $D(x_0, t_0)$ and the values of f inside and on the contour of the triangle.

Consider the rectangular grid $x_k = kh$, $t_j = j\tau (k = 0, \pm1, \pm2, \ldots;$ $j = 0, 1, 2, \ldots)$. We will call the set of mesh points $(k, j)(-\infty < k < \infty)$ the jth *series of the grid*. The simplest grid analog of problem (2.135), (2.136), (2.137) is

$$\square_h u_k \equiv \frac{u_{k,j+1} - 2u_{k,j} + u_{k,j-1}}{\tau^2} - \frac{u_{k+1,j} - 2u_{k,j} + u_{k-1,j}}{h^2} = (f)_{k,j} \quad (2.139)$$

$$\begin{aligned}(k = 0, \pm1, \pm2, \ldots \quad j = 1, 2, \ldots),\\ u_{k,0} = \varphi(kh) \quad (k = 0, \pm1, \pm2, \ldots),\end{aligned} \quad (2.140)$$

$$\frac{u_{k,1} - u_{k,0}}{\tau} = g(kh) \quad (k = 0, \pm1, \pm2, \ldots). \quad (2.141)$$

Equations (2.140) and (2.141) are used to determine u_h in the zeroth and first series of the grid $(u_{k,0} = \varphi(kh), u_{k,1} = \varphi(kh) + \tau g(kh))$. Equations (2.139) are such that $u_{k,j+1}$ is uniquely determined in terms of the values of the grid function u_h at the mesh points of the jth and $(j - 1)$-th series $(j = 1, 2, \ldots)$, and it follows that system (2.139), (2.140), (2.141) has a unique solution.

We introduce the notation $\tau/h = \sigma$ and $D_{-\sigma}(x_{-0}, t_{-0})$ is the triangle bounded by the axis $t = 0$ and the lines $\sigma x + t = \sigma x_0 + t_0$, $\sigma x - t = \sigma x_0 - t_0$ passing through (x_0, t_0). It is not difficult to see that the value of the grid solution u_h of system (2.139), (2.140), (2.141) at the mesh point (k_0, j_0) is uniquely determined by the values of φ and g at the mesh points on the base of the triangle $D_\sigma(k_0h, j_0\tau)$ and the values of f at the interior and boundary mesh points of $D_\sigma(k_0h, j_0\tau)$.

Assume that there is a sequence of grids such that $h \to 0$, $\tau = \sigma h$, $\sigma = $ const. > 1 and a point $(x_0, t_0)(t_0 > 0)$ is a mesh point in each grid of the sequence. If $u_h(x_0, t_0)$ has a limit $u_0(x_0, t_0)$ for $h \to 0$, the limit is determined by the values of f, φ, and g in $D_\sigma(x_0, t_0)$ and, generally speaking, is different from $u(x_0, t_0)$, the value taken at (x_0, t_0) by the solution of problem (2.135), (2.136),

(2.137), which is determined by the values of f, φ, and g in the triangle D (x_0, t_0), which contains $D_\sigma(x_0, t_0)$ when $\sigma > 1$. In the case $\sigma > 1$, therefore, the sequence u_h generally does not converge to the exact solution of problem (2.135), (2.136), (2.137).

Assume that the functions $f(x, t)$, $\varphi(x)$, and $g(x)$ are sufficiently smooth in the half-plane $t \geqslant 0$ and on the axis $-\infty < x < \infty$, respectively.

Theorem 4. If $\sigma = \text{const} \leqslant 1$, then, as $h \to 0$, the sequence u_h of solutions of Problem (2.139), (2.140), (2.141) uniformly converges to the exact solution $u(x, t)$ of Problem (2.135), (2.136), (2.137) in any finite region of the half-plane $t \geqslant 0$.

When $\sigma = 1$, there is a simple error estimate.

(α) If φ' and g are continuous and $\delta_f(h)$, $\delta_{\varphi'}(h)$ and $\delta_g(h)$ are the moduli of continuity inside (for f) and on the base (for φ', g) of the triangle $D(x, t)$, then

$$|u_h(x, t) - u(x, t)| \leqslant t(\| f \| \cdot h + \delta_f(h) + \delta_g(h) + \delta_{\varphi'}(h)), \quad (2.142)$$

where

$$\| f \| = \max_{D(x,t)} |f|.$$

(β) If $f \in C^2$, $g \in C^2$, $\varphi \in C^2$, and $\varphi \in C^2$,

$$|u_h(x, t) - u(x, t)| \leqslant (\| f \| + M_f^{(2)} \cdot th + M_g^{(2)} \cdot h + M_\varphi^{(2)})th. \quad (2.143)$$

(γ) If we introduce the auxiliary mesh points $(k, -1)$, add the equation for $j = 0$ to system (2.139), and substitute

$$\frac{u_{k,1} - u_{k,-1}}{2\tau} = g(kh) \quad (2.144)$$

for (2.141), the new system will also have a unique solution and $\| f \|$, $\delta_{\varphi'}(h)$, and $M_\varphi^{(2)}$ must be replaced by zeros in the right-hand sides of inequalities (2.142) and (2.143). Inequalities (2.142) and (2.143) are examples of error estimates in terms of the given functions of the problem.

(b) *Parabolic Equations.* The simplest parabolic equation is that for thermal conduction in a rod (Fourier's equation) in the presence of heat sources ($f \not\equiv 0$):

$$\frac{\partial u}{\partial t} - \frac{\partial^2 u}{\partial x^2} = f(x, t). \quad (2.145)$$

If there are no heat sources, we have

$$\frac{\partial u}{\partial t} - \frac{\partial^2 u}{\partial x^2} = 0. \quad (2.146)$$

The Cauchy problem for Eq. (2.145) is stated as follows. In the half-plane

$-\infty < x < \infty$, $t \geqslant 0$, find the solution of Eq. (2.145) that satisfies initial condition (2.136) on the boundary $t = 0$.

It is known [98] that the solution $u(x, t)$ of problem (2.145), (2.136) at a point (x_0, t_0) is determined by the values of $f(x, t)$ in the strip $D_0(x_0, t_0)$ $(0 \leqslant t \leqslant t_0, -\infty < x < \infty)$ and by the values of $\varphi(x)$ everywhere on the real line $-\infty < x < \infty$ ("infinite speed of thermal propagation").

For a rectangular grid $(x_k = kh, t_j = j\tau, \tau = \sigma h)$, it is natural to replace Eq. (2.145) by the grid equation

$$\frac{u_{k,j+1} - u_{k,j}}{\tau} - \frac{u_{k+1,j} - 2u_{k,j} + u_{k-1,j}}{h^2} = (f)_{k,j} \tag{2.147}$$

$$(k = 0, \pm 1, \pm 2, \ldots; \quad j = 0, 1, 2, \ldots),$$

and it is natural to substitute condition (2.140) for condition (2.136). System (2.147), (2.140) has a unique solution, since (2.147) uniquely determines u_h on the $(j + 1)$-th series, if u_h is known for the jth series of mesh points $(j \geqslant 0)$, and (2.140) yields u_h for the zeroth series.

It is not difficult to see that the value of the grid solution u_h of system (2.147), (2.140) at the mesh point k_0, j_0) is uniquely determined by the values of $f(x, t)$ inside and on the boundary of the triangle $D_\sigma(k_0 h, j_0 \tau)$ and the values of $\varphi(x)$ at the mesh points on the base of the triangle $D_\sigma(k_0 h, j_0 \tau)$, which lies inside the strip $D_0(k_0 h, j_0 \tau)$ for all arbitrarily small $\sigma > 0$. If there is a sequence of grids $(h \to 0, \tau = \sigma h, \sigma = \text{const.})$ and the point (x_0, t_0) is a mesh point of each grid, $u_h(x_0, t_0)$ generally does not approach the value $u(x_0, t_0)$ of the exact solution. For $u_h(x_0, t_0) \to u(x_0, t_0)$ for any given $f(x, t)$ and $\varphi(x)$, it is necessary that $\sigma \to 0$ as $h \to 0$ (i.e., it is necessary that the sides of the isosceles triangle $D_\sigma(x_0, t_0)$ tend to merge with the half-lines $t = t_0, x < x_0, x > x_0$).

Set $r = \tau/h^2$, and let $u(x, t)$ have uniformly continuous derivatives $\partial u/\partial t$ and $\partial^2 u/\partial x^2$ in the strip $0 \leqslant t \leqslant T$.

Theorem 5. If $r \leqslant 1/2$, the grid solution u_h of system (2.147), (2.140) uniformly approaches (in the strip $0 \leqslant t \leqslant T$) the exact solution $u(x, t)$ of problem (2.145), (2.136) as $h \to 0$.

We now consider the more general parabolic equation

$$\frac{\partial u}{\partial t} - a(x, t)\frac{\partial^2 u}{\partial x^2} - b(x, t)\frac{\partial u}{\partial x} + g(x, t)u = f(x, t), \tag{2.148}$$

where, in the strip $0 \leqslant t \leqslant T$, the coefficients $a(x, t)$, $b(x, t)$, and $g(x, t)$ satisfy the conditions

$$0 < a(x, t) \leqslant A, \qquad |b(x, t)| \leqslant Ma(x, t), \qquad 0 \leqslant g(x, t) \leqslant G, \tag{2.149}$$

and A, M and G are constants $(A > 0, M \geqslant 0, G \geqslant 0)$.

The grid equation

$$\frac{u_{k,j+1} - u_{k,j}}{\tau} - (a)_{k,j}\frac{u_{k+1,j} - 2u_{k,j} + u_{k-1,j}}{h^2}$$

$$-(b)_{k,j}\frac{u_{k+1,j} - u_{k-1,j}}{2h} + (g)_{k,j}\,u_{k,j} = (f)_{k,j} \qquad (2.150)$$

replaces Eq. (2.148). System (2.150), (2.140) also has a unique solution. If $h < 2/M$ and $\tau < h^2(2A + Gh^2)^{-1}$, then, in virtue of (2.149), the system obtained from (2.150), (2.140) by multiplication of each equation by -1 satisfies the principle of the maximum (see Section 1.3a, A). The mesh point $(k, j + 1)$ is an interior mesh point for the star consisting of the mesh points $(k, j + 1)$, $(k + 1, j)$, (k, j), $(k - 1, j)$; the mesh point $(k, 0)$ is a boundary point. The functions $v_0(x, t) \equiv t$ and $v_1(x, t) \equiv 1$ satisfy the conditions of Lemma 2 (Section 1.3). Equation (2.150) approximates Eq. (2.148) in the class U of functions with uniformly continuous derivatives $\partial u/\partial t$ and $\partial^2 u/\partial x^2$ in the strip $0 \leqslant t \leqslant T$. It then follows from Theorem 3 (Section 1.3) that the grid solution uniformly converges to the exact solution $u(x, t)$ and, in particular, Theorem 4 follows. Error estimates can also be obtained from Theorem 3 (Section 1.3). We will limit our discussion to an estimate of the error in the solution of system (2.147), (2.140) under the assumption that $u \in U$ and $u(x, t)$ has bounded derivatives $\partial^2 u/\partial t^2$ and $\partial^4 u/\partial x^4$ in the strip $0 \leqslant t \leqslant T$:

$$\|u_h - u\| \leqslant T\left[\frac{r}{2}\left\|\frac{\partial^2 u}{\partial t^2}\right\| + \frac{1}{12}\left\|\frac{\partial^4 u}{\partial x^4}\right\|\right]h^2 \qquad (2.151)$$

Remark 1. Assume that $u \in U$ and $u(x, t)$ has bounded derivatives $\partial^3 u/\partial t^3$ and $\partial^6 u/\partial x^6$ in the strip $0 \leqslant t \leqslant T$ and let u_h be the solution of the system obtained from (2.147), (2.140) for $r = \tau/h^2 = 1/6$ by replacing $(f)_{k,j}$ in the right-hand sides of (2.147) by

$$\left(f + \frac{h^2}{12}\left(\frac{\partial f}{\partial t} + \frac{\partial^2 f}{\partial x^2}\right)\right)_{k,j}$$

(see Section 1.2, Example 6). Then

$$\|u_h - u\| \leqslant T\left[\frac{1}{216}\left\|\frac{\partial^3 u}{\partial t^3}\right\| + \frac{1}{360}\left\|\frac{\partial^6 u}{\partial x^6}\right\|\right] \cdot h^4. \qquad (2.152)$$

Remark 2. If $f \equiv 0$, then

$$\frac{\partial^k u}{\partial t^k} = \frac{\partial^{2k} u}{\partial x^{2k}} \quad \text{and} \quad \left\|\frac{\partial^{2k} u}{\partial x^{2k}}\right\|$$

do not exceed $\|\varphi^{(2k)}(x)\|$. In this case, estimates (2.151) and (2.152) take simpler forms and we obtain the following estimates in terms of the given data of the problem:

$$\|u_h - u\| \leqslant T\!\left(\frac{r}{2} + \frac{1}{12}\right)\|\varphi^{(4)}\| \cdot h^2;$$

$$\|u_h - u\| \leqslant \frac{T}{135}\|\varphi^{(6)}\| \cdot h^4.$$

(c) *Computational Instability.* Let u_h be the solution of system (2.147), (2.140). For u_h to converge to the exact solution u, it is necessary that $\sigma \to 0$ as $h \to 0$, and sufficient that $r \leqslant \frac{1}{2}$. If $r = \text{const.}$ when $h \to 0$, then $\sigma \to 0$ ($\sigma = rh$), but u_h generally does not converge to u when $r > \frac{1}{2}$. When $r > \frac{1}{2}$, moreover, system (2.147), (2.140) is extremely sensitive to computational errors, in particular, round-off errors, which are inevitable in practical computations.

Table 19

	j \ k	0	1	2	3	4	5	6
	1	ε	0	0	0	0	0	0
	2	$\dfrac{\varepsilon}{2}$	$\dfrac{\varepsilon}{4}$	0	0	0	0	0
	3	$\dfrac{3\varepsilon}{8}$	$\dfrac{\varepsilon}{4}$	$\dfrac{\varepsilon}{16}$	0	0	0	0
$r=\dfrac{1}{4}$	4	$\dfrac{5\varepsilon}{16}$	$\dfrac{15\varepsilon}{64}$	$\dfrac{3\varepsilon}{32}$	$\dfrac{\varepsilon}{64}$	0	0	0
	5	$\dfrac{35\varepsilon}{128}$	$\dfrac{7\varepsilon}{32}$	$\dfrac{7\varepsilon}{64}$	$\dfrac{\varepsilon}{32}$	$\dfrac{\varepsilon}{256}$	0	0
	6	$\dfrac{63\varepsilon}{256}$	$\dfrac{105\varepsilon}{512}$	$\dfrac{15\varepsilon}{128}$	$\dfrac{45\varepsilon}{1024}$	$\dfrac{5\varepsilon}{512}$	$\dfrac{\varepsilon}{1024}$	0
	7	$\dfrac{231\varepsilon}{1024}$	$\dfrac{99\varepsilon}{512}$	$\dfrac{495\varepsilon}{4096}$	$\dfrac{55\varepsilon}{1024}$	$\dfrac{33\varepsilon}{2048}$	$\dfrac{3\varepsilon}{1024}$	$\dfrac{\varepsilon}{4096}$
	1	ε	0	0	0	0	0	0
	2	$-\dfrac{\varepsilon}{2}$	$\dfrac{3\varepsilon}{4}$	0	0	0	0	0
	3	$\dfrac{11\varepsilon}{8}$	$-\dfrac{3\varepsilon}{4}$	$\dfrac{9\varepsilon}{16}$	0	0	0	0
$r=\dfrac{3}{4}$	4	$-\dfrac{29\varepsilon}{16}$	$\dfrac{117\varepsilon}{64}$	$-\dfrac{27\varepsilon}{32}$	$\dfrac{27\varepsilon}{64}$	0	0	0
	5	$\dfrac{467\varepsilon}{128}$	$-\dfrac{93\varepsilon}{32}$	$\dfrac{135\varepsilon}{64}$	$-\dfrac{27\varepsilon}{32}$	$\dfrac{81\varepsilon}{256}$	0	0
	6	$-\dfrac{1583\varepsilon}{256}$	$\dfrac{2955\varepsilon}{512}$	$\dfrac{495\varepsilon}{128}$	$\dfrac{2295\varepsilon}{1024}$	$\dfrac{405\varepsilon}{512}$	$\dfrac{243\varepsilon}{1024}$	0
	7	$\dfrac{12031\varepsilon}{1024}$	$-\dfrac{5337\varepsilon}{512}$	$\dfrac{32{,}535\varepsilon}{4096}$	$-\dfrac{4725\varepsilon}{1024}$	$\dfrac{4617\varepsilon}{2048}$	$-\dfrac{729\varepsilon}{1024}$	$\dfrac{729\varepsilon}{4096}$

Computation of u_h proceeds as follows: (2.140) provides u_h at the mesh points $(k, 0)$; these values and (2.147) for $j = 0$ are used to compute the values at the mesh points $(k, 1)$, and then for the mesh points $(k, 2)$, etc.

Assume that in computing $u_{0,1}$ there is a round-off error ε, but that all subsequent computations are absolutely exact. Table 19 shows the total error, as computed with the formula

$$\varepsilon_{k,j+1} = \varepsilon_{k,j} + r(\varepsilon_{k+1,j} - 2\varepsilon_{k,j} + \varepsilon_{k-1,j}), \quad \varepsilon_{0,1} = \varepsilon, \quad \varepsilon_{k,1} = 0 \quad (k \neq 0).$$

It is clear from Table 19 that for $r = \frac{1}{4}$ the single error ε has increasingly less influence on the value of $u_{k,j}$. It is also clear from Table 19 that for $r = \frac{3}{4}$ the error begins to have an increasingly larger influence (oscillates) and the computation becomes meaningless. Thus, it is not desirable to use grid equations (2.147) and (2.140) with $r > \frac{1}{2}$ for approximate calculation of u_h, even when it is theoretically possible for u_h to converge to the exact solution $u(x, t)$. A similar statement holds for grid system (2.139), (2.140), (2.141) with $\sigma > 1$.

2.2 Mixed problems. Explicit and implicit schemes. Here we will consider mixed problems for Eqs. (2.135) and (2.145) in the simplest possible form.

Let Ω be the region $0 \leqslant x \leqslant 1$, $t \geqslant 0$, in the Oxt plane, let Γ_0 be the segment $0 \leqslant x \leqslant 1$, $t = 0$, let Γ_1 be the half-line $x = 0$, $t \geqslant 0$, and let Γ_2 be the half-line $x = 1, t \geqslant 0$; Γ_0, Γ_1, and Γ_2 are parts of the boundary Γ of the region Ω. The problem is stated as follows: In the region Ω, find the solution of Eq. (2.135) [(2.145)] that satisfies initial condition (2.136), (2.137) [(2.136)] on Γ_0, and on Γ_1 and Γ_2, the boundary conditions

$$l_1 u \big|_{\Gamma_1} \equiv u \big|_{\Gamma_1} = \psi_1(t), \tag{2.153}$$

$$l_2 u \big|_{\Gamma_2} \equiv u \big|_{\Gamma_2} = \psi_2(t). \tag{2.154}$$

Conditions for consistency of data. If the solution of the problem stated above is continuous in the closed region Ω, it is also continuous at the points joining Γ_1 to Γ_0 and Γ_2 to Γ_0; in addition, $u(0, 0)$ is defined by the given of the problem either as $\varphi(0)$ or $\psi_1(0)$. Thus, the solution $u(x, t)$ will be continuous only if the condition

$$\varphi(0) = \psi_1(0)$$

is satisfied, and, similarly,

$$\varphi(1) = \psi_2(0).$$

Continuity of $\partial u/\partial t$ requires that

$$g(0) = \psi_1'(0), \qquad g(1) = \psi_2'(0)$$

[for Problem (2.135), (2.136), (2.137), (2.153), (2.154)] and $\varphi''(0) + f(0, 0) = \psi_1'(0)$, $\varphi''(1) + f(1, 0) = \psi_2'(0)$ [for Problem (2.145), (2.136), (2.153), (2.154)].

The necessary conditions obtained here for continuity of the solution $u(x, t)$ and its derivatives at the points $(0, 0)$ and $(1, 0)$ are called the *conditions for consistency of the given data* of mixed problems.

This list of conditions can be extended by writing necessary conditions for continuity of $\dfrac{\partial^2 u}{\partial t^2}, \dfrac{\partial^3 u}{\partial t^3}, \ldots$ at $(0, 0)$ and $(1, 0)$. In what follows we will assume that the consistency conditions are satisfied up to some order, and we will assume that the exact solution $u(x, t)$ is continuous, together with its derivatives of up to some order, in the closed region $\Omega + \Gamma$.

The following discussion will be devoted primarily to grid solutions of mixed Problem (2.145), (2.136), (2.153), (2.154).

We use a rectangular grid for approximate solution of this problem, setting $h = 1/N$ (N is a positive integer), and letting τ be an arbitrary positive number. The grid Ω_h ($x_h = kh$, $t_j = j\tau$, $0 \leqslant k \leqslant N$, $j = 0, 1, 2, \ldots$) is such that the mesh points $(0, j)$ and (N, j) lie on Γ_1 and Γ_2. At mesh points on Γ_0, Γ_1, or Γ_2, we assume that u_h is equal to the corresponding values of φ, ψ_1, or ψ_2.

To determine u_h at the remaining mesh points, we use various systems of grid equations with the following common property: The values of u_h at the mesh points of the $(j + 1)$-th series are determined after the values of u_h for the preceding $(j, j - 1, \ldots)$ series are found (solution "step by step"). Some set of equations relating $u_{k, j+1}$ and $u_{k', j'}$ ($j' \leqslant j$) is used to determine $u_{k, j+1}$. We will denote this set of equations by A_{j+1}.

A system of grid equations is said to be an *explicit scheme* if each equation in the set A_{j+1} contains only one of the $u_{k, j+1}$ and, thus, each of the $u_{k, j+1}$ ($k = 1, 2, \ldots, N - 1$) is determined independently of the others [(2.147) is an example].

A system of grid equations is said to be an *implicit scheme* if at least some of the equations in the set A_{j+1} contain more than one $u_{k, j+1}$. In this case, the system containing all the equations in the set A_{j+1} must be solved in order to find $u_{k, j+1}$.

(a) *An Explicit Scheme.* We will now give an example of a simple explicit scheme. We will call the mesh points $(k, j + 1)(1 \leqslant k \leqslant N - 1, j \geqslant 0)$ *interior*, and with each such mesh point associate Eq. (2.147); with the mesh points on Γ_0 we associate Eq. (2.140), and with the mesh points on Γ_1 and Γ_2 associate the equations

$$u_{0, j} = \psi_1(j\tau), \quad u_{N, j} = \psi_2(j\tau) \quad (j = 1, 2, \ldots). \tag{2.155}$$

System (2.147), (2.140), (2.155) has a unique solution, and it is not difficult to see that u_{k_0, j_0} is determined by the values of $\varphi(x)$, $\psi_1(t)$, $\psi_2(t)$ at the mesh points in the triangle $D_\sigma(k_0 h, j_0 \tau)$; the exact solution $u(k_0 h, j_0 \tau)$, however, is determined by the values of φ on Γ_0, ψ_1 and ψ_2 on the sections $t \leqslant j_0 \tau$ of the half-lines Γ_1 and Γ_2, and the value of f in the rectangle $0 \leqslant x \leqslant 1, 0 \leqslant t \leqslant j_0\tau$. As in the Cauchy problem, it thus follows that u_h converges to the exact solution as $N \to \infty$, $\tau \to 0$, only if $\sigma = \tau/h \to 0$ as $N \to \infty$.

Assume that the exact solution $u(x, t)$ of Problem (2.145), (2.136), (2.153), (2.154) and its derivatives $\partial u/\partial t$ and $\partial^2 u/\partial x^2$ are continuous in the rectangle $\Delta(T)(0 \leqslant x \leqslant 1, 0 \leqslant t \leqslant T)$, where $T > 0$ is some number, and let $r = \tau/h^2$.

Theorem 6. If $r \leqslant \frac{1}{2}$, $h \to 0$, the grid solution u_h of system (2.147), (2.140), (2.155) uniformly approaches the exact solution $u(x, t)$ in $\Delta(T)$.

Remark 1. Theorem 6 also holds for the more general equation (2.148) and the region $\tilde{\Delta}(T)$ in which the half-lines Γ_1 and Γ_2 have been replaced by the curves $x = x_1(t)$ and $x = x_2(t)$ $(x_1(t) < x_2(t))$. It is assumed that grid equation (2.150) is used, and that the conditions $u(x_1(t), t) = \psi_1(t)$, $u(x_2(t), t) = \psi_2(t)$ are taken into account by simple shifting. In this case the grid system satisfies the principle of the maximum and is valid (see Theorem 5), from which our assertion follows.

Remark 2. Error estimates (2.151) and (2.152) hold for system (2.147), (2.140), (2.155).

Remark 3. If $f \equiv 0$, then

$$\frac{\partial^k u}{\partial t^k} = \frac{\partial^{2k} u}{\partial x^{2k}}.$$

In this case

$$\frac{\partial^{2k} u}{\partial x^{2k}} = v$$

satisfies Eq. (2.146) and the conditions

$$v\big|_{\Gamma_0} = \varphi^{(2k)}(x), \qquad v\big|_{\Gamma_1} = \psi_1^{(k)}(t), \qquad v\big|_{\Gamma_2} = \psi_2^{(k)}(t).$$

It is known [77] that

$$\max_{\Delta(T)} |v| \leqslant \max \left\{ \max_{\Gamma_0} |v|; \quad \max_{0 \leqslant t \leqslant T} |v|\Big|_{\Gamma}; \quad \max_{0 \leqslant t \leqslant T} |v|\Big|_{\Gamma_2} \right\}.$$

As a result, it is possible to obtain an estimate of $\|u_h - u\|$ in terms of the given φ, ψ_1, and ψ_2 when $f \equiv 0$ and φ, ψ_1, and ψ_2 are sufficiently smooth.

The constraint $r = \tau/h^2 \leqslant \frac{1}{2}$ is very burdensome, since the number of interior mesh points in $\Delta(T)$ increases no slower than $2N^3T$ as $N \to \infty$. Certain implicit schemes for solution of the same problem are free of the constraint $r \leqslant \frac{1}{2}$.

(b) *An Implicit Scheme.* Instead of Eq. (2.147), we associate the equation

$$\frac{u_{k, j+1} - u_{k, j}}{\tau} - \frac{u_{k+1, j+1} - 2u_{k, j+1} + u_{k-1, j+1}}{h^2} = (f)_{k, j+1} \qquad (2.156)$$

with each interior mesh point. Now the grid system consists of Eqs. (2.156), (2.140), and (2.155). If the values of u_h in the series $(0, 1, \ldots, j)$ are known, determination of $u_{k,j+1}$ $(k = 1, 2, \ldots, N - 1)$ requires us to solve the system

$$-\frac{1}{h^2} u_{k-1,j+1} + \left(\frac{1}{\tau} + \frac{2}{h^2}\right) u_{k,j+1} - \frac{1}{h^2} u_{k+1,j+1} = (f)_{k,j+1} + \frac{u_{k,j}}{\tau} \Bigg\}$$

$$(k = 1, 2, \ldots, N - 1), \tag{2.157}$$

$$u_{0,j+1} = \psi_1((j + 1)\tau), \qquad u_{N,j+1} = \psi_2((j + 1)\tau),$$

so system (2.156), (2.140), (2.155) constitutes an implicit scheme. It is not difficult to see that system (2.157) has a unique solution, and therefore, because u_h is known at mesh points on Γ_0, Γ_1, and Γ_2, it is possible to use (2.157) to determine successively the values in the various series: the first ($j = 0$), the second ($j = 1$), etc., i.e., system (2.156), (2.140), (2.155) has a unique solution.

Converge and error estimation. For any $\sigma = \tau/h$, system (2.156), (2.140), (2.155) satisfies the principle of the maximum, where Eqs. (2.156) correspond to the mesh points $(k, j + 1)$ of the first kind, and Eqs. (2.140) and (2.155) correspond to mesh points of the second kind. It is clear that each mesh point of the first kind can be connected with a mesh point of the second kind (at worst, by a horizontal line segment). By Theorem 2, the system has a unique solution [to avoid an infinite system of equations, we limit the discussion to mesh points in $\Delta(T)$]. Now, let $N \to \infty$ and $\tau \to 0$ in an arbitrary manner. For the region $\Delta(T)$, grid system (2.156), (2.140), (2.155) is valid because of Lemma 2, since the functions $v_0(x, t) \equiv t$ and $v_1(x, t) \equiv 1$ satisfy the hypothesis of the lemma.

If $u(x, t)$ is the solution of a mixed problem and is continuous together with its derivatives $\partial u/\partial t$ and $\partial^2 u/\partial x^2$ in $\Delta(T)$, then Eq. (2.156) approximates (2.145) and, by Theorem 2, we have

Theorem 7. If $N \to \infty$, $\tau \to 0$ in an arbitrary manner, then u_h uniformly converges to $u(x, t)$ in $\Delta(t)$.

If, moreover, we assume that $\partial^2 u/\partial t^2$ and $\partial^4 u/\partial x^4$ are bounded in $\Delta(T)$, we have the error estimate

$$\|u_h - u\| < T\left(\frac{\tau}{2}\left\|\frac{\partial^2 u}{\partial t^2}\right\| + \frac{h^2}{12}\left\|\frac{\partial^4 u}{\partial x^4}\right\|\right). \tag{2.158}$$

Remark. If $f \equiv 0$, then $\left\|\dfrac{\partial^2 u}{\partial t^2}\right\|$ and $\left\|\dfrac{\partial^4 u}{\partial x^4}\right\|$ in (2.158) can be replaced by

$$\max\left(\|\varphi^{(4)}(x)\|, \quad \max_{0 \leqslant t \leqslant T} |\psi_1''(t)|, \quad \max_{0 \leqslant t \leqslant T} |\psi_1''(t)|\right)$$

(see Remark 3 on Theorem 6).

Remark 2.   If we use the equation

$$\frac{u_{k,j+1} - u_{k,j}}{\tau} - (a)_{k,j+1} \frac{u_{k+1,j+1} - 2u_{k,j+1} + u_{k-1,j+1}}{h^2}$$

$$-(b)_{k,j+1} \frac{u_{k+1,j+1} - u_{k-1,j+1}}{2h} + (g)_{k,j+1} u_{k,j+1} = (f)_{k,j+1}$$

instead of Eq. (2.150), then Theorem 7 holds for the region $\tilde{\Delta}(T)$ (see Remark 1 on Theorem 6) with arbitrary convergence $h \to 0$, $\tau \to 0$.

(c) *The Pivot Method* (*see* [2, 17, 81, 90]).   A method called the *pivot or sweep method* has been proposed for solution of linear systems of the form

$$\left.\begin{aligned} -A_k v_{k-1} + B_k v_k - C_k v_{k+1} = D_k \\ (k = 1, 2, \ldots, N - 1), \\ v_0 = a, \quad v_N = b \end{aligned}\right\} \tag{2.159}$$

under the condition that the coefficients satisfy the conditions

$$A_k > 0, \quad B_k > 0, \quad C_k > 0, \quad A_k + C_k < B_k. \tag{2.160}$$

System (2.157) is a special case of system (2.159).

To solve system (2.159), we must

(α) compute the numbers E_k and F_k ($k = 0, 1, \ldots, N - 1$):

$$E_0 = 0, \quad E_k = \frac{C_k}{B_k - A_k E_{k-1}} \quad (k = 1, 2, \ldots, N - 1),$$

$$F_0 = a, \quad F_k = \frac{D_k + A_k F_{k-1}}{B_k - A_k E_{k-1}} \quad (k = 1, 2, \ldots, N - 1)$$

(*forward pivot*);

(β) compute the numbers

$$v_N = b, \quad v_k = E_k v_{k-1} + F_k \quad (k = N - 1, N - 2, \ldots, 1)$$

(*reverse pivot*).

When this method is used, the numbers E_k will, in virtue of conditions (2.160), satisfy the inequality $0 < E_k < 1$ ($k = 1, 2, \ldots, N - 1$), which distinguishes the pivot method from other possible exact methods of solving system (2.159).

(d) *An Example of a Family of Implicit Schemes.* Let α and θ be arbitrary constants. The equation

$$\frac{u_{k,j+1} - u_{k,j}}{\tau} - \left\{ \alpha \frac{u_{k+1,j+1} - 2u_{k,j+1} + u_{k-1,j+1}}{h^2} \right.$$

$$\left. + (1-\alpha) \frac{u_{k+1,j} - 2u_{k,j} + u_{k-1,j}}{h^2} \right\} = f(kh, (j+\theta)\tau)$$

$$(2.161)$$

approximates Eq. (2.145) in the class of functions that are continuous together with their derivatives $\partial u/\partial t$ and $\partial^2 u/\partial x^2$ in $\Delta(T)$.

When $\alpha = \theta = 0$, we obtain Eq. (2.147), while when $\alpha = \theta = 1$, we obtain Eq. (2.156). For each $\alpha \neq 0$, system (2.161), (2.140), (2.155) is an implicit scheme. This system has a unique solution when $\alpha \geqslant 0$, satisfies the principle of the maximum, and is valid in $\Delta(T)$ upon satisfaction of the conditions

$$0 \leqslant \alpha \leqslant 1, \qquad r = \frac{\tau}{h^2} \leqslant \frac{1}{2(1-\alpha)}. \qquad (2.162)$$

When conditions (2.162) are satisfied, therefore, the solution u_h of system (2.162), (2.140), (2.155) uniformly approaches the exact solution $u(x, t)$ in $\Delta(T)$.

2.3 Stability of difference schemes. Stability tests.

(a) *Example* 23.   Consider the following problem: in the region $\Omega(0 \leqslant x \leqslant 1, t \geqslant 0)$, find the solution of Eq. (2.145) that satisfies initial condition (2.136) on the segment $\Gamma_0(t = 0, 0 \leqslant x \leqslant 1)$, boundary condition (2.153) on the half-line $\Gamma_1(x = 0, t \geqslant 0)$, and the boundary condition

$$\frac{\partial u}{\partial x}\bigg|_{x=1} = \psi_2(t) \qquad (2.163)$$

on the half-line $\Gamma_2(x = 1, t \geqslant 0)$. The following grid equations can be proposed for the rectangular grid $\Omega_h(x_k = kh, t_j = j\tau, h = \dfrac{1}{N + \frac{1}{2}}$, where N is an integer). We will call the mesh points (k, j) $(1 \leqslant k \leqslant N, j \geqslant 2)$ *interior*, and for each such mesh point we write the equation (Richardson, 1910)

$$\frac{u_{k,j+1} - u_{k,j-1}}{2\tau} - \frac{u_{k+1,j} - 2u_{k,j} + u_{k-1,j}}{h^2} = (f)_{k,j} \qquad (2.164)$$

$$(k = 1, 2, \ldots, N; \quad j = 2, 3, \ldots);$$

each of these equations approximates Eq. (2.145) with error

$$\frac{1}{3}\left\|\frac{\partial^3 u}{\partial t^3}\right\| \tau^2 + \frac{1}{12}\left\|\frac{\partial^4 u}{\partial x^4}\right\| h^2$$

in the class of functions that can be extended to the half-line Γ_2 and have continuous first through fourth derivatives with respect to x. The approximation of eq. (2.145) by Eq. (2.164) is better than the approximation by Eq. (2.147) or Eq. (2.156). At mesh points Γ_0 and Γ_1, we set u_h equal to φ and φ_1, respectively. For grid replacement of condition (2.163), we introduce auxiliary mesh points $(N + 1, j)$ at a distance of $h/2$ from Γ_2. The equation

$$\frac{u_{N+1,j} - u_{N,j}}{h} = \psi_2(j\tau) \qquad (j = 1, 2, \ldots) \qquad (2.165)$$

approximates Eq. (2.163) with error $\dfrac{1}{24} \left\| \dfrac{\partial^3 u}{\partial x^3} \right\| h^2$. Equation (2.165) makes it possible to find $u_{N+1,j}$ if $u_{N,j}$ is known. Equation (2.164) makes it possible to find u_h at interior mesh points of the $(j + 1)$-th series if the values of u_h for the two preceding series—the jth and $(j - 1)$-th—are known. Therefore, for complete determination of the grid function everywhere in the grid Ω_h, it is sufficient to find the values of u_h at the interior mesh points of the first series. Then

$$u_{0,1} = \psi_1(\tau), \quad u_{N+1,1} = u_{N,1} + h\psi_2(\tau)$$

and u_h will be known for all mesh points of the first series. Equation (2.164) with $j = 1$ is used to determine u_h at the interior mesh points of the second series, and then at all of its mesh points. This method is used to find u_h everywhere in the grid.

In order to determine u_h for the first series, we use, for example, the following method. It follows from Eq. (2.145) for $t = 0$ and from (2.136) that

$$\frac{\partial u}{\partial t}\bigg|_{t=0} = \varphi''(x) + f(x, 0).$$

Thus, because $u(x, \tau) \approx \varphi(x) + \tau \left(\dfrac{\partial u}{\partial t} \right)_{t=0}$, it is natural to set

$$u_{k,1} = \varphi(kh) + \tau[\varphi''(kh) + f(kh, 0)] \qquad (k = 1, 2, \ldots, N).$$

Differentiation of Eq. (2.145) with respect to t similarly yields $\dfrac{\partial^2 u}{\partial t^2}\bigg|_{t=0}$ and makes it possible to refine $u_{k,1}$ or to compute u_h in several subsequent series

At first glance, the scheme described here for approximate solution of a problem is convenient in the sense of providing good estimates for the approximations of the grid equations used. However, later we will reject this scheme because it is unstable.

(b) *Grid (difference) Scheme for Solution of Mixed Problems for Hyperbolic and Parabolic Equations.* Let Lu be an sth order linear differential operator for differentiation with respect to only x, and assume that it has coefficients depending on x and t. Moreover, let p be a positive integer. The problem is as follows. In the region $\Omega(0 \leqslant x \leqslant 1, t \geqslant 0)$, find the solution of the equation

$$\frac{\partial^p u}{\partial t^p} - Lu = f(x, t), \tag{2.166}$$

that satisfies the p initial conditions

$$u \mid_{t=0} = \varphi_0(x), \quad \frac{\partial u}{\partial t}\bigg|_{t=0} = \varphi_1(x), \ldots, \quad \frac{\partial^{p-1} u}{\partial x^{p-1}} = \varphi_{p-1}(x), \tag{2.167}$$

$$0 \leqslant x \leqslant 1,$$

and the linear boundary conditions

$$\bar{l}_1 u = \psi_1(t), \quad \bar{l}_2 u = \psi_2(t), \ldots, \bar{l}_s u = \psi_s(t), \tag{2.168}$$

where $\bar{l}_i u$ is a linear combination of values of $u(x, t)$ and its derivatives with respect to x with coefficients depending on t; the equation

$$\alpha(t)u(0, t) + \beta(t)\frac{\partial u}{\partial x}\bigg|_{x=0} + \gamma(t)u(1, t) + \delta(t)\frac{\partial u}{\partial x}\bigg|_{x=1} = \psi(t)$$

is an example of Eqs. (2.168).

The mixed problems indicated above (see Paragraph 2) for hyperbolic and parabolic equations are special cases of Problem (2.166), (2.167), (2.168) as we have stated it.

Let ω_h denote some finite set of points on the segment $-\varepsilon \leqslant x \leqslant 1 + \varepsilon$ ($\varepsilon > 0$):

$$\omega_h\{x_1, x_2, \ldots, x_{N_h}\}$$

and let $\tau > 0$ be an arbitrary number. We will assume that the grid consists of the mesh points with coordinates $(x_k, j\tau)$ $(x_k \in \omega_h, j \geqslant 0)$. By the layer S_j we will mean the set of mesh points on the line $t = j\tau$. Let u_h be some grid function and let $u_h^{(j)}$ be the N_h-dimensional vector whose components are the values of the function u_h at the mesh points of the layer S_j. We use the following criterion to separate the set of grid equations approximating Eq. (2.166) into two groups: The group with index j includes the equations containing values of u_h in S_j and not in $S_{j'}$, where $j' > j$. It is assumed that the matrix form of each such group of equations is

$$R^j u_h \equiv \sum_{m=0}^{q} A_h^{(j, m)} u_h^{(j-m)} = \Pi_h^{(0, j)}(f; \varphi_0, \ldots, \varphi_{p-1}; \psi_1, \ldots, \psi_s), \tag{2.169}$$

where $A_h^{(j,m)}$ is a rectangular matrix with $N_h - s$ rows and N_h columns, and $\Pi_h^{(0,j)}$ is an operator that associates an $(N_h - s)$-dimensional vector with the group of functions $f; \varphi_0, \ldots, \varphi_{p-1}; \psi_1, \ldots, \psi_s$. Each equation in the jth group relates the values of the grid function on the $q + 1$ previous layers $S_{j-q}, S_{j-q+1}, \ldots, S_{j-1}, S_j$, where $q > p$ (in Example 23, $p = 1, q = 2$).

We will assume that the grid equations replacing boundary conditions (2.168) are written so that each equation contains the value of u_h in only one layer and is linear with respect to these values; to each layer there correspond s equations, which we write in the form

$$(a_h^{(j,n)}, u_h^{(j)}) = \Pi_h^{(j,n)}(f; \varphi_0, \ldots, \varphi_{p-1}; \psi_1, \ldots, \psi_s)$$

$$(n = 1, 2, \ldots, s; j = q, q+1, \ldots), \tag{2.170}$$

where $a_h^{(j,n)}$ is an N_h-dimensional vector, (a, b) denotes the scalar product of the vectors a and b, and $\Pi_h^{(j,n)}$ is a functional over the group of functions $(f: \varphi_0, \ldots, \varphi_{p-1}; \psi_1, \ldots, \psi_s)$.

Proposition A. For each j ($j \geq q$), Eqs. (2.169) and (2.170) have a unique simultaneous solution for $u_h^{(j)}$.

It follows from Proposition A that if $u_h^{(0)}, u_h^{(1)}, \ldots, u_h^{(q-1)}$ are known, then u_h is uniquely determined on $S_q, S_{q+1}, \ldots$.

Let $\Pi_h(f; \varphi_0, \ldots, \varphi_{p-1}; \psi_1, \ldots, \psi_s)$ be the operator that, with the group $(f; \omega_0, \ldots, \varphi_{p-1}; \psi_1, \ldots, \psi_s)$, associates the $(N_h \cdot q)$-dimensional vector whose components are the values of u_h on the layers $S_0, S_1, \ldots, S_{q-1}$; in Example 23 the operator is such that

$$u_{k,0} = \varphi(kh), \quad u_{k,1} = \varphi(kh) + \tau(\varphi''(kh) + f(kh, 0))$$

$$(k = 1, 2, \ldots, N).$$

$$u_{0,1} = \psi_1(\tau), \quad u_{N+1,1} = u_{N,1} + h\psi_2(\tau).$$

If we are given the operator Π_h and grid equations (2.169), (2.170) satisfying Proposition A have been written, the grid function u_h is uniquely determined.

Consider the solution of problem (2.166), (2.167), (2.168) in the fixed rectangle $\Delta(T)(0 \leq x \leq 1, 0 \leq t \leq T)$, and assume that the grid sequence $\{\Omega_h\}, h \to 0$, under discussion is such that $\tau \to 0$, $N_h \to \infty$. Now, let M_h denote the number of layers in $\Delta(T)$, i.e., the smallest integer larger than or equal to T/τ. We will then have the following vector spaces: an $(N_h \cdot M_h)$-dimensional space U_h, and $(N_h - s)$ $(M_h - q)$-dimensional space F_h, and $(M_h - q)$-dimensional space ψ_{nh} ($n = 1, 2, \ldots, s$), and an $(N_h \cdot q)$-dimensional space Φ_h. We assume that norms consistent with the corresponding functional norms $\|u\|_U$, $\|f\|_F$, and $\|\psi_n\|_{\psi_n}$ (see Section 1.2) have been introduced into the spaces U_h, F_h, and ψ_{nh}. In Φ_h we introduce a vector norm that we assume is consistent with several functional norms $\|\varphi_0\|, \|\varphi_1\|, \ldots, \|\varphi_{p-1}\|$ in the sense that for any function $u(x, t) \in U$ we have the equation

$$\lim_{h \to 0} \|\Pi_h(f; \varphi_0, \ldots, \varphi_{p-1}; \psi_1, \ldots, \psi_s)\|_{\Phi_h} = K(\|\varphi_0\|, \|\varphi_1\|, \ldots, \|\varphi_{p-1}\|),$$

$$\tag{2.171}$$

where $f, \varphi_0, \ldots, \varphi_{p-1}, \psi_1, \ldots, \psi_s$ are defined by Eqs. (2.166), (2.167), and (2.168), and K is some homogeneous first-degree positive function of all of its arguments (e.g., $\|\varphi_0\| + \|\varphi_1\| + \cdots + \|\varphi_{p-1}\|$ for

$$\sqrt{\|\varphi_0\|^2 + \|\varphi_1\|^2 + \cdots + \|\varphi_{p-1}\|^2}).$$

We will say that Π_h approximates (ux, t) in norm if $\|u - \Pi_h\| \to 0$ as $h \to 0$.

Definition 1. We will say that grid problem (2.169), (2.170) is *stable with respect to the initial conditions* if for any grid function u_h satisfying the homogeneous equations corresponding to inhomogeneous equations (2.169) and (2.170) [obtained from (2.169) and (2.170) by equating them to zero] we have the inequality

$$\|u_h\|_{U_h} \leqslant N^{(0)} \|u_h\|_{\Phi_h}, \qquad (2.172)$$

where N^0 is a positive constant not depending on h.

Definition 2. We will say that grid problem (2.169), (2.170) is *stable with respect to the right-hand side* if for any grid function u_h that vanishes on the layers $S_0, S_1, \ldots, S_{q-1}$ and satisfies the homogeneous equations corresponding to (2.170) we have the inequality

$$\|u_h\|_{U_h} \leqslant N^{(1)} \|R_h u_h\|_{F_h},$$

where $N^{(1)}$ is independent of h, and $R_h u_h$ is the operator mapping U_h into F_h and the set of left-hand sides of (2.169). The definition of *stability with respect to boundary conditions* is similar:

$$\|u_h\|_{U_h} \leqslant N^{(2)} \sum_{n=1}^{s} \|r_{nh} u_h\|_{\Psi_{nh}},$$

if u_h is equal to zero on $S_0, \ldots, S_{q-1}$ and satisfies homogeneous equations (2.169).

It follows from the linearity of the grid problem that if the grid problem is stable with respect to the initial conditions, the right-hand side, and the boundary conditions, it is well posed (see Section 1.3b). If $u(x, t) \in U$, Eqs. (2.169) and (2.170) approximate Eqs. (2.166) and (2.168), and Π_h approximates $u(x, t)$, then u_h converges to $u(x, t)$ as $h \to 0$ (Section 1.3, Theorem 3).

Considerably more attention has been devoted to the study of stability with respect to initial conditions than to the study of stability with respect to the right-hand side or stability with respect to boundary conditions. This stems from two sources:

1. In many cases ([83, 116]), stability relative to initial conditions (so-called *uniform stability*) implies stability with respect to the right-hand side;

2. The greatest part of the problems under discussion are such that the boundary conditions are accounted for exactly and the corresponding term in the error estimate is equal to zero;

3. The study of the influence of errors inherited from computation of u_h

on certain layers S_j on the value of u_h on the subsequent layers $S_{j+1}, S_{j+2}, \dots$ reduces to the study of stability with respect to initial conditions. Apparently, this last fact has proved decisive. The book [17] presents a discussion of problems on stability with respect to the right-hand side and stability with respect to boundary conditions.

In the following discussion, *stability of a difference scheme* will mean stability with respect to initial conditions.

(c) *Stability of Difference Schemes.* Let U_h^0 denote a set of grid functions u_h satisfying homogeneous equations (2.169) and (2.170).

Consider the following norms: $\|u_h\|_{U_h}$ for the $(N_h \cdot M_h)$-dimensional vector u_h, $\|u_h^{(j)}\|$ for the N_h-dimensional vector $u_h^{(j)}$, $\|u_h^{(j,q)}\|$ for the $(N_h \cdot q)$-dimensional vector whose components are the values of u_h on the q layers $S_{j-q+1}, S_{j-q+2}, \dots, S_j$, and a norm $\|u_h\|_{\Phi_h}$ consistent with the functional norms in the sense of (2.171). It is assumed that for any grid function $u_h \in U_h^0$, these norms are related by the inequalities

$$\|u_h\|_{U_h^0} \leqslant C_0 \max_j \|u_h^{(j)}\| \qquad (0 \leqslant j \leqslant M_h - 1), \qquad (2.173)$$

$$\|u_h^{(j)}\| \leqslant C_1 \|u_h^{(j,q)}\|, \qquad (2.174)$$

$$\|u_h^{(q-1,q)}\| \leqslant C_2 \|u_h\|_{\Phi_h}, \qquad (2.175)$$

where C_0, C_1, and C_2 are positive constants that do not depend on h. In particular, if we take the maximum modulus of the vector components for the norms of the vectors, these inequalities are satisfied for $C_0 = C_1 = C_2 = 1$.

Theorem 8. If there exists a nonnegative constant C such that for any $u_h \in U_h^0$

$$\|u_h^{(j,q)}\| \leqslant (1 + C\tau)\|u_h^{(j-1,q)}\|, \qquad q \leqslant j \leqslant M_h - 1, \qquad (2.176)$$

then grid scheme (2.169)–(2.170) is stable, i.e., inequality (2.172) holds for any $u_h \in U_h^0$.

Special case. If $p = q = 1$, we can assume that the norm $\|u_h^{(j,q)}\|$ coincides with $\|u_h^{(j)}\|$, and then (2.176) takes the form

$$\|u_h^{(j)}\| \leqslant (1 + C\tau)\|u_h^{(j-1)}\|, \qquad 1 \leqslant j \leqslant M_h - 1. \qquad (2.177)$$

EXAMPLE 24. In the rectangle $\Delta(T)$, consider Grid Equation (2.150) ($h = 1/N$) for $(f)_{k,j} = 0$ under the conditions $u_{0,j} = u_{N,j} = 0$ on the half-lines Γ_1 and Γ_2. If $g(x, t) \geqslant 0$ and $\tau \leqslant h^2(2A + Gg^2)^{-1}$, then the principle of the maximum holds and the grid problem is well posed, as a result of which it is stable relative to the initial conditions. If $g(x, t)$ also takes negative values in $\Delta(T)$, the grid system does not satisfy the principle of the maximum, but stability does occur when $r = \tau/h^2 < 1/2A$, since it is clear that (2.177) is valid where $C = g(x, t)$. It can be shown that here u_h also converges to $u(x, t)$.

Remark. When $p = q = 1$, we obtain

$$u_h^{(j)} = B_h^{(j)} u_h^{(j-1)},$$

where $B_h^{(j)}$ is an $N_h \times N_h$ matrix, by solving the homogeneous equations corresponding to (2.169) and (2.170) for $u_h^{(j)}$. Assume that the matrix norm is chosen so that it is consistent [104] with the vector norm. Then a sufficient condition for stability will be

$$\|B_h^{(j)}\| \leqslant 1 + C\tau, \qquad 1 \leqslant j \leqslant M_h - 1.$$

If the coefficients of the operator L and the boundary conditions are independent of t, it is natural to choose the coefficients of grid equations (2.169) and (2.170) so that they do not depend on j. In this case the matrix $B_h^{(j)}$ is independent of j, so

$$u_h^{(j)} = (B_h)^j u_h^{(0)},$$

Then a necessary and sufficient condition for stability is boundedness of the norms of the family of matrices

$$\|(B_h)^j\| \qquad (h \to 0, 1 \leqslant j \leqslant M_h - 1),$$

(d) *The Index of a Difference Scheme* ([30]).   It follows from Proposition A for system (2.169)–(2.170) that an individual component $(u_h^{(j)})_k$ of the vector $u_h^{(j)}$ is a linear combination of the values of u_h on the layers $S_{j-1}, \ldots, S_{j-q}$ (it is assumed that $u_h \in U_h^0$), i.e.,

$$(u_h^{(j)})_k = \sum_{\substack{x_\nu \in \omega_h \\ j-q \leqslant \mu \leqslant j-1}} C_{\mu,\nu}^{(k,j)} (u_h^{(\mu)})_\nu,$$

where the $C_{\mu,\nu}^{(k,j)}$ are the coefficients of the linear combination. The quantity

$$J = \max_{q \leqslant j \leqslant M_h-1} \max_{x_k \in \omega_h} \sum_{\substack{x_\nu \in \omega_h \\ j-q \leqslant \mu \leqslant j-1}} |C_{\mu,\nu}^{(k,j)}|$$

is called the *index of the difference scheme.*
   If there exists a constant C that is independent of h and such that $J < 1 + C\tau$, it follows from Theorem 8 that the difference scheme is stable (the vector norm is the maximum modulus of the components.).

(e) *Stability Tests Obtained by the Method of Separation of Variables.*   We assume that the coefficients of the operator L [see (2.166)] and the linear combinations $\bar{l}_n u$ [see (2.168)] are independent of t. It is then natural to choose the matrices $A_h^{(j,m)}$ and vectors $a_h^{(j,n)}$ [see (2.169) and (2.170)] so that they do not depend on j; in this case we write $A_h^{(m)}$ and $a_h^{(n)}$. Now all of the vectors $u_h^{(j)}$ ($j = 0, 1, \ldots$) must satisfy the conditions

$$(a_h^{(n)}, u_h^{(j)}) = 0 \qquad (n = 1, 2, \ldots, s) \tag{2.178}$$

and consequently, belong to some $(M_h - s)$-dimensional vector subspace V_h of the space of N_h-dimensional vectors.

Let $N_h - s$ of the mesh points of ω_h be interior, and let s be boundary mesh points. Now assume that the vector $v_h \in V_h$ be uniquely determined by its values at the interior mesh points, and assume that the rows of the matrix $A_h^{(m)}$ correspond to the interior mesh points of ω_h, i.e., $A_h^{(m)} u_h^{(j)}$ is the vector whose components are the values of some grid function at the interior mesh points of ω_h. In virtue of our assumptions, this vector can be uniquely extended to a vector in the subspace V_h. In this sense, the rectangular matrices $A_h^{(m)}$ can be treated as mappings of any vector in V_h into a vector in V_h.

Proposition B. It is possible to provide V_h with a scalar product such that V_h will contain an orthonormal basis such that each vector is a characteristic vector for each matrix $A_h^{(m)}$.

We denote this scalar product by $[v_h, v_h']$, where v_h and v_h' are two vectors in V_h; we denote the basis vectors by $v_h^{(1)}$ ($l = 1, 2, \ldots, N_h - s$), and we denote the eigenvalues of the matrix $A_{h,}^{(m)}$ by $\rho_h^{(m,l)}$. Then the grid function u_h, whose value on the layer S_j is given by the equation

$$u_h^{(j)} = \lambda^j v_h^{(l)},$$

where λ is some constant, satisfies boundary conditions (2.178); u_h satisfies homogeneous equation (2.169) if, and only if, λ satisfies the equation

$$\sum_{m=0}^{q} \rho_h^{(m,l)} \lambda^{j-m} \equiv \lambda^{j-q} \sum_{m=0}^{q} \rho_h^{(m,l)} \lambda^{q-m} = 0,$$

i.e., (assuming that $\lambda \neq 0$) the equation

$$\rho_h^{(0,l)} \lambda^q + \rho_h^{(1,l)} \lambda^{q-1} + \ldots + \rho_h^{(q-1,l)} \lambda + \rho_h^{(q,l)} = 0 \tag{2.179}$$

We denote the roots of Eq. (2.179) by $\lambda_h^{(\mu,l)}$ ($\mu = 1, 2, \ldots, q$), and we will call them the *growth coefficients*. We introduce the norms

$$\left.\begin{aligned}
\|u_h^{(j)}\| &= \sqrt{[u_h^{(j)}, u_h^{(j)}]}, \\
\|u_h\|_{U_h^0} &= \max_{0 \leqslant j \leqslant M_h - 1} \|u_h^{(j)}\|
\end{aligned}\right\} \tag{2.180}$$

and, in the case $p = 1$

$$\|u_h\|_{\Phi_h} = \sqrt{\sum_{m=0}^{q-1} \|u_h^{(m)}\|^2}. \tag{2.181}$$

Theorem 9. A grid problem is stable (in the case $p = 1$) with respect to norms (2.180) and (2.181) if and only if there exists a nonnegative constant

C such that for $\mu = 1, 2, \ldots, q$ and $l = 1, 2, \ldots, N_h - s$ the growth coefficients satisfy the inequality

$$\|\lambda_h^{(\mu, l)}\| \leqslant 1 + C\tau. \tag{2.182}$$

Remark 1. Conditions for stability were discussed in [83] for the case $p > 1$ and a specially selected form $\|u_h\|_{\Phi_h}$. In particular, approach of the upper bound of the moduli of the growth coefficients to unity is a necessary condition for stability. This means that if one of the growth coefficients is such that $|\lambda_h^{(\mu, l)}| \geqslant 1 + \varepsilon$ for all h, where ε is small and fixed, the grid problem is not stable.

Remark 2. When $p = 1$, the condition

$$|\lambda_h^{(\mu, l)}| \leqslant 1 \tag{2.183}$$

is sufficient for stability. Under condition (2.183), $\|u_h^{(j)}\|$ remains bounded as $j \to \infty$. Some authors [90, 112] who define stability as boundedness of $\|u_h^{(j)}\|$ when $j \to \infty$, use (2.183) as a necessary and sufficient condition for stability.

(f) EXAMPLES. In the following examples we will consider grid schemes for Eq. (2.146). We will use $\dfrac{1}{h^2}(u_{k-1, j} - 2u_{k, j} + u_{k+1, j})$. as the approximation for $\left(\dfrac{\partial^2 u}{\partial x^2}\right)_{k, j}$. For the boundary conditions we will use

$$(\alpha) \qquad u\,\big|_{x=0} = u\,\big|_{x=1} = 0,$$

$$(\beta) \qquad u\,\big|_{x=0} = \frac{\partial u}{\partial x}\,\big|_{x=1} = 0,$$

$$(\gamma) \qquad \frac{\partial u}{\partial x}\,\big|_{x=0} = \frac{\partial u}{\partial x}\,\big|_{x=1} = 0.$$

For the set ω_h we take

$$(\alpha) \qquad x_k = kh, \quad h = \frac{1}{N}, \quad 0 \leqslant k \leqslant N,$$

$$(\beta) \qquad x_k = kh, \quad h = \frac{1}{N + \frac{1}{2}}, \quad 0 \leqslant k \leqslant D + 1,$$

$$(\gamma) \qquad x_k = \left(k + \frac{1}{2}\right)h, \quad h = \frac{1}{N}, \quad -1 \leqslant k \leqslant N.$$

For the grid boundary condition we take

$(\alpha)\ u_{0, j} = u_{N, j} = 0,$

$(\beta)\ u_{0, j} = 0, \quad u_{N+1, j} - u_{N, j} = 0,$

$(\gamma)\ u_{0, j} - u_{-1, j} = 0, \quad u_{N, j} - u_{N-1, j} = 0.$

The grid functions $v_h^{(j)}(k)$,

(α) $v_h^{(l)}(k) \equiv \sin\left(k\dfrac{\pi l}{N}\right)$ $(l = 1, 2, \ldots . N - 1)$,

(β) $v_h^{(l)}(k) \equiv \sin\left(k\dfrac{\pi(2l + 1)}{2N + 1}\right)$ $(l = 0, 1, \ldots, N)$,

(γ) $v_h^{(l)}(k) \equiv \cos\left(\left(k + \dfrac{1}{2}\right)\dfrac{\pi l}{N}\right)$ $(l = 0, 1, \ldots, N - 1)$,

are the characteristic functions of the difference operator

$$(\delta_h^2 v)_k \equiv h^{-2}[v(k - 1) - 2v(k) + v(k + 1)],$$

where

(α) $\delta_h^2 v_h^{(l)} = \left(-\dfrac{4}{h^2}\sin^2\dfrac{\pi l}{2N}\right)v_h^{(l)}$,

(β) $\delta_h^2 v_h^{(l)} = \left(-\dfrac{4}{h^2}\sin^2\dfrac{\pi(2l + 1)}{2(2N + 1)}\right)v_h^{(l)}$,

(γ) $\delta_h^2 v_h^{(l)} = \left(-\dfrac{4}{h^2}\sin^2\dfrac{\pi l}{2N}\right)v_h^{(l)}$.

We should note that in cases (α), (β), and (γ) the factors $\sin^2\dfrac{\pi l}{2N}$, $\sin^2\dfrac{\pi(2l + 1)}{2(2N + 1)}$, and $\sin^2 \pi l/2N$ are positive (except in case γ) when $l = 0$ and when l varies within the given limits, take values arbitrarily close to 0 or 1 as $N \to \infty$. In what follows we will denote these factors by $\rho_h^{(l)}$ and in the following examples the boundary conditions may be any of (α), (β), or (γ) and we will write only the grid equation replacing Eq. (2.146) for the interior points of the mesh.

EXAMPLE 25: Consider homogeneous equation (2.164) [see (a)]. Substituting the expression $\lambda^j v_h^{(l)}(k)$ for $u_{k,j}$ in (2.164), we find, after division by $\lambda^{j-1} v_h^{(l)}(k)$, that

$$\lambda^2 + 8r\rho_h^{(l)}\lambda - 1 = 0 \qquad \left(r = \frac{\tau}{h^2}\right).$$

The constant term of this quadratic equation is negative, so its roots are real, of different signs, and the negative root has modulus greater than one. We denote this root by $\lambda_h^{(1,l)}$. For fixed r and sufficiently small τ and h, there exists an l such that

$$|\lambda_h^{(1,l)}| > 1 + 4r,$$

and, consequently, the difference scheme with (2.164) is unstable when

$$\tau \to 0, \ h \to 0, \frac{\tau}{h^2} = r \geqslant r > 0.$$

EXAMPLE 26:   We consider a family of implicit schemes (2.161). Substitution of $\lambda^j v_h^{(1)}(k)$ for $u_{k,j}$ in Eq. (2.161) and division by $\lambda^j v_h^{(1)}(k)$ yields

$$\lambda - 1 + 4r[\alpha\lambda + (1 - \alpha)]\rho_h^{(l)} = 0.$$

It follows that

$$\lambda = 1 - \frac{4r\rho_h^{(l)}}{1 + 4r\rho_h^{(l)}\alpha},$$

and therefore, we have $\lambda < 1$ for $\alpha > 0$. If the inequality $2r(1 - 2\alpha) \leqslant 1$ is satisfied, we will have $\lambda \geqslant -1$ because $0 \leqslant \rho_h^{(l)} \leqslant 1$ and, consequently, $|\lambda| \geqslant 1$. It follows that scheme (2.161) is stable if $2r(1 - 2\alpha) \leqslant 1$. In particular, if $\alpha \geqslant \frac{1}{2}$ the scheme is stable for any $r > 0$, i.e., it is stable for any means in which τ and h approach zero. If $\alpha < \frac{1}{2}$, the scheme will be stable if and only if $r = \frac{\tau}{h^2} \leqslant \frac{1}{2(1 - 2a)}$. We should note that for $0 \leqslant \alpha \leqslant 1$ the principle of the maximum (see Paragraph 2) yields the inequality $r \leqslant \frac{1}{2(1 - \alpha)}$, which guarantees validity and therefore stability in a uniform norm; as a result, stability in norm (2.180) is also guaranteed. For $r = \frac{1}{6(1 - 2\alpha)} \left(\alpha < \frac{1}{2}\right)$ we obtain an equation with a good approximation.

EXAMPLE 27:   When $\alpha > 0$, scheme (2.161) is implicit and transition to the following layer requires solution of a system of linear equations. The equation (Dufort and Frankel, 1953)

$$\frac{u_{k,j+1} - u_{k,j-1}}{2\tau} - \frac{u_{k+1,j} - u_{k,j+1} - u_{k,j-1} + u_{k-1\ j}}{h^2} = 0 \qquad (2.184)$$

leads to an explicit scheme that is stable for any means in which τ and h approach zero. Indeed,

$$v_h^{(l)}(k + 1) + v_h^{(l)}(k - 1) = 2\cos\mu_h^{(l)} \cdot v_h^{(l)}(k),$$

where $\mu_h^{(l)} = \frac{\pi l}{N}$ in cases (α) and (γ), while $\mu_h^{(l)} = \frac{\pi(2l + 1)}{2N + 1}$ in case (β). Thus, after substitution of $\lambda^j v_h^{(1)}$ for $u_{k,j}$ in (2.184), elementary operations yield

$$\lambda^2 - 1 - 2r[\lambda \cdot 2\cos\mu_h^{(l)} - (\lambda^2 + 1)] = 0$$

or

$$\lambda^2 - \frac{4r\cos\mu_h^{(l)}}{1 + 2r}\lambda - \frac{1 - 2r}{1 + 2r} = 0,$$

whose roots have moduli less than one for all $r > 0$ and $\mu_h^{(1)}$, so (2.184) is stable for any means in which τ and h approach zero. We should, however, note that Eq. (2.184) approximates Eq. (2.146) only when $\tau/h \to 0$. If $\tau/h = \sigma$ remains constant ($\sigma > 0$), Eq. (2.184) approximates the hyperbolic equation

$$\frac{\partial u}{\partial t} - \frac{\partial^2 u}{\partial x^2} + \sigma^2 \frac{\partial^2 u}{\partial t^2} = 0.$$

Therefore when Eq. (2.184) is used for approximate solution of Eq. (2.146), the grid must be chosen with a sufficiently small $\sigma = \tau/h$. The books [81, 90] contain tables of grid equations approximating Eq. (2.146) and conditions for stability of these grid equations.

(h) *A Stability Test for Equations with Constant Coefficients.* Let: (a) the coefficients of an operator Lu be constant; and (b) homogeneous boundary conditions for $x = 0$ and $x = 1$ be such that the solution $u(x, t)$ of the equation

$$\frac{\partial u}{\partial t} - Lu = 0 \qquad (2.185)$$

can be extended to the entire half-plane ($-\infty < x < \infty$, $t \geqslant 0$) so that the new function is a solution of Eq. (2.185) and is periodic with respect to x with period m, where m is a positive integer.

To solve this problem we use the rectangular grid

$$x_k = x^{(0)}(h) + kh, \quad t_j = j\tau$$

$$\left(k = 0, \pm 1, \pm 2, \ldots ; \; j = 0, 1, 2, \ldots ; \; h = \frac{m}{N}\right)$$

and a grid equation replacing (2.185) of the form ($q = 1$)

$$\sum_{v=-s}^{s} a_h^{(v)} u_{k+v, j} + \sum_{v=-s}^{s} b_h^{(v)} u_{k+v, j-1} = 0, \qquad (2.186)$$

where s is some positive integer, while $a_h^{(v)}$ and $b_h^{(v)}$—the coefficients of the grid equation—depend on τ and h, but not on k and j. The boundary conditions are replaced by a condition requiring the grid solution to be periodic. Grid equations (2.186) have solutions of the form

$$v_h^{(l)}(k, j) = (\lambda_h^{(l)})^j \, e^{i(2\pi l/N)k}, \quad i = \sqrt{-1},$$

where l is an arbitrary integer, and the $\lambda_h^{(l)}$ are constants that do not depend on l (or h and τ). Equation (2.186) yields

$$\lambda_h^{(l)} = -\frac{\displaystyle\sum_{v=-s}^{s} b_h^{(v)} \zeta^v}{\displaystyle\sum_{v=-s}^{s} a_h^{(v)} \zeta^v} \; (\zeta = e^{i \, 2\pi l/N}). \qquad (2.187)$$

If the inequality

$$|\lambda_h^{(l)}| \leqslant 1 + C\tau, \tag{2.188}$$

holds for every l as $h \to 0$, $\tau \to 0$, the grid problem is stable.

The book [81] contains a discussion of the theory of stability of difference equations that approximate equations of the form (2.185) in the case $q \geqslant 1$. The test (2.188) under discussion here is a result of this theory.

We should not that this theory can be used to obtain the conclusions of Examples 25, 26, and 27 [see (f)].

The following example is such that Proposition B of (e) does not hold, and therefore it does not yield to the method of Paragraph (f).

EXAMPLE 28: *An asymmetric grid equation* [90]. The problem is stated as follows: Find the solution of Eq. (2.146) under the boundary conditions $u\big|_{x=0} = u\big|_{x=1} = 0$ and the initial condition $u\big|_{t=0} = \varphi(x)$. It is not difficult to see that if the solution $u(x, t)$ of this problem is extended to $(-1 \leqslant x \leqslant 0,\ t \geqslant 0)$ by setting $u(x, t) = -u(-x, t)$, and then extended periodically with period 2 relative to x to the entire half-plane $t \geqslant 0$, the function $u(x, t)$ thus obtained is a solution of Eq. (2.146).

Let α be an arbitrary real number. For each interior mesh point of the grid

$$x_k = kh,\ t_j = j\tau \left(h = \frac{1}{N}\ ;\ k = 1, 2, \ldots, N-1;\ j = 1, 2, \ldots \right)$$

we write the equation

$$(1 + r\alpha)\frac{u_{k,j+1} - u_{k,j}}{\tau} - r\alpha\frac{u_{k-1,j+1} - u_{k-1,j}}{\tau}$$

$$- \frac{u_{k+1,j} - 2u_{k,j} + u_{k-1,j}}{h^2} = 0,\quad r = \frac{\tau}{h^2}, \tag{2.189}$$

which approximates Eq. (2.146) when $\tau h \to 0$ with estimate

$$\left\|\frac{\partial^4 u}{\partial x^4}\right\| h^2 + \left\|\frac{\partial^2 u}{\partial t^2}\right\| \tau + \left\|\frac{\partial^2 u}{\partial t\, \partial x}\right\| \alpha\frac{\tau}{h}\ .$$

Despite the fact that Eq. (2.189) leads to an implicit scheme, it is easy to compute $u_h^{(j+1)}$. Namely, (2.189) uniquely determines $u_{k,j+1}$ when $(1 + r\alpha) \neq 0$ if $u_h^{(j)}$ and $u_{k-1,j+1}$ are known. But $u_{0,j+1} = 0$ because of the boundary condition, so $u_{1,j+1}, u_{2,j+1}, \ldots, u_{N-1,j+1}$ can be successively computed if $u_h^{(j)}$ is known and we can then set $u_{N,j+1} = 0$.

Equation (2.189) yields

$$[(1 + r\alpha)u_{k,j+1} - r\alpha u_{k-1,j+1}]$$

$$+ [(2r - 1 - r\alpha)u_{k,j} - r(1 - \alpha)u_{k-1,j} - ru_{k+1,j}] = 0$$

and, by (2.187), we therefore have

$$\lambda_h^{(l)} = \frac{r(1 - \alpha)\zeta^{-1} + r\zeta - (2r - 1 - r\alpha)}{(1 + r\alpha) - r\alpha\zeta^{-1}}, \ \zeta = e^{i\,2\pi l/N} = e^{i\mu}.$$

It is clear that when $\alpha = 1$ we have

$$|\lambda_h^{(l)}|^2 = \frac{r\zeta + (1 - r)}{(1 + r) - r\zeta^{-1}} \frac{r\bar{\zeta} + (1 - r)}{(1 + r) - r\bar{\zeta}^{-1}} = \frac{r^2 + (1 - r)^2 + 2r(1 - r)\cos\mu}{r^2 + (1 + r)^2 - 2r(1 + r)\cos\mu}$$

$$= 1 - \frac{4r(1 - \cos\mu)}{r^2 + (1 + r)^2 - 2r(1 + r)\cos\mu} \quad \left(\bar{\zeta} = e^{-i\mu} = \frac{1}{\zeta}\right).$$

which implies that $0 \leqslant |\lambda_h + |\, 2 \leqslant 1$ and, therefore, grid scheme (2.189) is stable for $\alpha = 1$ and arbitrary r. Nonetheless, when scheme (2.189) is used we must remember that the approximation holds only if $\tau/h \to 0$, so for concrete computations τ must be small in comparison with h. We should note that when $\alpha = r = 1$, scheme (2.189) leads to the formula

$$u_{k\,j+1} = \frac{u_{k+1,j} + u_{k-1,j+1}}{2}$$

which is very easy for computation.

2.4 Examples of stable difference schemes. (a) *An Alternating Scheme.* We will consider explicit scheme (2.147) and implicit scheme (2.156) for approximate solution of Eq. (2.146) under the boundary conditions $u\,|_{x=0} = u\,|_{x=1} = 0$ and initial condition (2.136). The explicit scheme is stable only when $r = \tau/h^2 \leqslant \frac{1}{2}$, but computation of u_h on successive layers S_j is simple; the implicit scheme is stable for all $\tau \to 0$, $h \to 0$, but determination of u_h on successive layers S_j requires solution of a system of linear equations by, for example, the pivot method, although there are no constraints on the ratio $\sigma = \frac{\tau}{h}\,(\tau \to 0, h \to 0)$. It turns out that if the explicit scheme is used to compute $u_h^{(j)}$ for even j (odd j) and the implicit scheme is used for odd j (even j), the entire scheme is stable. Indeed, the solution of the grid problem is the sum of terms of the form

$$w_l(j) \sin k\frac{l\pi}{N} \qquad (l = 1, 2, \ldots, N - 1).$$

When the explicit scheme is used, we obtain

$$\frac{w_l(j)}{w_l(j - 1)} = 1 - 4r\rho_h^{(l)} \qquad \left(r = \frac{\tau}{h^2}, \rho_h^{(l)} = \sin^2\frac{\pi l}{2N}\right)$$

upon transition form S_{j-1} to S_j, and upon transition from S_j to S_{j+1} by the implicit scheme, we obtain

$$\frac{w_l(j+1)}{w_l(j)} = \frac{1}{1 + 4r\rho_h^{(l)}}.$$

As a result, for each pair of transitions from S_{j-1} to S_{j+1} we have

$$\left| \frac{w_l(j+1)}{w_l(j-1)} \right| = \left| \frac{1 - 4r\rho_h^{(l)}}{1 + 4r\rho_h^{(l)}} \right| < 1,$$

which ensures stability of the scheme for arbitrary r; the stability and approximation hold no matter how h and τ go to zero.

A large number of difference schemes for solution of parabolic equations is studied in [90].

(b) *Stable Difference Schemes for $p = q = 2$.* Consider Eq. (2.166) with $p = 2$. If we set up difference scheme (2.169) for the case $q = 2$ and set the norm in Φ_h equal to

$$\sqrt{[u_h^{(0)}, u_h^{(0)}] + \left[\frac{u_h^{(1)} - u_h^{(0)}}{\tau}, \frac{u_h^{(1)} - u_h^{(0)}}{\tau} \right]},$$

the following sufficient conditions for stability can be given. If the grid problem is such that the growth coefficients (see Section 2.3,e) $\lambda_h^{(\mu, l)}$ ($\mu = 1, 2$: $l = 1, 2, \ldots, N_h - s$) can be represented in the form $\lambda_h^{(1,l)} = e^{i\gamma l}$, $\lambda_h^{(2,l)} = e^{-i\gamma l}$, the grid problem is stable if $\cos \gamma_l \geq -1 + \nu$, where $\nu > 0$ is some arbitrary constant [83].

EXAMPLE 29: To solve the mixed problem

$$\frac{\partial^2 u}{\partial t^2} - \frac{\partial^2 u}{\partial x^2} = 0,$$

$$u \mid_{x=0} = u \mid_{x=1} = 0, \quad u \mid_{t=0} = \varphi(x), \quad \frac{\partial u}{\partial t} \Big|_{t=0} = g(x)$$

we use the grid $x_k = kh$, $t_j = j\tau$ $\left(h = \frac{1}{N}; k = 0, 1, \ldots, N; j = 0, 1, 2, \ldots \right).$

Consider the family of implicit schemes

$$\frac{u_{k,j+1} - 2u_{k,j} + u_{k,j-1}}{\tau^2} - [\alpha \delta_h^2 u_h^{(j+1)} + (1 - \alpha - \beta) \delta_h^2 u_h^{(j)}$$

$$+ \beta \delta_h^2 u_h^{(j-1)}]_k = 0 \quad \left([\delta_h^2 u_h^{(j)}]_k = \frac{u_{k+1,j} - 2u_{k,j} + u_{k-1,j}}{h^2} \right),$$

$$u_{0,j} = u_{N,j} = 0, \quad u_{k,0} = \varphi(kh), \quad u_{k,1} = \varphi(kh) + \tau g(kh).$$

Choosing $v_h^{(l)}(k) = \sin k \dfrac{\pi l}{N} \, (l = 1, 2, \ldots, N - 1)$, we can easily obtain the following equation for $\lambda_h^{(\mu, l)}$:

$$\lambda^2 - 2\lambda + 1 + 4\rho_h^{(l)}\sigma^2[\alpha\lambda^2 + (1 - \alpha - \beta)\lambda + \beta] = 0$$

$$\left(\rho_h^{(l)} = \sin^2\frac{\pi l}{2N}, \quad \sigma = \frac{\tau}{h}\right),$$

i.e.,

$$\lambda^2 - 2\left[\frac{1 - 2\rho_h^{(l)}\sigma^2(1 - \alpha - \beta)}{1 + 4\rho_h^{(l)}\sigma^2\alpha}\right]\lambda + \frac{1 + 4\rho_h^{(l)}\sigma^2\beta}{1 + 4\rho_h^{(l)}\sigma^2\alpha} = 0.$$

For $\alpha = \beta \geqslant 0$ and $\rho_h^{(l)}\sigma^2(1 - 4\alpha) \leqslant 1$, the roots of the last quadratic equation are of the form $e^{i\gamma l}$ and $e^{-i\gamma l}$, where

$$\cos\gamma_l = 1 - \frac{2\rho_h^{(l)}\sigma^2}{1 + 4\rho_h^{(l)}\sigma^2\alpha} \geqslant 1 - \frac{2\sigma^2}{1 + 4\sigma^2\alpha} = -1 + 2\frac{1 + \sigma^2(4\alpha - 1)}{1 + 4\sigma^2\alpha}.$$

For $\alpha > \frac{1}{4}$, therefore, the scheme is stable for all $h \to 0, \tau \to 0$. For $\alpha = \frac{1}{4}$ the scheme is stable when $\tau h \leqslant \sigma_0$, where σ_0 is an arbitrary constant. For $\alpha = 0$ the scheme is stable when $\sigma < 1$, i.e., when $\tau/h \leqslant \sigma_0 < 1$; for $\alpha = 0$ and $\alpha = 1$ the scheme is unstable [83].

EXAMPLE 30: The problem of elastic vibrations of a rod is stated as follows: In the region $0 \leqslant x \leqslant 1, t \geqslant 0$, solve the equation

$$\frac{\partial^2 u}{\partial t^2} + \frac{\partial^4 u}{\partial x^4} = 0 \tag{2.190}$$

under initial conditions (2.136) and (2.137), and the boundary conditions

$$u\bigg|_{x=0} = \frac{\partial^2 u}{\partial x^2}\bigg|_{x=0} = u\bigg|_{x=1} = \frac{\partial^2 u}{\partial x^2}\bigg|_{x=1} = 0. \tag{2.191}$$

(Other boundary conditions can also be considered.)

We will use the grid $x_k = kh, \, t_j = j\tau \left(h = \dfrac{1}{N}; k = -1, 0, \ldots, N, N + 1; \, j = 0, 1, 2, \ldots\right)$.

Grid boundary equations are written in the form

$$u_{0,j} = u_{N,j} = 0, \quad u_{-1,j} + u_{1,j} = 0, \quad u_{N-1,j} + u_{N+1,j} = 0. \tag{2.192}$$

Consider the operator

$$\delta_h^4 u_h^{(j)} \equiv \frac{1}{h^4}(u_{k+2,j} - 4u_{k+1,j} + 6u_{k,j} - 4u_{k-1,j} + u_{k-2,j}).$$

Then the equation

$$\frac{u_{k,j+1} - 2u_{k,j} + u_{k-1,j}}{\tau^2} + \{\alpha\delta_h^4 u_h^{(j+1)} + (1 - \alpha - \beta)\delta_h^4 u_h^{(j)} + \beta\delta_h^4 u_h^{(j-1)}\} = 0$$

$$(k = 1, 2, \ldots, N - 1; \; j = 1, 2, \ldots)$$

with $0 \leqslant \alpha$, $0 \leqslant \beta$, and $\alpha + \beta \leqslant 1$ approximation Eq. (2.190). It is not difficult to see that the grid functions $v_h^{(l)}(k) = \sin\dfrac{\pi kl}{N}$ satisfy boundary conditions (2.192) and are the characteristic functions of the operator δ_h'' for the eigenvalues $\dfrac{16}{h^4}\sin^4\dfrac{\pi l}{2N}$. As a result, the growth coefficients $\lambda_h^{(\mu,1)}$ satisfy the equation

$$\lambda^2 - 2\lambda + 1 + 16r^2[\alpha\lambda^2 + (1 - \alpha - \beta)\lambda + \beta]c_h^{(l)} = 0$$

$$\left(r = \frac{\tau}{h^2}, \; c_h^{(l)} = \sin^4\frac{\pi l}{2N}\right),$$

i.e.,

$$\lambda^2 - 2\frac{1 - 8c_h^{(l)}r^2(1 - \alpha - \beta)}{1 + 16ac_h^{(l)}}\lambda + \frac{1 + 16c_h^{(l)}r^2\beta}{1 + 16c_h^{(l)}r^2\alpha} = 0.$$

For $\alpha = \beta \geqslant 0$, $4c_h^{(l)}r^2(1 - 4\alpha) \leqslant 1$, the roots of the equation are representable in the form $e^{i\gamma_1}$ and $e^{-i\gamma_b}$, where

$$\cos\gamma_l = 1 - \frac{8c_h^{(l)}r^2}{1 + 16c_h^{(l)}r^2\alpha} \geqslant 1 - \frac{8r^2}{1 + 16r^2\alpha}$$

$$= -1 + 2\frac{1 + 4r^2(4\alpha - 1)}{1 + 16r^2\alpha}.$$

For $\alpha > \frac{1}{4}$, therefore, the scheme is stable no matter how h and τ approach zero; for $\alpha = \frac{1}{4}$ the scheme is stable when $\tau/h^2 \leqslant r_0$, where r_0 is an arbitrary constant; for $\alpha = 0$ the scheme is stable when $\dfrac{\tau}{h^2} \leqslant r_0 < \frac{1}{2}$.

3. NONLINEAR PROBLEMS

Nonlinear problems exist for hyperbolic and parabolic equations where the region for which the solution exists is not known beforehand. This makes it difficult to choose a grid for their approximate solution.

In Sections 3.1 and 3.2 we will consider grid methods for solution of such problems.

3.1 Quasi-linear hyperbolic systems.
Consider the following system of two quasi-linear differential equations of the first order with respect to two

functions $u(x, y)$ and $v(x, y)$:

$$\left.\begin{array}{l} a_{11}\dfrac{\partial u}{\partial x} + a_{12}\dfrac{\partial v}{\partial x} + b_{11}\dfrac{\partial u}{\partial y} + b_{12}\dfrac{\partial v}{\partial y} = f_1, \\[3mm] a_{21}\dfrac{\partial u}{\partial x} + a_{22}\dfrac{\partial v}{\partial x} + b_{21}\dfrac{\partial u}{\partial y} + b_{22}\dfrac{\partial v}{\partial y} = f_2, \end{array}\right\} \tag{2.193}$$

where $a_{i,j}$, $b_{i,j}$, and $f_i (i, j = 1, 2)$ are functions of x, y, u, and v that are defined for all $-\infty < x, y, u, v < \infty$. By introducing vectors $X(x, y)$, $U(u, v)$, and $F(f_1, f_2)$ and matrices A and B with entries $a_{i,j}$ and $b_{i,j}$, respectively, we can write system (2.193) in the form

$$A\frac{\partial U}{\partial x} + B\frac{\partial U}{\partial y} = F. \tag{2.194}$$

The determinant of the matrix $A\alpha - B\beta$, where α and β are scalars, is a quadratic form $Q(\alpha, \beta)$ in α and β.

System (2.193) is said to be *hyperbolic* for (X_0, U_0) if the quadratic form $Q(\alpha, \beta)$ decomposes into real linear factors when $X = X_0$ and $U = U_0$:

$$Q(\alpha, \beta) \equiv (\mu_1\alpha - \nu_1\beta)(\mu_2\alpha - \nu_2\beta),$$

where the vectors (μ_1, ν_1) and (μ_2, ν_2) are not colinear. For the sake of brevity, we will say that $Q(\alpha, \beta)$ is linearly decomposable. The two directions determined by the vectors (μ_1, ν_1) and (μ_2, ν_2) on the Oxy plane are called the *characteristic directions* of (X_0, U_0). Let $U(x, y)$ be some vector function $U\{u(x, y), v(x, y)\}$. Then the quadratic form $Q(\alpha, \beta)$ is defined at every point of the Oxy plane, and we assume that at each point of some region Ω this form is linearly decomposable, so that two characteristic directions are associated with each point in this region. By a *characteristic curve* in the Oxy plane, we will mean a curve such that the tangent at each point has a characteristic direction.

If we assume that $a_{i,j}$ and $b_{i,j}$ are sufficiently smooth functions of X and U, each sufficiently smooth vector function $U(x, y)$ will generate two families of characteristics in the region Ω in which the quadratic form $Q(\alpha, \beta)$ is linearly decomposable (if such a region exists).

Now, let $U(x, y)$ be a solution of system (2.193) and assume that Ω is the region of linearly decomposability of the quadratic form $Q(\alpha, \beta)$ for this solution. Assume that for some part of any characteristic the tangent is not parallel to the Oy axis, i.e., for each of the points on this section $\mu \neq 0$. It then turns out that along the section

$$\frac{dy}{dx} = \rho, \tag{2.195}$$

where ρ is one of the roots of the quadratic equation

$$|A\rho - B| = \begin{vmatrix} a_{11}\rho - b_{11} & a_{12}\rho - b_{12} \\ a_{21}\rho - b_{21} & a_{22}\rho - b_{22} \end{vmatrix} = 0, \qquad (2.196)$$

and du/dx and dv/dx are related by the expression

$$\begin{vmatrix} a_{11}\dfrac{du}{dx} + a_{12}\dfrac{dv}{dx} - f_1 & a_{12}\rho - b_{12} \\[2mm] a_{21}\dfrac{du}{dx} + a_{22}\dfrac{dv}{dx} - f_2 & a_{22}\rho - b_{22} \end{vmatrix} = 0,$$

which, after multiplication by dx, can be written in the form

$$M\,du + N\,dv + P\,dx = 0, \qquad (2.197)$$

where

$$M = \begin{vmatrix} a_{11} & a_{12}\rho - b_{12} \\ a_{21} & a_{22}\rho - b_{22} \end{vmatrix} = \begin{vmatrix} a_{11} & a_{12} \\ a_{21} & a_{22} \end{vmatrix}\rho - \begin{vmatrix} a_{11} & b_{12} \\ a_{21} & b_{22} \end{vmatrix},$$

$$N = \begin{vmatrix} a_{12} & a_{12}\rho - b_{12} \\ a_{22} & a_{22}\rho - b_{22} \end{vmatrix} = -\begin{vmatrix} a_{12} & b_{12} \\ a_{22} & b_{22} \end{vmatrix},$$

$$P = \begin{vmatrix} -f_1 & a_{12}\rho - b_{12} \\ -f_2 & a_{22}\rho - b_{22} \end{vmatrix} = \begin{vmatrix} f_1 & b_{12} \\ f_2 & b_{22} \end{vmatrix} - \rho\begin{vmatrix} f_1 & a_{12} \\ f_2 & a_{22} \end{vmatrix}.$$

Assume that $\mu_1 \neq 0$ and $\mu_2 \neq 0$ in Ω, i.e., that no characteristic is parallel to the Oy axis. Then both roots of Eq. (2.196) are finite at each point in the region Ω; we label them so that $\rho_1 < \rho_2$. By the first family of characteristics we will mean the one for which (2.195) holds when ρ_1 is substituted for ρ, and by the second family we will mean the one for which ρ_2 is substituted for ρ in (2.195).

Now, assume that two points X_1 and X_2 in the Oxy plane are given with the following properties: They do not lie on the same characteristic and are sufficiently close to each other. Moreover, assume that we know the values u_1, v_1 and u_2, v_2 of the functions u and v at these points, and assume that it is required to find the point x_3 at which the characteristic of the first family that passes through X_1 intersects the characteristic of the second family that passes through X_2 and the values u_2 and v_3 of the functions u and v at X_3.

The following approach can be taken toward approximate solution of this problem. At the point X_1 we know the values of u and v, so we know the roots $\rho_1^{(1)}$ and $\rho_2^{(1)}$ of Eq. (2.196). Similarly, for the point X_2 we know the roots $\rho_1^{(2)}$ and $\rho_2^{(2)}$ of Eq. (2.196). If we substitute $(y_3 - y_1)/(x_3 - x_1)$ and $(y_3 - y_2)/(x_3 - x_2)$ for dy/dx in (2.195), we obtain the following two equations for approximate computation of the coordinate of the point X_3:

$$y_3 - y_1 = \rho_1^{(1)}(x_3 - x_1), \quad y_3 - y_2 = \rho_2^{(2)}(x_3 - x_2). \qquad (2.198)$$

For approximate calculation of the values of u_3 and v_3 we use equations obtained from (2.197) by substituting $u_3 - u_1$, $v_3 - v_1$ and $u_3 - u_2$, $v_3 - v_2$ for du and dv in (2.197) for the first and second characteristics, respectively:

$$\left. \begin{array}{l} M_1^{(1)}(u_3 - u_1) + N_1^{(1)}(v_3 - v_1) + P_1^{(1)}(x_3 - x_1) = 0, \\ M_2^{(2)}(u_3 - u_2) + N_2^{(2)}(v_3 - v_2) + P_2^{(2)}(x_3 - x_2) = 0, \end{array} \right\} \quad (2.199)$$

where $M_i^{(j)}$, $N_i^{(j)}$, and $P_i^{(j)}$ ($i, j = 1, 2$) are the values of the functions M, N and P for $x = x_i$, $y = y_i$, $u = u_i$, $v = v_i$, $\rho = \rho_i^{(j)}$. Thus, determination of x_3, y_3, u_3 and v_3 requires solution of two systems of linear equations, each in one pair of unknowns x_3 and y_3 or u_3 and v_3.

The x_3, y_3, u_3, and v_3 found in this manner are, generally speaking, crude approximations of the desired quantities. Various methods for refining these values [2, 76, 116] have been proposed; some of these methods are iterative, and the values found with Eqs. (2.198) and (2.199) for x_3, y_3, u_3, and v_3 are used as the initial approximations for the iteration process. For example, one of the iteration processes proceeds as follows. The values of x_3, y_3, u_3, and v_3 are used to find $\rho_1^{(3)}$ and $\rho_2^{(3)}$; $\tilde{\rho}_1 = \frac{1}{2}(\rho_1^{(1)} + \rho_1^{(3)})$ and $\tilde{\rho}_2 = \frac{1}{2}(\rho_2^{(2)} + \rho_2^{(3)})$ are, respectively, substituted for $\rho_1^{(1)}$ and $\rho_2^{(1)}$, and the system thus obtained is used to find x_3' and y_3'.

Then, $x_3' - x_1$ and $x_3' - x_2$ are substituted for $x_3 - x_1$ and $x_3 - x_2$ in Eqs. (2.199), while $\frac{1}{2}(M_1^{(1)} + M_1^{(3)})$, $\frac{1}{2}(N_1^{(1)} + N_1^{(3)})$, ..., $\frac{1}{2}(P_2^{(2)} + P_2^{(3)})$ are substituted for $M_1^{(1)}$, $N_1^{(1)}$, ..., $P_2^{(2)}$, respectively [$M_i^{(j)}$, ... denotes the value of M, ... for x_j, y_j, u_j, v_j, $\rho_i^{(j)}$)]. By solving the system (2.199) obtained in this way, values of u_3' and v_3' are found, which ends one iteration step

If $|x_3' - x_3|$, $|y_3' - y_3|$, $|u_3' - u_3|$, and $|v_3' - v_3|$ are not small, the refinement process continues and x_3', y_3', u_3', and v_3' are used to find x_3'', y_3'', u_3'', and v_3'' in the same way as the former were found by means of x_3, y_3, u_3, and v_3.

The method we have described for using (x_1, y_1, u_1, v_1) and (x_2, y_2, u_2, v_2) to find (x_3, y_3, u_3, v_3) is used for approximate solution of a number of boundary problems for system (2.193). We will call this method the elementary-step method.

The Cauchy Problem. The Cauchy problem for system (2.193) is stated as follows: In the Oxy plane, assume that a line $C(x = x(\tau), y = y(\tau))$ is given, and that the values U of a vector $U\{u = \tilde{u}(\tau), v = v(\tau)\}$ are given at the points of C. In the neighborhood of C, it is required to find a vector function $U\{u(x, y), v(x, y)\}$ that is a solution of system (2.193) and coincides with $\tilde{U}$ on C.

Since (x, y, u, v) is known at each point of the line C, the quadratic form $Q(\alpha, \beta)$ is also known at each point.

Proposition 1. The line C and the vector U given on it are such that system (2.193) is hyperbolic at each point of the line C. (Under certain additional assumptions, this means that the roots ρ_1 and ρ_2 or Eq. (2.196) are real and different.)

Proposition 2.   The line C is not a characteristic, i.e., at each point of the line

$$\frac{dy}{dx} \neq \rho_1, \quad \frac{dy}{dx} \neq \rho_2.$$

To solve the Cauchy problem, we choose several sufficiently close points $X_1, X_2, \ldots, X_k$ on the line C and label them in the order that they occur on C. Then, we apply the elementary-step method, using

$$(x_i, y_i, u_i, v_i), \quad (x_{i+1}, y_{i+1}, u_{i+1}, v_{i+1})$$

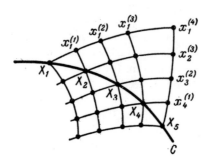

Fig. 13

to find

$$(x_i^{(1)}, y_i^{(1)}, u_i^{(1)}, v_i^{(1)}) \quad (i = 1, 2, \ldots, k - 1).$$

Applying the elementary-step method to these points

$$(x_i^{(1)}, y_i^{(1)}, u_i^{(1)}, v_i^{(1)}), \quad (x_{i+1}^{(1)}, y_{i+1}^{(1)}, u_{i+1}^{(1)}, v_{i+1}^{(1)})$$

$$(i = 1, 2, \ldots, k - 2),$$

we find

$$(x_i^{(2)}. y_i^{(2)}. u_i^{(2)}. v_i^{(2)}) \quad (i = 1, 2, \ldots, k - 2)$$

and after k steps we obtain the single point

$$(x_1^{(k-1)}, y_1^{(k-1)}, u_1^{(k-1)}, v_1^{(k-1)}).$$

As a result, we obtain a table of coordinates for the points $X_i^{(j)}(j = 1, 2, \ldots, k - 1; \ i = 1, 2, \ldots, k - j)$ and the corresponding values of $U_i^{(j)}$ (Fig. 13). It may occur that this computation process must be stopped—if the roots of Eq. (2.196) for some $X_i^{(j)}$ and $U_i^{(j)}$ prove to be complex (and the quadratic form $Q(\alpha, \beta)$ is no longer linearly decomposable.)

To find the analogous table for the approximate solution in the other direction along the line C, the roles of ρ_1 and ρ_2 must be exchanged, i.e., a characteristic of the second family (ρ_2) must be drawn to the point X_i, and a characteristic of the first family (ρ_1) must be drawn through the point X_{i+1}.

Goursat's Problem.   We are given two lines C_1 and C_2 with a common point A, and the values $\tilde{U}_1$ and $\tilde{U}_2$ of a vector U on C_1 and C_2, where U_1 and U_2 coincide at A. On each of the lines Proposition 1 is satisfied (system (2.193) is hyperbolic on C_1 for $\tilde{U}_1$ and on C_2 for $\tilde{U}_2$); moreover, $dy/dx = \rho_1$ on C_1 and $dy/dx = \rho_2$ on C_2 (i.e., the lines C_1 and C_2 are characteristics of the first and second families, respectively). It is required to find a solution $U(x, y)$ of system (2.193) in the neighborhood of the point A that coincides with $\tilde{U}_1$ and $\tilde{U}_2$ on C_1 and C_2, respectively.

In order to solve Goursat's problem we select points $X_1, X_2, \ldots, X_k$ and $Y_1, Y_2, \ldots, Y_l$ on the lines C_1 and C_2, respectively, where X_1 and Y_1 are points closest to A on C_1 and C_2.

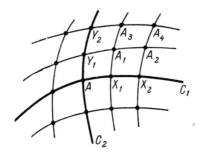

Fig. 14

Applying the elementary-step method to X_1 and Y_1 and the values of $\tilde{U}$ given there, we find the point A_1 and $U(A_1)$. Let X_2 be the point closest to X_1 on C_1. By applying the elementary-step method to X_2 and A, we find A_2 and $U(A_2)$, etc.

After kl iterations, approximate values of the points A_i ($i = 1, 2, \ldots, kl$) and the functions $u(A_i)$ and $v(A_i)$ will have been found (Fig. 14).

3.2 Parabolic equations; a problem with a moving boundary (modified single-sheeted Stefan problem). The problem is stated as follows: Find a nonnegative function $x = \xi(t)$, ($t \geqslant 0$, $\xi(0) = a > 0$) and a function $u(x, t)$ that satisfies the equation

$$\frac{\partial u}{\partial t} - \frac{\partial^2 u}{\partial x^2} = 0 \tag{2.200}$$

in the region $0 \leqslant x \leqslant \xi(t)$, $t \geqslant 0$, and the conditions

$$\left.\frac{\partial u}{\partial x}\right|_{x=0} = -1, \tag{2.201}$$

$$u\,|_{t=0} = \varphi(x) \quad (0 \leqslant x \leqslant a), \tag{2.202}$$

$$u(\xi(t),t) = 0, \tag{2.203}$$

$$-\left.\frac{\partial u}{\partial x}\right|_{x=\xi(t)} = \frac{d\xi}{dt}, \tag{2.204}$$

on its boundary, where it is assumed that

$$\varphi(x) > 0 \quad (0 \leqslant x \leqslant a), \quad \varphi'(0) = -1, \quad \varphi(a) = 0. \qquad (2.205)$$

It is not difficult to see that if the problem has a solution, it is nonnegative and, in virtue of (2.203), we have $\left. \dfrac{\partial u}{\partial x} \right|_{x=\xi} \leqslant 0$ so, by (2.204), we have $d\xi/dt \geqslant 0$, i.e., $\xi(t)$ is a nondecreasing function.

Let $h = a/N$, where N is a positive integer, and, in what follows, let $x_k = kh$. Moreover, let t_n denote the value of t such that $\xi(t_n) = x_{N+n}$.

If the function $x = \xi(t)$ were known, we would know t_n and then, for determination of the grid function $u_{k,n}$ replacing $u(x, t)$, it would be natural to write the following grid equations, in which $\tau_n = t_{n+1} - t_n$:

$$\frac{u_{k,n+1} - u_{k,n}}{\tau_n} - \frac{u_{k+1,n+1} - 2u_{k,n+1} + u_{k-1,n+1}}{h^2} = 0 \qquad (2.206)$$

$$(n = 0.\ 1.\ 2.\ \ldots\ ; \quad k = 1.\ 2, \ldots, D + n), \qquad (2.207)$$

$$u_{0,n+1} - u_{1,n+1} = h \quad (n = 0, 1, 2, \ldots),$$

$$u_{k,0} = \varphi(kh), \qquad (2.208)$$

$$u_{N+n+1,n+1} = 0. \qquad (2.209)$$

these would replace Eqs. (2.200)–(2.203). If we know τ_n and $u_{k,n}$ ($k = 0, 1, \ldots, N + n$), then $u_{k,n+1}$ is uniquely determined by (2.206), (2.207), and (2.209). To determine τ_n, we might, for example, use the equation

$$\left. \frac{d\xi}{dt} \right|_{t=t_n} \approx \frac{h}{\tau_n} = \frac{u_{N+n-1,n}}{h} \approx - \left. \frac{\partial u}{\partial x} \right|_{x=\xi(t_n)}$$

to replace Eq. (2.204). It follows from the last equation that

$$\tau_n = \frac{h^2}{u_{N+n-1,n}},$$

and that the grid problem has a unique solution (if $u_{N+n-1,n} > 0$, $n = 0, 1, 2, \ldots$) because $u_{k,0}$ is given by (2.208). This method of computing τ_n is apparently rather crude, and other methods of taking condition (2.204) into account are known.

For example, the following formula is known for solution of problem (2.200)–(2.204):

$$\xi(t) = t - \int_0^{\xi(t)} u(x, t)\, dx + a + \int_0^a \varphi(x)\, dx,$$

for $t = t_{n+1} = t_n + \tau_n$ this formula takes the form

$$\underset{(N+n+1)h}{(N + n + 1)h} = t_n + \tau_n - \int_0^{(N+n+1)h} u(x, t_{n+1})\, dx + a + \int_0^a \varphi(x)\, dx.$$

Substituting a sum for the integral, we set

$$\tau_n = \left[n + 1 + \sum_{k=0}^{N+n} u_{k,n+1} \right] h - \int_0^a \varphi(x)\, dx - t_n. \tag{2.210}$$

If it is assumed that $u_{k,n}$ and t_n are already known, τ_n and $u_{k,n+1}$ can be determined from system (2.206), (2.207), (2.209) (2.210), which can be solved by an iteration method that proceeds as follows: With $\tau_n^{(0)}$ selected, system (2.206), (2.207), (2.209) is used to find $u_{k,n+1}^{(0)}$, and then formula (2.210) is used to find $\tau_n^{(1)}$.

Convergence of this iteration process and convergence of the grid solution to the exact solution as $h \to p$ were proved in [115].

3.3 The Dirichlet problem for weakly nonlinear elliptic equations [111].

Let Ω be a finite region bounded by a contour Γ in the Oxy plane, and let $F(x, y, z\ p, q)$ be a function that is defined for $(x, y) \in \Omega, -\infty < z, p, q > \infty$, is continuous, and is such that the first derivatives with respect to z, p, and q exist and satisfy the conditions

$$F_z \geqslant 0. \quad |F_p| \leqslant A. \quad |F_q| \leqslant A \tag{2.211}$$

where A is some positive constant.

The Dirichlet problem of the equation

$$\frac{\partial^2 u}{\partial x^2} + \frac{\partial^2 u}{\partial y^2} - F\left(x, y, u, \frac{\partial u}{\partial x}, \frac{\partial u}{\partial y} \right) = 0 \tag{2.212}$$

is stated as follows: In the region $\Omega + \Gamma$, find a twice continuously differentiable function $u(x, y)$ that satisfies Eq. (2.212) and the boundary condition

$$u(x, y)\,|_{\Gamma} = \varphi(x, y), \tag{2.213}$$

where $\varphi(x, y)$ is a function given on Γ.

If the problem has a solution, then, because $F_z \geqslant 0$, it is unique.

We will use a square grid with step h satisfying the inequality $Ah < 2$ to solve Problem (2.212)–(2.213) approximately.

Let Ω_h be the set of all mesh points inside Ω or on the boundary Γ, let Ω_h^0 and Ω_h^1 be the sets of interior and boundary mesh points (in the sense of a five-pointed star), and let N_h and N_h^0 be the numbers of mesh points in Ω_h and Ω_h^0. We index all mesh points in Ω_h^0 with the numbers from 1 through N_h^0, and the mesh points in Ω_h^1 with the numbers from $N_h^0 + 1$ through N_h.

For the star with center at an interior mesh point X_j, we use $j(1), j(2), j(3)$, and $j(4)$ to denote the indices of the star points different from the center. For each interior mesh point $X_j(x_j, y_j)$ we write the grid equation

$$\frac{\sum_{k=1}^{4} u_{j(k)} - 4u_j}{h^2} - F\left(x_j, y_j, u_j, \frac{u_{j(1)} - u_{j(3)}}{2h}, \frac{u_{j(2)} - u_{j(4)}}{2h} \right) = 0 \tag{2.214}$$

$$(j = 1, 2, \ldots, N_h^0)$$

and for each boundary mesh point

$$u_j = \varphi(Q_j) \qquad (j = N_h^0 + 1, \ldots, N_h), \tag{2.215}$$

where Q_j is the boundary point closest to X_j.

It has been proved that system (2.214)–(2.215) has a unique solution (provided condition (2.211) is satisfied and $Ah < 2$).

If $u(x, y) \in C^4$, where $u(x, y)$ is the solution of Problem (2.212)–(2.213), we have the estimate

$$\|u_h - u(x, y)\| \leqslant N(2M^{(3)} + M^{(4)})h^2 + M^{(1)}h,$$

where N is some positive constant that depends on A and the diameter of the region Ω. It thus follows that the grid solution u_h uniformly converges to the exact solution $u(x, y) \in C^4$. If, however, $u(x, y) \in C^4$, the convergence of u_h to $u(x, y)$ remains subject to the statements we made above about the linear Dirichlet problem (see Assertions 4 and 5 in Section 1.4, a).

The following iteration method has been proposed for solution of grid problem (2.214)–(2.215). Because $F_z \geqslant 0$, the equation

$$z + \frac{h^2}{4} F(x, y, z, p, q) = S \tag{2.216}$$

has a unique solution for z for all fixed $(x, y) \in \Omega$, $-\infty < p, q < \infty$. Let

$$z = \Psi_h(x, y, S, p, q)$$

be this solution.

We rewrite Eq. (2.214) in the form

$$\frac{1}{4} \sum_{k=1}^{4} u_{j(k)} = u_j + \frac{h^2}{4} F\left(x_j, y_j, u_j, \frac{u_{j(1)} - u_{j(3)}}{2h}, \frac{u_{j(2)} - u_{j(4)}}{2h}\right),$$

from which it follows that the grid function u_h satisfies Eq. (2.214) at each interior mesh point (x_j, y_j) if and only if the equation

$$u_j = \Psi_h\left(x_j, y_j, \frac{\sum_{k=1}^{4} u_{j(k)}}{4}, \frac{u_{j(1)} - u_{j(3)}}{2h}, \frac{u_{j(2)} - u_{j(4)}}{2h}\right),$$

which we rewrite in the form

$$u_j = \Phi_h(x_j, y_j, u_{j(1)}, u_{j(2)}, u_{j(3)}, u_{j(4)}) \tag{2.217}$$

holds at every interior mesh point (x_j, y_j).

Let $u_h^{(0)}$ be some grid function satisfying condition (2.215). We then construct a sequence of grid function $u_h^{(m)}$ whose values at the boundary mesh points are determined by (2.215) and, at the interior mesh points, by the formula

$$u_j^{(m)} = \Phi_h(x_j, y_j, u_{j(1)}^{(m-1)}, u_{j(2)}^{(m-1)}, u_{j(3)}^{(m-1)}, u_{j(4)}^{(m-1)}) \tag{2.218}$$

$$(j = 1, 2, \ldots, N_h^0).$$

This iteration process converges if $F_z \geqslant \eta > 0$ (where η is an arbitrarily small positive constant), a more stringent condition than the assumption that $F_z \geqslant 0$. The iteration process with formula (2.218) is the analog of simple iteration for systems of linear equations.

Let $\tilde{u}_{j(k)}^{(m-1)}$ denote $u_{j(k)}^{(m)}$ if $j(k) < j$, and $u_{j(k)}^{(m-1)}$ for $j(k) > j$. Then the iteration process

$$u_j^{(m)} = \Phi_h(x_j, y_j, \tilde{u}_{j(1)}^{(m-1)}, \tilde{u}_{j(2)}^{(m-1)}, \tilde{u}_{j(2)}^{(m-1)}, \tilde{u}_{j(4)}^{(m-1)}) \qquad (2.219)$$

$$(j = 1, 2, \ldots, N_h^0)$$

is the analog of Seidel iteration for linear systems. Process (2.219) also converges (provided that $F_z \geqslant \eta > 0$).

The process is stopped after several computations with formulas (2.218) [or (2.219)] and the result of the last iteration is taken as the approximate solution of (2.217), (2.215), which is equivalent to system (2.214), (2.215).

We will consider one iteration step with formula (2.218). Let (x_j, y_j) be some interior mesh point, and assume that we are given the values $u_{j(1)}$, $u_{j(2)}$, $u_{j(3)}$, and $u_{j(4)}$ of the grid function at mesh points adjacent to (x_j, y_j). Then we know the values

$$P_j = \frac{u_{j(1)} - u_{j(3)}}{2h}, \qquad q_j = \frac{u_{j(2)} - u_{j(4)}}{2h}, \qquad S_j = \frac{1}{4} \sum_{k=1}^{4} u_{j(k)}$$

and it remains to solve Eq. (2.216). To do so, it is apparently desirable to iterate with the formula

$$z^{(l)} = S_j - \frac{h^2}{4} F(x_j, y_j, z^{(l-1)}, p_j, q_j) \qquad (2.220)$$

$$(l = 1, 2, \ldots; \quad z^{(0)} = S_j).$$

This iteration process converges if F_z is bounded above by some number B and $(h^2/4) B < 1$. In this case the exact solution of Eq. (2.216) lies between two successive approximations $z^{(l-1)}$ and $z^{(l)}$. After several iterations with formula (2.220), the process is stopped and the result of the last calculation is taken for the approximate value of the right-hand side of (2.218) [or (2.220)].

These results carry over to the case of the equations obtained from (2.212) by substituting

$$Lu \equiv a(x, y) \frac{\partial^2 u}{\partial x^2} + 2e(x, y) \frac{\partial^2 u}{\partial x \, \partial y} + b(x, y) \frac{\partial^2 u}{\partial y^2} \qquad (ab - e^2 > 0)$$

for $\dfrac{\partial^2 u}{\partial x^2} + \dfrac{\partial^2 u}{\partial y^2}$ under the condition that the equation $Lu = f$ can be approximated by equations of the form (2.50) that form, together with grid boundary equations, a system satisfying the principle maximum.

BIBLIOGRAPHIC COMMENTS

Systematic discussions of the grid method as a whole or of specialized techniques are contained in the books [2, 25, 30, 75, 81, 83, 90, 116], and in the articles [34, 35]. Many numerical examples of the grid method for solution for fundamental problems in mathematical physics are presented in [75].

The fundamental notions (norms in functional and vector spaces, consistency of norms, validity and stability of grid problems, etc.) were first systematically discussed in [83]. Some of these notions pertaining to application of the grid method to the fundamental equations of mathematical physics were discussed in [77].

Problems concerning approximations, solvability, and error estimates for elliptic grid Dirichlet problems satisfying the principle of the maximum were discussed in [2, 25, 30, 54, 75, 116].

For grid problems replacing the Dirichlet problem in the case of self-adjoint (and almost self-adjoint) elliptic equations, solvability, validity, and convergence problems were discussed in [35] (see also [34, 38]).

The books [90, 116] discuss the advantages and disadvantages of individual methods for solution of systems of linear elliptic grid equations.

Much attention has been devoted in the recent past to problems on the stability of the difference schemes corresponding to the method of using grid equations to replace mixed problems for hyperbolic and parabolic equations. A discussion of these problems is contained in [17, 81, 83, 90, 116] (see also [25, 30]). The new stability tests discussed in [17] were not referred to in Chapter Two of this book.

A very complete discussion of various grid methods and an extensive bibliography may be found in [116].

We should note the groups of papers [85–88, 101–103] on problems of stability, convergence, and error estimates for difference schemes approximating parabolic equations with discontinuous coefficients and the corresponding elliptic equations. These problems were not discussed in Chapter Two of this book.

Chapter Three

VARIATIONAL METHODS

I. POSITIVE OPERATORS AND ENERGY

1.1 The operators of boundary-value problems. Every boundary-value problem in mathematical physics can be reduced to an equation of the form

$$Au = f, \tag{3.1}$$

where u is an element sought in some functional space,* A is a given operator, and f is a given element in the same or a different functional space. We will call the operator A an *operator* of the given boundary-value problem.

EXAMPLE 1: We state the Dirichlet problem as follows: In some region Ω bounded by a surface S, it is required to find a function $u(x)$ [x is a variable point] that, inside the region, satisfies the Poisson equation $-\Delta u = f(x)$, where Δ is the Laplace operator, and on the boundary S satisfies the boundary $u\,|_S = 0$.

We assume that, as frequently occurs, $f(x)$ is continuous and square summable in Ω, and we require that the desired function $u(x)$ be continuous in the closed region $\bar{\Omega} = \Omega + S$, and that its first and second derivatives be continuous and square summable in the open region Ω.† Then u and f can be treated as elements—desired and given—of the Hilbert space of functions that are square summable in Ω; here the operator A can be defined as the Laplace operator (with opposite sign) defined on the functions that are continuous in the closed region $\bar{\Omega} = \Omega + S$, are twice continuously differentiable in the open region Ω, have square summable Laplacian in Ω, and vanish on the boundary S.

EXAMPLE 2: Again we consider the same problem as in Example 1, but introduce the new unknown $v = \operatorname{grad} u$. Then the desired vector function v can be treated as an element of the Hilbert space generated by the gradients of functions that vanish on the boundary S; as before, the given function $f(x)$ can be treated as an element of the Hilbert space of functions that are square summable in Ω. Since $\Delta u = \operatorname{div} \operatorname{grad} u = \operatorname{div} v$, the equation

$$-\Delta u = f(x)$$

---

* Information about function spaces, in particular, about Hilbert space, can be found, for example, in [13, 24, 63, 95].

† Here we will not consider whether it is always possible to satisfy the requirements stated in the text.

takes the form

$$-\operatorname{div} v = f(x).$$

In this case, we will take the divergence operator with opposite sign for A.

In problems in the theory of elasticity or in hydrodynamics, the desired element u may constitute some set of functions (a vector of displacements or velocities, stress, deformation, deformation-velocity tensors, etc.). The same pertains to the given element f.

A boundary-value problem may either be linear or nonlinear and, correspondingly, the operator A will be linear or nonlinear.

Throughout this chapter, with the exception of Section 10, we will consider only linear problems and linear operators without specifically saying so.

We will also assume (unless we specifically say otherwise) that the given element f and the desired element u belong to the same real Hilbert space.

1.2 Positive and positive definite operators.   A symmetric operator A defined on some Hilbert space is said to be *positive* if for any element in the domain of existence of this operator we have the inequality

$$(Au, u) \geqslant 0,$$

where equality occurs if, and only if, $u = 0$, i.e., u is the zero element of the space.

If A is a positive operator, the scalar product (Au, u) is called the *energy* of the element u relative to the operator A. This terminology is used because in all cases in which the element u can be treated as a translation of some system, the quantity (Au, u) coincides, at least when the units of measurement are appropriately selected, with the potential energy of deformation of this system.

Theorem 1.   If an operator A is positive, then Eq. (3.1) has no more than one solution.

A symmetric operator A is said to be *positive definite* if there exists a positive constant γ^2 such that for any element u in the domain of existence of the operator A we have the inequality

$$(Au, u) \geqslant \gamma^2 \|u\|^2. \tag{3.2}$$

EXAMPLE 3:   We consider the very elementary boundary-value problem of determining a function $u(x)$ that satisfies the differential equation $-u'' = f(x)$ inside the interval $0 \leqslant x \leqslant 1$, and the boundary conditions $u(0) = u(1) = 0$ at the ends of this interval.

In the Hilbert space $L_2(0, 1)$ of functions that are square summable in the interval $0 \leqslant x \leqslant 1$, our problem generates the operator $A = -d^2/dx^2$, and for the domain of existence of this operator, it is natural to take the set of functions that are continuous, together with their first and second derivatives, in the interval $0 \leqslant x \leqslant 1$, and vanish at the ends of this interval. Integration by parts with allowance for the boundary conditions yields (u and v are functions in the domain of existence of the operator A)

$$(Au, v) = -\int_0^1 vu'' \, dx = -vu' \Big|_0^1 + \int_0^1 u'v' \, dx = \int_0^1 u'v' \, dx;$$

in particular, when $v = u$

$$(Au, u) = \int_0^1 u'^2 \, dx.$$

Symmetry follows from the first formula, and positivity of the operator A follows from the second. Furthermore, we have

$$u(x) = u(x) - u(0) = \int_0^x u'(t) \, dt$$

and, by the Cauchy inequality,

$$u^2(x) \leqslant x \int_0^x u'^2(t) \, dt \leqslant \int_0^1 u'^2(t) \, dt.$$

Integrating with respect to x from zero to one, we can easily see that $(Au, u) \geqslant \|u\|^2$; the operator A is positive definite and, in our example, we can take $\gamma^2 = 1$.

Positive operators that are not positive definite exist. This can be seen from the following example. Let B denote the operator $-d^2/dx^2$ defined on functions given on the infinite interval $(0, \infty)$. We assume that these functions are continuous and have continuous first and second derivatives when $x \geqslant 0$, are nonzero only on some finite interval (different for each function), and vanish when $x = 0$. It follows from the easily proved formulas

$$(Bu, v) = \int_0^\infty u'v' \, dx, \qquad (Bu, u) = \int_0^\infty u'^2 \, dx$$

that the operator B is symmetric and positive, but, however, is not positive definite. This is a consequence of the fact that for the function

$$u_n(x) = \begin{cases} x(n - x)^3, & 0 \leqslant x \leqslant n, \\ 0 & x > n, \end{cases}$$

which satisfies all of the conditions given above, the ratio

$$\frac{(Bu_n, u_n)}{\|u_n\|^2} = O\left(\frac{1}{n^2}\right)$$

can be made arbitrarily small by choosing a sufficiently large n.

The notions of positiveness and positive definiteness admit the following physical interpretation.

Treat u as a translation of some system. Then positivity of an operator means that the system cannot translate without consumption of energy. If the size of the translation is estimated in terms of a norm, a positive-definite operator means that the system can support a large translation only when a sufficiently large quantity of energy is consumed. If, however, the operator is positive and not positive definite, the system may admit a translation that is arbitrarily large in norm, but brought about by an arbitrarily small consumption of energy.

1.3 Energy space. With any positive (in particular, with any positive definite) operator, we can associate a special Hilbert space which we will call *energy space*. Let A be a positive operator defined on some Hilbert space H, and let $M = D(A)$ be the domain of existence of this operator. On M we define a new scalar product (which we denote by square brackets) as follows: If u and v are elements of M, we set

$$[u, v] = (Au, v). \qquad (3.3)$$

We call the quantity $[u, v]$ the *energy product* of the elements u and v. It turns out that the energy product satisfies all of the axioms of scalar products.

Once the new scalar product is defined on the set M, it becomes a Hilbert space. In the general case it is incomplete and we must complete it. We will call the new Hilbert space constructed in this manner the *energy space* and denote it by H_A.

We call the norm in the energy space the *energy norm* and denote it by $|u|$. For the elements of the domain M of existence of the operator A, the energy norm is given by the formula

$$|u| = \sqrt{(Au, u)}. \qquad (3.4)$$

Convergence in the energy space is called *convergence in energy*.

An important role is played by the problem of the nature of the elements that are used to complete an energy space. If the operator A is positive definite, we have a theorem that states that all elements in the space H_A also belong to the initial Hilbert space H; if u is an element of the space H_A, we have the inequality

$$\|u\| \leqslant \frac{1}{\gamma} |u|, \qquad (3.5)$$

where the symbol $\|\ \ \|$ denotes the norm in the initial space H and γ is the constant of inequality (3.2).

If A is a positive-definite operator, convergence of a sequence in energy implies that it also converges in the norm of the initial space; if $u_n \in H_A$, $u \in H_A$ and $|u_n - u| \to 0$, then $\|u_n - u\| \to 0$ as well.

1.4 Generalized derivatives. Let Ω be some finite region in m-dimensional space, and let S be its boundary. By a *bounded strip in the region* Ω we will mean the set of its points whose distance to the boundary S is no greater than some given number δ; this number is called the *width* of the bounded strip.

A region Ω' is said to be a *subregion* of Ω if all points of Ω' belong to Ω, and an *interior subregion* if Ω contains not only all points of the region Ω', but all of its boundary points, i.e., if there exists a bounded strip in the region Ω that does not contain points of the subregion Ω'.

By Φ_k we denote the set of functions that are k-times continuously differentiable in Ω and vanish in a bounded strip (different for each function) in this region.

At first, we assume that in the closed region $\bar\Omega = \Omega + S$ the function $u(x)$ has a continuous derivative

$$\frac{\partial^k u}{\partial x_{i_1} \partial x_{i_2} \cdots \partial x_{i_k}};$$

at the same time, it also has all of the preceding derivatives, also continuous in $\bar\Omega$. Let $\varphi(x)$ be any function in the set Φ_k. On the surface S the function $\varphi(x)$ and all of its derivatives vanish, so integration by parts yields the formula

$$\int_\Omega u \frac{\partial^k \varphi}{\partial x_{i_1} \partial x_{i_2} \cdots \partial x_{i_k}}\, dx = (-1)^k \int_\Omega \varphi \frac{\partial^k u}{\partial x_{i_1} \partial x_{i_2} \cdots \partial x_{i_k}}\, dx.$$

Now, let $u(x)$ be some function that is summable in any interior subregion of Ω, and assume that there exists a function $w(x)$ that is also summable in any interior subregion of Ω and is such that for any function $\varphi(x) \in \Phi_k$ we have the identity

$$\int_\Omega u \frac{\partial^k \varphi}{\partial x_{i_1} \partial x_{i_2} \cdots \partial x_{i_k}}\, dx = (-1)^k \int_\Omega \varphi w\, dx.$$

Then $w(x)$ is called the *generalized kth derivative with respect to $x_{i_1}, x_{i_2}, \ldots,$* x_{i_k} *of the function* u(x) *in the region* Ω. A generalized derivative is denoted by the usual symbol

$$w(x) = \frac{\partial^k u}{\partial x_{i_1} \partial x_{i_2} \cdots \partial x_{i_k}}. \tag{3.6}$$

EXAMPLE 4: Let $f(t)$ and $g(t)$ be two summable but not nondifferentiable functions of t, say, in the interval $0 \leqslant t \leqslant 1$. Then the function

$$u(x_1, x_2) = f(x_1) + g(x_2),$$

which is summable in the square Ω defined in the (x_1, x_2) plane by the inequalities $0 \leqslant x_1 \leqslant 1$, $0 \leqslant x_2 \leqslant 1$, has a second generalized derivative $\partial^2 u / \partial x_1 \partial x_2$ in this square, and this derivative is identically equal to zero.

Indeed, let $\varphi(x) \in \Phi_2$. Then

$$\int_\Omega u \frac{\partial^2 \varphi}{\partial x_1 \partial x_2} \, dx = \int_0^1 \int_0^1 f(x_1) \frac{\partial^2 \varphi}{\partial x_1 \partial x_2} \, dx_1 \, dx_2 + \int_0^1 \int_0^1 g(x_2) \frac{\partial^2 \varphi}{\partial x_1 \partial x_2} \, dx_1 \, dx_2$$

$$= \int_0^1 f(x_1) \, dx_1 \int_0^1 \frac{\partial^2 \varphi}{\partial x_1 \partial x_2} \, dx_2 + \int_0^1 g(x_2) \, dx_2 \int_0^1 \frac{\partial^2 \varphi}{\partial x_1 \partial x_2} \, dx_1 = 0$$

$$= \int_\Omega 0 \cdot \varphi \, dx.$$

It is clear from this example that a function with a generalized derivative of order $k > 1$ need not have preceding generalized derivatives; in our example, the function $u(x_1, x_2)$ does not have generalized first derivatives.

Theorem 2. If functions $u_r(x)(r = 1, 2, \ldots, n)$ in a region Ω have generalized derivatives of the same form

$$w_r(x) = \frac{\partial^k u_r}{\partial x_{i_1} \partial x_{i_2} \cdots \partial x_{i_k}},$$

and if c_r $(r = 1, 2, \ldots, n)$ are constants, the function $\sum_{r=1}^n c_r u_r(x)$ has a generalized derivative of the same form and

$$\frac{\partial^k}{\partial x_{i_1} \partial x_{i_2} \cdots \partial x_{i_k}} \sum_{r=1}^n c_r u_r(x) = \sum_{r=1}^n c_r w_r(x).$$

Theorem 3. Let Ω' be a subregion of Ω. If $w(x)$ is some generalized derivative of $u(x)$ in Ω, then $w(x)$ is the same generalized derivative of $u(x)$ in Ω'.

Theorem 4. If a function $v(x)$ in a region Ω is the kth generalized derivative of $u(x)$ with respect to $x_{i_1}, x_{i_2}, \ldots, x_{i_k}$,

$$v(x) = \frac{\partial^k u}{\partial x_{i_1} \partial x_{i_2} \cdots \partial x_{i_k}},$$

and a function $w(x)$ is the lth derivative of $v(x)$ with respect to $x_{j_1}, x_{j_2}, \ldots, x_{j_l}$,

$$w(x) = \frac{\partial^l v}{\partial x_{j_1} \partial x_{j_2} \cdots \partial x_{j_l}},$$

then $w(x)$ is a generalized derivative of $u(x)$ of the form

$$w(x) = \frac{\partial^{k+l} u}{\partial x_{i_1} \partial x_{i_2} \cdots \partial x_{i_k} \partial x_{j_1} \partial x_{j_2} \cdots \partial x_{j_l}}$$

in the same region Ω.

Theorem 5. Let $u_n(x)(n = 1, 2, \ldots)$ be a sequence of functions defined almost everywhere and summable with some power $p > 1$ in a region Ω, and assume that generalized derivatives

$$w_n(x) = \frac{\partial^k u_n}{\partial x_{i_1} \partial x_{i_2} \cdots \partial x_{i_k}}$$

exist and are summable in Ω with some power $q > 1$. If the function $u_n(x)$ in any subregion $\Omega' \subset \Omega$ converges weakly to some function $u(x)$ in L_p (Ω') and the functions $w_n(x)$ converge weakly in $L_q(\Omega')$ to some function $w(x)$, then the limit function $u(x)$ has the generalized derivative

$$\frac{\partial^k u}{\partial x_{i_1} \partial x_{i_2} \cdots \partial x_{i_k}}$$

in Ω, and this derivative is equal to $w(x)$.

We can define the generalized derivative in a different way that is equivalent to the above definition. Let $u(x)$ and $w(x)$ be summable in any interior subregion Ω' of a region Ω. We will say that the function $w(x)$ is a *generalized derivative* of the form (2.6) of $u(x)$ if there exists a sequence of functions $u_n(x)$ that are k-times continuously differentiable in Ω, such that $u_n \to u$, and

$$\frac{\partial^k u_n}{\partial x_{i_1} \partial x_{i_2} \cdots \partial x_{i_k}} \to w$$

in the metric of the space $L(\Omega')$, i.e., if

$$\lim_{n \to \infty} \int_{\Omega'} |u_n(x) - u(x)| \, dx = 0$$

and

$$\lim_{n \to \infty} \int_{\Omega'} \left| \frac{\partial^k u_n}{\partial x_{i_1} \partial x_{i_2} \cdots \partial x_{i_k}} - w(x) \right| dx = 0;$$

here Ω' denotes any interior subregion of the region Ω.

1.5 Embedding theorems. We will say that a region is *star shaped* with respect to a given point if any ray beginning at this point intersects the boundary only once. Thus, for example, any convex region is star shaped with respect to any of its points.

Here and below we will consider only finite regions that can be represented in the form of the union of a finite number of overlapping subregions that are each star-shaped with respect to any point in some ball.

Theorem 6. Let a function $u(x)$ that is summable in a region Ω have all generalized derivatives of some order $k > 1$, with the derivatives also summable in Ω. Then $u(x)$ has all possible generalized derivatives of orders less than k and they are summable in Ω.

Sobolev's Space $W_p^{(l)}(\Omega)$, where $p > 1$, consists of functions that, in Ω, have all generalized derivatives of order l, where both the functions and their lth derivatives are summable in Ω with power p; the norm in this space is given by the formula

$$\|u\|_{W_p^{(l)}(\Omega)}^p = \int_\Omega |u|^p \, dx + \int_\Omega \sum \left| \frac{\partial^l u}{\partial x_{i_1} \partial x_{i_2} \cdots \partial x_{i_l}} \right|^p dx, \qquad (3.7)$$

where the sum is taken over all possible sets of equal or different indices $i_1, i_2, \ldots, i_l$ that are each no greater than m, the dimension of the region Ω.

Theorem 7. If $u(x) \in W_p^{(l)}(\Omega)$ and $pl > m$, then $u(x)$ is equivalent to a function that is continuous in the closed region $\bar\Omega$. We have the inequality

$$\|u\|_{C(\Omega)} \leqslant M \|u\|_{W_p^{(l)}(\Omega)}, \qquad (3.8)$$

where $C(\Omega)$ denotes the space of functions that are continuous in the closed region $\bar\Omega$, and M is a constant that does not depend on the function $u(x)$. Any bounded set in $W_p^{(1)}(\Omega)$ is compact in $C(\Omega)$.

Corollary. If $u(x) \in W_p^{(l)}(\Omega)$ and k, a natural number, is such that $p(1 - k) > m$, then $u(x) \in C^{(k)}(\Omega)^*$, we have

$$\|u\|_{C^{(k)}(\Omega)} \leqslant M \|u\|_{W_p^{(l)}(\Omega)}$$

and any set that is bounded in $W_p^{(1)}(\Omega)$ is compact in $C^{(k)}(\Omega)$.

Theorem 8. Let Γ_s, $s \leqslant m$, be a sufficiently smooth manifold whose points all belong to Ω. If $pl \leqslant m$ and $s > m - pl$, then any function $u(x) \in W_p^{(1)}(\Omega)$ is equivalent to a function that is defined almost everywhere in Γ_s and is summable on Γ_s with any power q that satisfies the inequality

$$q \leqslant \frac{ps}{m - pl} ; \qquad (3.9)$$

in this case we have the inequality

$$\|u\|_{L_q(\Gamma_s)} \leqslant M_1 \|u\|_{W_p^{(l)}(\Omega)}, \qquad (3.10)$$

where the constant M_1 does not depend on the function $u(x)$. If q satisfies the strict inequality

$$q < \frac{ps}{m - pl}, \qquad (3.11)$$

---

* That is, the kth derivatives of $u(x)$ are continuous in $\bar\Omega$.

then a set that is bounded in $W_q^{(1)}(\Omega)$ is compact in $L_q(\Gamma_s)$.

Corollary. If $u \in W_p^{(l)}(\Omega)$ and $k < l$, then

$$u \in W_q^{(l-k)}(\Omega),$$

where

$$q \leqslant \frac{mp}{m - p(1 - k)}, \qquad (3.12)$$

and we have the inequality

$$\|u\|_{W_p^{(l-k)}} \leqslant M_2 \|u\|_{W_k^{(l)}}, \qquad (3.13)$$

where the constant M_2 does not depend on the function $u(x)$.

Theorem 9. Let N be the number of linearly independent polynomials of degree $\leqslant l - 1$ in the m variables $x_1, x_2, \ldots, x_m$. Moreover, assume that linear functions $l_j u (j = 1, 2, \ldots, n)$ are bounded in $W_p^{(1)}(\Omega)$ and are such that they do not simultaneously vanish on any polynomial of degree $\leqslant l - 1$. Then the norm defined by the formula

$$\|u\|^p = \sum_{j=1}^N |l_j u|^p + \int_\Omega \sum \left| \frac{\partial^l u}{\partial x_{i_1} \partial x_{i_2} \cdots \partial x_{i_l}} \right|^p dx, \qquad (3.14)$$

is equivalent to norm (3.7).

We should note the following two extremely simple and important consequences of the embedding theorems above.

1. *Poincare's Inequality.* If $u(x) \in W_2^{(1)}(\Omega)$, then

$$\int_\Omega u^2\, dx \leqslant A \int_\Omega (\text{grad } u)^2\, dx + A' \left(\int_\Omega u\, dx \right)^2. \qquad (3.15)$$

2. If $u(x) \in W_2^{(1)}(\Omega)$ and $u = 0$ on part of the boundary S, then

$$\int_\Omega u^2\, dx \leqslant B \int_\Omega (\text{grad } u)^2\, dx. \qquad (3.16)$$

If $u = 0$ everywhere on the boundary S, inequality (3.16) is called *Friedrichs' inequality*. In inequalities (3.15) and (3.16), A, A', and B are constants that do not depend on the choice of the functions $u(x)$, but do depend on the choice of the region Ω.

2. THE ENERGY METHOD

2.1 The functional of the energy method. If the operator A is positive, solution of Eq. (3.1) can be reduced to solution of some variational problem as the following theorem implies.

Theorem 10.   Let A be a positive operator. If the equation $Au = f$ has a solution, this solution minimizes the functional

$$F(u) = (Au, u) - 2(u, f) \qquad (3.17)$$

Conversely, if there exists an element that minimizes functional (3.17), this element satisfies the equation $Au = f$.

The method of solving boundary-value problems that consists in replacing Eq. (3.1) by the problem of minimizing the functional in Eq. (3.17) is called, in the literature, the *energy method*. We will call functional $F(u)$ the *functional of the energy method*.

Theorem 10 yields no information on the conditions required for existence of a solution of a variational problem, nor on how such a solution can be constructed. Such information may be obtained if the operator of the boundary-value problem is positive definite. In that case, we introduce the energy space H_A. By Formula (3.4), $(Au, u) = |u|^2$. Moreover, by the Cauchy inequality and inequality (3.5), $|(u, f)| \leqslant \|f\| \|u\| \leqslant \dfrac{\|f\|}{\gamma} |u|$. This means that the linear functional (u, f) is bounded in H_A; by the Riesz theorem, there exists an element $u_p \in H_A$ such that $(u, f) = [u, u_0]$, provided that $u \in H_A$. Now, functional (3.17) reduces to the form

$$F(u) = |u|^2 - 2(u, f) = |u|^2 - 2[u, u_0] = |u - u_0|^2 - |u_0|^2. \quad (3.18)$$

Formula (3.18) has two simple and important corollaries:

1. this formula makes it possible to determine the functional $F(u)$ not only on elements of the domain of existence of the operator A, but on all elements of the energy space H_A;

2. in the space H_A the functional $F(u)$ achieves a minimum at $u = u_0$.

If $u_0 \in D(A)$, then, by Theorem 10, u_0 satisfies the equation $Au = f$; in general, however, the energy space H_A is larger than $D(A)$ and we can assume that the element u_0 that is provided by the Riesz theorem, and minimizes the functional $F(u)$ in the energy space, does not lie in $D(A)$. In this case we can treat u_0 as the generalized solution of the equation $Au = f$.

The notion of a generalized solution is related to that of an *extension* of a positive-definite operator. Let A be such an operator, and with each element f in a given Hilbert space H, associate the element $u_0 \in H_A$ that minimizes the functional $F(u)$ in the energy space; this correspondence generates some operator G such that $Gf = u_0$. It turns out that *there exists an inverse operator* $\tilde{A} = G^{-1}$ that is a self-adjoint extension of the operator A; the generalized solution of the equation $Au = f$ is the ordinary solution of the equation $\tilde{A}u = f$.

2.2 Construction of solutions of variational problems. Here we will present two general methods for constructing an element u_0 that minimizes the functional $F(u)$; the very important Rayleigh-Ritz method, which is a concrete form of the methods discussed above, is considered in Paragraph 3.

1. We assume that the space H_A contains a complete orthonormal (in the sense of the metric of this space) countable system* ω_n $(n = 1, 2, \ldots)$ such that

$$[\omega_n, \omega_k] = \begin{cases} 1, n = k, \\ 0, n \neq k. \end{cases}$$

Then

$$u_0 = \sum_{n=1}^{\infty} (f, \omega_n)\omega_n. \tag{3.19}$$

Series (3.19) is the Fourier series (in the energy space) of the element u_0 in the orthonormal system $\{\omega_n\}$; this series converges both in the metric of the space H_A (i.e., in energy), and in the metric of the space H.

EXAMPLE 5: Consider an elastic rod of *rectangular* cross section that is bounded by the lines $x = 0$, $x = a$, $y = 0$, and $y = b$. The problem on the bending of such a rod can easily be reduced to integration of the equation

$$-\Delta u = 1 \tag{3.20}$$

under the boundary conditions

$$u(0, y) = u(a, y) = u(x, 0) = u(x, b) = 0, \tag{3.21}$$

which state that the desired function vanishes on the contour of the cross section. In our case, the operator A of the boundary-value problem may be defined as the operator $-\Delta$ defined on functions that are twice (say, continuously) differentiable in the region of the cross section, and vanish on the boundary of the cross section†; the initial Hilbert space H is the space of functions that are square summable in the region covered by the cross section. It can be shown that this operator is positive definite; in our case, the energy product is given by the formula

$$[u, v] = -\int_0^a \int_0^b v(x, y)\,\Delta u(x, y)\,dx\,dy;$$

---

* In other words, we assume that the space H_A is separable; a sufficient condition for this is that the initial space H be separable.

† The requirement of continuity for the second derivatives can be replaced by the weaker condition requiring that those derivatives exist as generalized derivatives and be square summable in the rectangle covered by the cross section.

integration by parts gives this formula a symmetric form:

$$[u, v] = \int_0^a \int_0^b \left[\frac{\partial u}{\partial x} \frac{\partial v}{\partial x} + \frac{\partial u}{\partial y} \frac{\partial v}{\partial y} \right] dx \, dy.$$

The space H_A consists of functions that have generalized derivatives that are square summable in the rectangle of the cross section and vanish on its contour; it follows from the theorems discussed in Section 1.3, as well as from Theorem 8, that the functions contained in H_A are square summable in the cross section.

A complete orthonormal system in H_A is, for example, provided by the functions

$$\omega_{kn}(x) = \frac{2}{\pi} \sqrt{\frac{ab}{b^2 k^2 + a^2 n^2}} \sin \frac{k\pi x}{a} \sin \frac{n\pi y}{b}$$

$$(k, n = 1, 2, \ldots);$$

Formula (3.19) provides the solution to the problem of bending of a rod with a rectangular cross section:

$$u(x, y) = \frac{16 a^2 b^2}{\pi^4} \sum_{k,n=1,3,5\ldots} \frac{\sin \dfrac{k\pi x}{a} \sin \dfrac{n\pi y}{b}}{kn(b^2 k^2 + a^2 n^2)}.$$

2. Let u_n be arbitrarily small minimizing sequence for the functional $F(u)$. Then $u_n \to u_0$ in energy and, consequently, in the metric of the initial space.

Any sufficiently distant term in the minimizing sequence can be treated as an approximate solution of the problem of minimizing functional (3.18).

2.3 The Ritz Method. In the space H_A we select a sequence of elements

$$\varphi_1, \varphi_2, \ldots, \varphi_n, \ldots, \tag{3.22}$$

that satisfy the following two conditions:

1. for any n, the elements, $\varphi_1, \varphi_2, \ldots, \varphi_n$ are linearly independent;

2. sequence (3.22) is complete with respect to energy, by which we mean the following: For any element $u \in H_A$ and any $\varepsilon > 0$, there exist a natural number N and constants $\alpha_1, \alpha_2, \ldots, \alpha_n$ such that

$$\left| u - \sum_{k=1}^N \alpha_k \varphi_k \right| < \varepsilon.$$

The elements (3.22) are called *coordinate* elements.

The Ritz method provides the natural number n and makes it possible to construct the approximate solution u_n of a variational problem in the form

$$u_n = \sum_{k=1}^n a_k \varphi_k, \tag{3.23}$$

where the a_k are *constants that are selected so that* $F(u_n)$ *is minimal;* in order to determine these constants, we use the linear algebraic system

$$\left.\begin{array}{l} [\varphi_1, \varphi_1]a_1 + [\varphi_2, \varphi_1]a_2 + \cdots + [\varphi_n, \varphi_1]a_n = (f, \varphi_1), \\ [\varphi_1, \varphi_2]a_1 + [\varphi_2, \varphi_2]a_2 + \cdots + [\varphi_n, \varphi_2]a_n = (f, \varphi_2), \\ \cdots\cdots\cdots\cdots\cdots\cdots\cdots\cdots\cdots\cdots\cdots\cdots \\ [\varphi_1, \varphi_n]a_1 + [\varphi_2 \, \varphi_n]a_2 + \cdots + [\varphi_n, \varphi_n]a_n = (f, \varphi_n), \end{array}\right\} \quad (3.24)$$

which is called the *Ritz system*.

Because $\varphi_1, \varphi_2, \ldots, \varphi_n$ are linearly independent, the determinant of the Ritz system is nonzero and the system has a unique solution.

The Ritz method is related closely to representation of solutions in the form of series (3.19). In the metric of H_A, we orthogonalize sequence (3.22) of coordinate elements, which leads to some system $\{\omega_n\}$ that is complete and orthonormal in H_A. Now the desired element u_0 can be represented in the form of series (3.19). It turns out that the *approximate solution* u_n *constructed with the Ritz method by means of Formulas* (3.23) *and* (3.24) *is the nth partial sum of series* (3.19).

A sequence of approximate solutions constructed with the Ritz method is also a minimizing sequence for functional (3.18).

As n increases, the energy norms of the approximate solutions given by the Ritz method increase (more accurately, do not decrease) and approach the energy form of the exact solution

$$|u_k| \leqslant |u_n|, \qquad k < n, \qquad \lim_{n \to \infty} |u_n| = |u_0|.$$

Moreover, we have the identity

$$|u_0 - u_n|^2 = |u_0|^2 - |u_n|^2. \qquad (3.25)$$

We agree to estimate the error of the approximate solution u_n by the quantity $|u_0 - u_n|$. It follows from Formula (3.25) that the *error of the approximate solution given by the Ritz method decreases* (*more accurately, does not increase*) *as new coordinate elements are added.*

If the coordinate elements belong not only to the space H_A, but to the domain of existence of the given operator A, then $[\varphi_j, \varphi_k] = (A\varphi_j, \varphi_k)$ and the Ritz system can be represented in the form

$$\left.\begin{array}{l} (A\varphi_1, \varphi_1)a_1 + (A\varphi_2, \varphi_1)a_2 + \cdots + (A\varphi_n, \varphi_1)a_n = (f, \varphi_1), \\ (A\varphi_1, \varphi_2)a_1 + (A\varphi_2, \varphi_2)a_2 + \cdots + (A\varphi_n, \varphi_2)a_n = (f, \varphi_2), \\ \cdots\cdots\cdots\cdots\cdots\cdots\cdots\cdots\cdots\cdots\cdots\cdots \\ (A\varphi_1, \varphi_n)a_1 + (A\varphi_2, \varphi_n)a_2 + \cdots + (A\varphi_n, \varphi_n)a_n = (f, \varphi_n). \end{array}\right\} \quad (3.24')$$

2.4 Methods for solving the Ritz System. The matrix of Ritz system (3.24) is positive definite, so this system yields to all methods used to solve systems of linear algebraic equations with positive definite matrices. These methods are discussed in detail in [104], so here we will consider only an iteration method.

We denote the matrix of system (3.24) by R_n, the vector composed of the unknowns $a_1, a_2, \ldots, a_n$ by a, and the vector composed of the free terms $(f, \varphi_1), (f, \varphi_2), \ldots, (f, \varphi_n)$ by b. System (3.24) can now be written as a single vector equation:

$$R_n a = b. \tag{3.26}$$

Equation (3.26) is clearly equivalent to the equation

$$a = (I - \alpha R_n)a + \alpha b, \tag{3.27}$$

where I is the nth-order identity matrix and α is any nonzero number. The eigenvalues $\lambda_1^{(n)}, \lambda_2^{(n)}, \ldots, \lambda_n^{(n)}$ of the matrix R_n are all positive, and we arrange them in increasing order:

$$0 < \lambda_1^{(n)} \leqslant \lambda_2^{(n)} \leqslant \cdots \leqslant \lambda_n^{(n)}.$$

The eigenvalues of the matrix $I - \alpha R_n$ are equal to $1 - \alpha \lambda_k^{(n)}$ $(k = 1, 2, \ldots, n)$; if we set

$$\alpha = \frac{2}{\lambda_1^{(n)} + \lambda_n^{(n)}}, \tag{3.28}$$

all of the eigenvalues of the matrix $I - \alpha R_n$ will lie between the numbers

$$-\frac{\lambda_n^{(n)} - \lambda_1^{(n)}}{\lambda_n^{(n)} + \lambda_1^{(n)}} \quad \text{and} \quad +\frac{\lambda_n^{(n)} - \lambda_1^{(n)}}{\lambda_n^{(n)} + \lambda_1^{(n)}}$$

and, consequently, will all have absolute value less than one; iteration with formula

$$a^{(k+1)} = \left(I - \frac{2}{\lambda_1^{(n)} + \lambda_n^{(n)}} R_n\right)a^{(k)} + \frac{2}{\lambda_1^{(n)} + \lambda_n^{(n)}} b; \tag{3.29}$$

converges to the solution of the Ritz system with the speed of a geometric progression with geometric mean

$$\frac{\lambda_n^{(n)} - \lambda_1^{(n)}}{\lambda_n^{(n)} + \lambda_1^{(n)}} = \frac{T_n - 1}{T_n + 1} \tag{3.30}$$

where $T_n = \lambda_n^{(n)}/\lambda_1^{(n)}$ is the Todd condition number of the matrix R_n.

If n increases, $\lambda_1^{(n)}$ does not increase, and $\lambda_n^{(n)}$ does not decrease. It can be assumed that at least one of the relations

$$\lambda_1^{(n)} \underset{n \to \infty}{\to} 0, \qquad \lambda_n^{(n)} \underset{n \to \infty}{\to} \infty;$$

holds; then (3.30) approaches one as $n \to \infty$. Here, at the large n required for the Ritz approximation to be sufficiently accurate, the iteration process converges very slowly. Consequently, a very important practical case is the one in which all of the eigenvalues of the matrix R_n lie between two positive constants that do not depend on n:

$$0 < c_1 \leqslant \lambda_k^{(n)} \leqslant c_2 < \infty; \tag{3.31}$$

in Section 8.2–4 of the present chapter, we will show how a coordinate system is chosen so that relation (3.31) holds. In this case we can take

$$\alpha = \frac{2}{c_1 + c_2}. \tag{3.32}$$

Then the eigenvalues of the matrix $I - \alpha R_n$ will lie between the numbers

$$-\frac{c_2 - c_1}{c_2 + c_1} \quad \text{and} \quad +\frac{c_2 - c_1}{c_2 + c_1};$$

iteration proceeding according to the formula

$$a^{(k+1)} = \left(I - \frac{2}{c_1 + c_2} R_n\right) a^{(k)} + \frac{2}{c_1 + c_2} b, \tag{3.33}$$

will, as a progression with mean

$$\frac{c_2 - c_1}{c_2 + c_1} \tag{3.34}$$

converge for any n.

2.5 Natural boundary conditions. In many cases of practical interest, the operator A of a boundary-value problem is a differential operator and its domain of existence is the set of functions with the requisite number of derivatives and such that at any given time they satisfy certain *homogeneous* boundary conditions, this second condition being, for us, the more important of the two. The corresponding space H_A is obtained from the domain of existence $D(A)$ of the operator A by adjoining new functions that may not satisfy all of the requirements imposed on the functions of $D(A)$. In particular, the functions of H_A may not satisfy one or another boundary conditions of the problem. A boundary condition satisfied by all functions in the domain of existence of a given positive operator A is called *natural* for this operator (or for the corresponding boundary-value problem) if the energy space H_A contains a function that does not satisfy this condition. The boundary conditions that must be satisfied by the elements of the energy space are called *principal*. In the theory of elasticity, the principal boundary conditions are called, conventionally, *geometric* or *kinematic*, while the natural boundary conditions are said to be *dynamic*.

The coordinate functions of the Ritz method need not be taken from the domain of existence of the operator, because it is sufficient for them to be elements of the energy space. It thus follows that the *coordinate functions must be subject to the natural boundary conditions;* this makes it much easier to select the coordinate functions.

A simpler rule convenient for a very large class of boundary-value problems can be given for distinguishing between natural and principal boundary conditions. Assume that the operator A is $2s$ times differentiable and positive on the set of functions satisfying certain homogeneous boundary conditions of the form $G_k u = 0$. Such a boundary condition will be natural if $G_k u$ contains sth and higher derivatives of u, while it will be principal if $G_k u$ contains no derivatives of u above the $(s - 1)$th.

EXAMPLE 6:   For the Laplace operator, $s = 1$; the boundary condition $u\,|_S = 0$ of the Dirichlet problem is principal or essential while the boundary condition of the mixed problem

$$\left[\frac{\partial u}{\partial \nu} + \sigma u\right]_S = 0, \qquad \sigma \geqslant 0,$$

is natural.

EXAMPLE 7:   For the biharmonic operator

$$\Delta^2 u = \frac{\partial^4 u}{\partial x^4} + 2\frac{\partial^4 u}{\partial x^2\,\partial y^2} + \frac{\partial^4 u}{\partial y^4},$$

in the equation for bending of thin plates, $s = 2$. The conditions for a rigidly fixed edge (ν is the exterior normal to the edge)

$$u\,|_S = 0, \qquad \frac{\partial u}{\partial \nu}\bigg|_S = 0$$

for this operator are principal, while of the conditions for a freely moving edge (σ is the Poisson constant, ρ is the radius of curvature of the edge)

$$u\,|_S = 0, \qquad \left[\Delta u - \frac{1 - \sigma}{\rho}\frac{\partial u}{\partial \nu}\right]_S = 0,$$

the first is principal, while the second is natural.

EXAMPLE 8:   The equations of the static theory of elasticity can, in the very general case of an inhomogeneous and nonisotropic medium, be written in the form

$$\mathbf{A}\mathbf{u} \equiv -\sum_{i,k,l,m=1}^{3}\frac{\partial}{\partial x_i}(c_{iklm}\varepsilon_{lm}(\mathbf{u})\mathbf{x}_k^{(0)}) = \mathbf{K}. \qquad (3.35)$$

Here $\mathbf{u}$ is the vector of elastic translations, $\mathbf{K}$ is the vector of body forces, and $\mathbf{x}_k^{(0)}$ is the vector of coordinates x_k,

$$\varepsilon_{lm}(\mathbf{u}) = \frac{1}{2}\left(\frac{\partial u_l}{\partial x_m} + \frac{\partial u_m}{\partial x_l}\right),$$

and the elasticity coefficients c_{iklm} satisfy the well-known symmetry conditions

$$c_{iklm} = c_{lmik} = c_{kilm}.$$

For Eq. (3.35), $s = 1$. The condition $\mathbf{u}\big|_S = 0$ for a rigidly fixed edge is principal; the condition that the edge of the object be free of external forces can be written in the form

$$\sum_{i,k,l,m=1}^{3} c_{iklm}\varepsilon_{lm}(\mathbf{u}) \cos(\nu, x_i)\mathbf{x}_k^{(0)} = 0,$$

and is clearly natural.

2.6 Inhomogeneous boundary conditions.   Also it is frequently possible to use the energy method when the boundary conditions of a problem are not homogeneous. We will explain this by means of two concrete boundary-value problems.

1. Consider the Poisson equation $-\Delta u = f(x)$ under the boundary condition $u\big|_S = g(x)$; we denote the bounded surface S of the region inside of which we seek the function $u(x)$ by Ω, and make the following additional assumption: There exists a function $\psi(x) \in W_2^{(2)}(\Omega)$ such that $\psi\big|_S = g(x)$. Set $v = u - \psi$. The function $v(x)$ satisfies the differential equation $-\Delta v = f(x) - \Delta\psi$ and the boundary condition $v\big|_S = 0$. As the initial Hilbert space we take the space $L_2(\Omega)$ of functions square summable in Ω. In this space the operator $-\Delta$ is positive definite on the set of functions that vanish on the boundary S, and the function $v(x)$ can be obtained as the solution of the problem of minimizing the functional

$$F(v) = -(\Delta v, v) - 2(v, f - \Delta\psi) = -\int_\Omega [v\,\Delta v + 2v(f - \Delta\psi)]\,dx$$

$$= \int_\Omega [(\operatorname{grad} v)^2 - 2v(f - \Delta\psi)]\,dx;$$

(3.36)

this minimum can be sought over the set of functions that belong to the space $W_2^{(1)}(S)$ and vanish on S.

Again setting $v = u - \psi$ in (3.36), elementary operations make it possible for us to show that $F(u)$ differs by only a constant from the functional

$$\int_\Omega [(\operatorname{grad} u)^2 - 2uf]\,dx.$$

(3.37)

It follows that the solution of our problem can be obtained as the solution of the problem of minimizing functional (3.37) over the set of those functions in $W_2^{(1)}(\Omega)$ that take the given value $g(x)$ on the boundary S.

We have reached this point by assuming that a function $\psi(x) \in W_2^{(2)}(\Omega)$ exists that satisfies the conditions $\psi\big|_S = g(x)$. This requirement can be weakened somewhat as follows: It is sufficient for $\psi(x) \in W_2^{(1)}(\Omega)$. This last requirement is also necessary: If $W_2^{(1)}(\Omega)$ does not contain a function that takes the value $g(x)$ on S, the problem of minimizing functional (3.37) is meaningless.

By applying the Ritz method to functional (3.37), we can choose a system of coordinate functions $\varphi_1(x), \varphi_2(x), \ldots$, that satisfy the conditions of Section 2.3; in particular, these functions must vanish on the boundary. The approximate solution given by the Ritz method must therefore be sought in the form

$$u_n = \psi(x) + \sum_{k=1}^{n} a_k \varphi_k(x).$$

2. For the second example, we consider the problem of integrating the same equation $-\Delta u = f(x)$ under the boundary condition

$$\left[\frac{\partial u}{\partial \nu} + \sigma u\right]_S = h(x),$$

where σ is a positive and, say, continuous function given on the boundary S. To reduce this problem to a variational problem, we assume, as above, that there exists a function $\psi(x) \in W_2^{(2)}(\Omega)$ that satisfies the boundary condition

$$\left[\frac{\partial \psi}{\partial \nu} + \sigma \psi\right]_S = h,$$

and we set $u - \psi = v$. Then $-\Delta v = f(x) - \Delta \psi$ and

$$\left[\frac{\partial v}{\partial \nu} + \sigma v\right]_S = 0.$$

This last problem reduces to the problem of minimizing the functional

$$(-\Delta v, v) - 2(v, f - \Delta \psi),$$

which, in our case, can be reduced by elementary operations to the form

$$\int_\Omega [(\operatorname{grad} v)^2 - 2v(f - \Delta \psi)] \, dx + \int_S \sigma v^2 \, dS. \tag{3.38}$$

For this functional the boundary condition

$$\left[\frac{\partial v}{\partial \nu} + \sigma v\right]_S = 0$$

is natural and the functional must be minimized over the functions of the space $W_2^{(1)}(\Omega)$ not subject to any boundary conditions. Setting $v = u - \varphi$ in (3.38), we can see, as above, that functional (3.38) differs by only a constant from the functional

$$\int_\Omega [(\operatorname{grad} u)^2 - 2uf] \, dx + \int_S (\sigma u^2 - 2uh) \, dS. \tag{3.39}$$

The inhomogeneous mixed problem therefore produces to the problem of minimizing functional (3.39), where minimization must be over the space $W_2^{(1)}(\Omega)$.

In our case, the assumption that the function $\psi(x)$ exists is, in fact, unnecessary.

2.7 The energy method in the case of a positive operator. We again consider the equation $Au = f$, assuming that in the selected Hilbert space the operator A is positive but not positive definite. By Theorem 10, our equation, as before, is equivalent to the problem of minimizing functional (3.17), although in this case the variational problem is, generally speaking, unsolvable, even in the generalized sense. Below we will present necessary and sufficient conditions for solvability of this problem.

As in the case of a positive-definite operator, we can construct an energy space H_A; but this time it contains not only the elements of the initial space, but certain new elements as well.

We have $(Au, u) = |u|^2$, so

$$F(u) = |u|^2 - 2(u, f).$$

The problem of minimizing the function $F(u)$ has a solution in H_A if and only if the linear functional (u, f) is bounded in this space. Here, by the Riesz theorem, there exists an element $u_0 \in H_A$ such that $(u, f) = [u, u_0]$ if $u \in H_A$; the element u_0 minimizes the functional $F(u)$ in the space H_A.

Boundary-value problems for infinite regions frequently lead to positive operators; this circumstance will be discussed in detail in Section 3.10.

The fact that $u_0 \in H_A$ can be interpreted physically as meaning that this element has finite energy; if the functional (u, f) is bounded in H_A, we will call the corresponding element u_0 a *solution with finite energy* of the equation $Au = f$.

We should note that in the case of a positive-definite operator we can also interpret an element minimizing $F(u)$ as a solution with finite energy.

3. APPLICATIONS TO PROBLEMS IN MATHEMATICAL PHYSICS

3.1 Second-order ordinary differential equations. Many important problems in mathematical physics reduce to second-order ordinary differential equations of the form

$$Lu \equiv -\frac{d}{dx}\left(p(x)\frac{du}{dx}\right) + q(x)u = f(x), \tag{3.40}$$

that must be integrated in an interval $a \leqslant x \leqslant b$ under the boundary conditions

$$\alpha u'(a) - \beta u(a) = 0, \quad \gamma u'(b) + \delta u(b) = 0, \tag{3.41}$$

where α, β, γ, and δ are constants. The simplest problem of this type is the problem of the static sag of a wire that, in the equilibrium state, occupies the segment $a \leqslant x \leqslant b$ of the x axis. The element $(x, x + dx)$ is under the influence of a restoring force $q(x)u \, dx$ and an external force $f(x) \, dx$, and tensions $p(x)$ and $p(x + dx)$ are applied to the ends x and $x + dx$ of the element, respectively. In the general case, boundary conditions (3.41) correspond to elastically fixed wire ends.

In the special case in which, for example, $\alpha \neq 0$, $\beta = 0$, the end $x = a$ of the wire is free; if, however, $\alpha = 0$ and $\beta \neq 0$, this end is rigidly fixed.

The operator L defined by the left-hand side of Eq. (3.40) and boundary conditions (3.41) is positive definite if the following conditions are satisfied:

1. When $a \leqslant x \leqslant b$ the functions $p(x)$ and $q(x)$ are piecewise-continuous and nonnegative.

2. The function $p(x)$ may vanish at certain points of the interval $a < x < b$, but only in such a manner that the integral

$$\int_a^b \frac{dx}{p(x)} \tag{3.42}$$

converges. We will also assume that $p(a) \neq 0$, $p(b) \neq 0$. The simplest case in which Condition 2 is satisfied is when $p(x) \geqslant p_0$, where p_0 is a positive constant.

3. The constants α, β, γ, and δ are nonnegative, and at least one of the constants β or δ is positive.

Upon satisfaction of the above conditions and the additional condition $\alpha \neq 0$, $\gamma \neq 0$, integration of Eq. (3.40) under conditions (3.41) reduces to the problem of minimizing the functional

$$\int_a^b [p(x)u'^2(x) + q(x)u^2(x) - 2f(x)u(x)] \, dx + \frac{\beta}{\alpha} p(a)u^2(a) + \frac{\delta}{\gamma} p(b)u^2(b); \tag{3.43}$$

boundary conditions (3.41) are natural in this case, and they need not be satisfied beforehand. If either of the constants α or γ is equal to zero, the corresponding term in the integrand of (3.43) must be eliminated and the corresponding condition (3.41) becomes a principal boundary condition. In particular, if $\alpha = \gamma = 0$, so that the boundary conditions take the form

$$u(a) = u(b) = 0, \tag{3.44}$$

the problem reduces to minimizing the integral

$$\int_a^b [p(x)u'^2(x) + q(x)u^2(x) - 2f(x)u(x)] \, dx \tag{3.45}$$

over the set of functions satisfying boundary conditions (3.44).

If $u_n(x)$ $(n = 1, 2, \ldots)$ is a minimizing sequence for functional (3.43), this sequence uniformly converges to the exact solution and the sequence of derivatives $u_n'(x)$ converges to the derivative of the exact solution in the mean with weight $p(x)$; this means that if $u_0(x)$ is the exact solution, then

$$\lim_{n \to \infty} \int_a^b p(x)[u_n'(x) - u_0'(x)]^2 \, dx = 0$$

In the special case in which $p(x)$ is bounded below by a positive number, $p(x) \geqslant p_0 > 0$, the sequence $u_n'(x)$ converges to $u_0'(x)$ in the mean:

$$\lim_{n \to \infty} \int_a^b [u_n'(x) - u_0'(x)]^2 \, dx = 0$$

We will now consider the previously inadmissible case $\beta = \delta = 0$; here the boundary conditions take the form

$$u'(a) = u'(b) = 0. \tag{3.46}$$

If, in this case, the function $q(x)$, which is nonnegative, by Condition 1, is not identically equal to zero, the operator L will be positive definite in this case as well; integration of Eq. (3.40) under boundary conditions (3.46) reduces to minimizing integral (3.45) over a set of functions that need not satisfy given boundary conditions. If, however, $q(x) \equiv 0$ and $\beta = \delta = 0$, the operator L, which must now take the form

$$Lu = -\frac{d}{dx}\left(p(x)\frac{du}{dx}\right), \tag{3.47}$$

will not, under boundary conditions (3.46), even be positive. Here the problem $Lu = f(x)$, $u'(a) = u'(b) = 0$, is unsolvable if the equation

$$(f, 1) = \int_a^b f(x) \, dx = 0, \tag{3.48}$$

is not satisfied, thus we will assume that the above condition is satisfied. Condition (3.48) means that $f(x)$ belongs to a subspace $\tilde{H}$, of the space $L_2(a, b)$, that is orthogonal to unity. In this subspace the operator (3.47) under boundary conditions (3.46) is positive definite, and the problem of integrating the equation

$$-\frac{d}{dx}\left(p(x)\frac{du}{dx}\right) = f(x) \tag{3.49}$$

under conditions (3.46) has a solution, which we can obtain by minimizing the integral

$$\int_a^b p(x)u'^2(x) \, dx$$

over the set of functions satisfying the condition $(u, 1) = 0$. We should also note that integration of Eq. (3.49) is elementary.

Another interesting case is the one in which the function $p(x)$ vanishes at one (or both) of the ends a or b. This case, for example, occurs in the study of translation of a heavy wire supported at its ends and under the influence of an external attracting force; in this case the functions $p(x)$, which is proportional to the weight of the section of the wire between the lowest point and the point x, vanishes at the lowest point.

For the sake of simplicity, we will limit the discussion to the case in which $p(a) = 0$, $p(b) \neq 0$, and the boundary condition at the end b is of the form $u(b) = 0$. It can be assumed that integral (3.42) converges, at which the problem will have a definite solution if we impose some boundary condition at $x = a$. We can use $u(a) = 0$, so that the operator L is positive definite and the problem reduces to minimizing functional (3.45) under boundary conditions (3.44). If integral (3.42) diverges, no boundary condition can be given at the end $x = a$; In the general case there is no solution satisfying this condition. When integral (3.42) diverges, the condition at the end $x = a$ is replaced by the requirement that the desired function $u(x)$ be square summable in the interval $a < x < b$. Under the above conditions, the operator L will be positive definite if the integral

$$\int_a^b \frac{(x - a)}{p(x)} \, dx \qquad (3.42')$$

converges; this occurs, for example, if the inequality $p(x) \geqslant C(x - a)^\alpha$, $C = \text{const} > 0$ holds for some constant $\alpha < 2$. If integral (3.42') converges, solving Eq. (3.40) under the condition $u(b) = 0$ with the solution square summable in the interval $a < x < b$ reduces to minimizing functional (3.45) over the set of functions that vanish at $x = b$. This also occurs when integral (3.42') diverges but the function $p(x)$ satisfies the inequality $p(x) \geqslant C(x - a)^2$, $C = \text{const} > 0$.

If $p(x)$ satisfies the inequality $p(x) \leqslant C(x - a)^\alpha$, where $\alpha > 2$, the operator L is positive on the set of functions that vanish at $x = b$, but not positive definite; the boundary-value problem stated here reduces, as before, to the problem of minimizing functional in equation (3.45) on the set of functions that vanishes at $x = b$; this variational problem, however, may not have a solution.

3.2 Higher-order ordinary differential equations. We consider the $2m$th-order equation

$$Lu \equiv \sum_{k=0}^{m} (-1)^k \frac{d^k}{dx^k} \left(p_k(x) \frac{d^k u}{dx^k} \right) = f(x), \qquad (3.50)$$

and we will attempt to solve this equation in the interval $a \leqslant x \leqslant b$ under the simple boundary conditions

$$u(a) = u'(a) = \cdots = u^{(m-1)}(a) = 0, \tag{3.51'}$$

$$u(b) = u'(b) = \cdots = u^{(m-1)}(b) = 0. \tag{3.51''}$$

We assume that all of the coefficients $p_k(x)$ are nonnegative, and that the last coefficient $p_m(x)$ satisfies the stronger condition $p_m(x) \geqslant c$, where c is a positive constant. Then the operator L will be positive definite on the set of functions that satisfy conditions (3.51); boundary problem (3.50)–(3.51) is equivalent to the problem of minimizing the functional

$$\int_a^b \left\{ \sum_{k=0}^m p_k(x) \left(\frac{d^k u}{dx^k} \right)^2 - 2f(x)u(x) \right\} dx \tag{3.52}$$

on the set of functions satisfying conditions (3.51). These conditions, incidentally, are principal or essential.

If $u_n(x)$ ($n = 1, 2, \ldots$) is a sequence of approximate solutions given by the Ritz method for our problem and $u_0(x)$ is the exact solution, then $u_n^{(m)}(x) \to u_0^{(m)}(x)$ in mean; the lower-order derivatives of the approximate solutions uniformly converge to the corresponding derivatives of the exact solution.

Now, assume that the last coefficient $p_m(x)$, which is positive when $a < x < b$, vanishes at $x = a$. We also assume that here

$$c_1(x - a)^\alpha \leqslant p_m(x) \leqslant c_2(x - a)^\alpha, \tag{3.53}$$

where c_1, c_2, and α are positive constants. If $\alpha \leqslant 2m$, the operator L is positive definite on the set of functions that satisfy conditions (3.51'') and, moreover, the conditions

$$u(a) = u'(a) = \cdots = u^{(m-\mu-1)}(a) = 0, \tag{3.54}$$

where μ is the integral part of α. In particular, if $\alpha < 1$, all of conditions (3.51') must be satisfied; in another extreme case, when $2m - 1 < \alpha \leqslant 2m$, it is not necessary to give all of the conditions at the end $x = a$. If inequality (3.53) is satisfied, the problem of integrating Eq. (3.50) under boundary conditions (3.51'') and (3.54) is equivalent to the problem of minimizing functional (3.52) on the set of functions satisfying boundary conditions (3.51'') and (3.54).

If, as before, we denote the exact solution of the problem by $u_0(x)$, and the approximate solution given by the Ritz method by $u_n(x)$, we can show that $u_n^{(m)}(x) \xrightarrow[n \to \infty]{} u_0^{(m)}(x)$ in mean with weight $(z - a)^\alpha$; this means that

$$\lim_{n \to \infty} \int_a^b (x - a)^\alpha [u_n^{(m)}(x) - u_0^{(m)}(x)]^2 \, dx = 0;$$

it follows that the mth and lower derivatives of the approximate solution uniformly converge to the corresponding derivative of the exact solution in the interval $a + \varepsilon \leqslant x \leqslant b$, where ε is any positive number.

If $\alpha > 2m$ in inequality (3.53) only boundary conditions (3.51″) may be stated; under these conditions the operator L is positive, but not positive definite. The boundary-value problem is equivalent to the problem of minimizing functional (3.52) on the set of functions satisfying conditions (3.51″) but this last problem may prove to be unsolvable.

The boundary conditions may have a form other than (3.51); some far from complete idea of the other possible types of boundary conditions may be obtained from the following example.

EXAMPLE 9: *Bending of a Shaft Resting on An Elastic Base.* Assume that the axis of the shaft coincides with the segment $(0, l)$ of the x axis. Generally speaking, we assume that the cross section of the shaft is variable. Denote the bend in the shaft at the cross section with abscissa x by $u(x)$, let $I(x)$ be the moment of inertia of this cross section, and let $K(x)$ and $f(x)$ be the compliance of the base and the force due to a normal load on the shaft at the same cross section. Finally, let E be Young's modulus for the material of which the shaft is made. The equation for bending of the shaft is of the form

$$Lu = \frac{d^2}{dx^2}\left(EI(x)\frac{d^2u}{dx^2}\right) + K(x)u = f(x). \tag{3.55}$$

First, we consider the case in which none of the cross sections of the shaft degenerate into a point or a line, so that the moment of inertia $I(x)$ is always larger than some positive constant. If the ends of the shaft are rigidly fixed, we have

$$u(0) = u'(0) = 0, \quad u(l) = u'(l) = 0 \tag{3.56}$$

and we are led to a special case of Problem (3.50)–(3.51). The bend $u(x)$ can be found as the solution to the problem of minimizing the functional

$$\int_0^l \left\{EI(x)\left(\frac{d^2u}{dx^2}\right)^2 + K(x)u^2(x) - 2f(x)u(x)\right\} dx \tag{3.57}$$

on the set of functions satisfying conditions (3.56). If $u_n(x)$ is the approximate solution given by the Ritz method and $u_0(x)$ is the exact solution, then $u_n''(x) \to u_0''(x)$ in mean, while $u(x)_n' \to u_0(x)$ and $u_n(x) \to u_0(x)$ uniformly.

If one of the ends of the shaft, say, for example, the end $x = l$, is free and the other is rigidly fixed, the second pair of conditions (3.56) is replaced by the conditions

$$u''(l) = 0, \quad \frac{d}{dx}[EI(x)u''(x)]_{x=l} = 0. \tag{3.58}$$

The operator L remains positive definite and the conditions (3.58) are natural.

We now assume that at some cross section $I(x)$ vanishes, and we will consider the special case in which the rod has the shape of a cone of arbitrary form with vertex at the point $x = 0$. In this case $I(x) = (x^4/l^4)I(l)$ and we are led to inequality (3.53) which, in this case, becomes an equation when $c_1 = c_2 = I(l)/l^4$ and $\alpha = 2m = 4$. It is impossible to give boundary conditions at the end $x = 0$; if the end $x = l$ is rigidly fixed, we must set $u(l) = u'(l) = 0$. In this case the operator L is positive definite and the problem reduces to the variational problem of minimizing the integral

$$\int_0^l \left\{ \frac{EI(l)}{l^4} x^4 \left(\frac{d^2u}{dx^2}\right)^2 + K(x)u^2(x) - 2f(x)u(x) \right\} dx$$

on the set of functions satisfying the conditions $u(l) = u'(l) = 0$. This variational problem is solvable: If $u_0(x)$ is its exact solution and $u_n(x)$ is the approximate solution given by the Ritz method, then $u_n''(x) \to u_0''(x)$ in mean with weight x^4, while $u_n'(x) \to u_0'(x)$ and $u_n(x) \to u_0(x)$ uniformly on the segment $\varepsilon \leqslant x \leqslant l$, where ε is any positive number.

3.3 Systems of ordinary differential equations. We consider the simple case in which the system is of the form

$$-\sum_{k=1}^s \left[\frac{d}{dx}\left(p_{jk}(x) \frac{du_k}{dx} \right) + q_{jk}(x)u_k \right] = f_j(x) \tag{3.59}$$

$$\{j = 1, 2, \ldots, s, a < x < b\},$$

and the boundary conditions take the simple form

$$u_j(a) = u_j(b) = 0 \qquad (j = 1, 2, \ldots, s). \tag{3.60}$$

We assume that the coefficients $p_{jk}(x)$ and $q_{jk}(x)$ are real, bounded, and measurable; practical interest is provided by the case in which these coefficients are continuous or piecewise-continuous.

The set of given functions $f_1(x), f_2(x), \ldots, f_s(x)$ and unknown functions $u_1(x), u_2(x), \ldots, u_s(x)$ can be treated as vectors $\mathbf{f}(x)$ and $\mathbf{u}(x)$ with s components. Together with boundary conditions (3.60), the left-hand sides of Eqs. (3.59) generate some operator in the space of s-component vector functions that are square summable in the interval (a, b). This operator is symmetric if $p_{jk}(x) = p_{kj}(x)$ and $q_{jk}(x) = q_{kj}(x)$, and it is positive definite if the matrix of coefficients $p_{jk}(x)$ is positive definite and the matrix of coefficients $q_{jk}(x)$ is nonnegative; more accurately, if for all real numbers $t_1, t_2, \ldots, t_s$ we have the inequalities

$$\sum_{j,k=1}^s p_{jk}(x)t_jt_k \geqslant \mu_0 \sum_{k=1}^s t_k^2, \quad \sum_{j,k=1}^s q_{jk}(x)t_jt_k \geqslant 0,$$

where μ_0 is some positive constant. When these conditions are satisfied, the problem of integrating system (3.59) under boundary conditions (3.60) is equivalent to the problem of finding a vector function that satisfies all of boundary conditions (3.60) and minimizes the functional

$$\int_a^b \left\{ \sum_{j,k=1}^s \left[p_{jk}(x) \frac{du_j}{dx} \frac{du_k}{dx} + q_{jk} u_j(x) u_k(x) \right] - \sum_{j=1}^s f_j(x) u_j(x) \right\} dx.$$

For the coordinate functions we take the vector functions

$$\boldsymbol{\varphi}_1(x) = \{\varphi_{11}(x), \varphi_{21}(x), \dots, \varphi_{s1}(x)\},$$

$$\boldsymbol{\varphi}_2(x) = \{\varphi_{12}(x), \varphi_{22}(x), \dots, \varphi_{s2}(x)\},$$

$$\cdot \; \cdot \; \cdot \; \cdot \; \cdot \; \cdot \; \cdot \; \cdot \; \cdot \; \cdot \; \cdot \; \cdot \; \cdot \; \cdot \; \cdot \; \cdot \; \cdot$$

$$\boldsymbol{\varphi}_n(x) = \{\varphi_{1n}(x), \varphi_{2n}(x), \dots, \varphi_{sn}(x)\},$$

$$\cdot \; \cdot \; \cdot \; \cdot \; \cdot \; \cdot \; \cdot \; \cdot \; \cdot \; \cdot \; \cdot \; \cdot \; \cdot \; \cdot \; \cdot \; \cdot \; \cdot$$

and because the boundary conditions are principal, we must have

$$\varphi_{jn}(a) = \varphi_{jn}(b) = 0 \qquad (j = 1, 2, \dots, s; \quad n = 1, 2, \dots).$$

Selecting n coordinate functions, we obtain the following expression for the nth Ritz approximation of the solution:

$$\mathbf{u}_n(x) = \sum_{k=1}^n a_k \boldsymbol{\varphi}_k(x)$$

or

$$u_{jn}(x) = \sum_{k=1}^n a_k \varphi_{jk}(x) \quad (j = 1, 2, \dots, s).$$

The coefficients a_k are determined from system (3.24); in this case

$$[\boldsymbol{\varphi}_j, \boldsymbol{\varphi}_k] = \int_a^b \left[\sum_{\alpha,\beta=1}^s p_{\alpha\beta} \frac{d\varphi_{\alpha j}}{dx} \frac{d\varphi_{\beta k}}{dx} + q_{\alpha\beta} \varphi_{\alpha j} \varphi_{\beta k} \right] dx.$$

If the coordinate functions belong to the domain of existence of the problem,* we can also use form (3.24') for the Ritz system; then

$$(A\boldsymbol{\varphi}_j, \boldsymbol{\varphi}_k) = \int_a^b \left[-\sum_{\alpha,\beta=1}^s \left(\frac{d}{dx} \left(p_{\alpha\beta} \frac{d\varphi_{\alpha j}}{dx} \right) + q_{\alpha\beta} \varphi_{\alpha j} \right) \varphi_{\beta k} \right] dx.$$

All of what we have said about the convergence of an approximate solution to the exact solution for a second-order equation holds in the present case (see Section 3.1 of this chapter).

If we denote the matrices with entries $p_{jk}(x)$ and $q_{jk}(x)$ by $p(x)$ and $q(x)$, respectively, Eqs. (3.59) and (3.60) take the form

$$-\frac{d}{dx} \left(p(x) \frac{d\mathbf{u}}{dx} \right) + q(x)\mathbf{u} = \mathbf{f}(x), \tag{3.59'}$$

$$\mathbf{u}(a) = \mathbf{u}(b) = 0, \tag{3.60'}$$

* In the simple case in which the coefficients $p_{jk}(x)$ are continuously differentiable and the coefficients $q_{jk}(x)$ are continuous, this occurs if the functions $\varphi_{jn}(x)$ have continuous second derivatives and vanish when $x = a$ and $x = b$.

which, in form, coincide with Eqs. (3.40) and (3.44). More complex boundary conditions under which the operator in the left-hand side of Eq. (3.59) is positive definite can be given. Thus, for example, we could use boundary conditions of the form

$$\mathbf{u}'(a) - \beta\mathbf{u}(a) = 0, \quad \mathbf{u}'(b) + \delta\mathbf{u}(b) = 0,$$

where β and δ are nonnegative matrices of which at least one is positive definite.

We can also consider a system of equations of order higher than second:

$$\sum_{k=0}^{m}(-1)^k \frac{d^k}{dx^k}\left(p_k(x)\frac{d^k\mathbf{u}}{dx^k}\right) = \mathbf{f}(x), \tag{3.50'}$$

where $\mathbf{u}(x)$ and $\mathbf{f}(x)$ are s-component vector functions and the $p_k(x)$ are symmetric matrices of order s. We will solve this system under boundary conditions (3.51), assuming, of course, that the function $u(x)$ contained in these conditions is a vector function. Thus it would be better to denote this function by $u(x)$. The operator generated by this problem will be positive definite if the matrices $p_k(x)$ ($k = 0, 1, 2, \ldots, m - 1$) are nonnegative for all x, $a \leqslant x \leqslant b$, and the matrices $p_m(x)$ are positive definite for the same x; more accurately, we assume that the eigenvalues of the matrix $p_m(x)$ [which generally depend on x] are bounded below by some positive constant.

3.4 Fundamental problems for elliptic equations. The Laplace and Poisson equations. Here we will consider the second-order self-adjoint elliptic equation

$$Au = -\sum_{i,j=1}^{m}\frac{\partial}{\partial x_j}\left(A_{ij}\frac{\partial u}{\partial x_j}\right) + C(x)u = f(x), \tag{3.61}$$

$$A_{ij} = A_{ji}.$$

In the general case, the coefficients A_{ij} and C are functions of the coordinates $x_1, x_2, \ldots, x_m$ of the variable point x; in special cases, these coefficients may also be constant. We will assume that the unknown function must be determined in some finite region Ω.

We assume that Eq. (3.61) is *elliptic* in the region Ω, which means that for any point $x \in \Omega$ and for any real numbers $t_1, t_2, \ldots, t_m$ there exists a positive constant $\mu(x)$ such that

$$\sum_{i,j=1}^{m}A_{ij}(x)t_it_j \geqslant \mu(x)\sum_{i=1}^{m}t_i^2.$$

Two cases must be distinguished:

1. The lower bound of $\mu(x)$ is positive. Then there exists a positive constant μ_0 such that for any point $x \in \Omega$ we have $\mu(x) \geqslant \mu_0$. In this case the elliptic

equation is said to be *nondegenerate*. The following inequality is valid for nondegenerate equations:

$$\sum_{i,j=1}^{m} A_{ij}(x)t_i t_j \geqslant \mu_0 \sum_{i=1}^{m} t_i^2, \quad \mu_0 = \text{const} > 0.$$

2. The lower bound of $\mu(x)$ is equal to zero. In this case the elliptic equation is said to be *degenerate*. If the coefficients A_{ij} are continuous in the closed region $\Omega + S$, then $\mu(x) = 0$ on some set of points of the surface S. Depending on its structure, this set is said to be linearly, surface, etc., degenerate.

The following problems, which are distinguished by the types of boundary conditions (which, for the present we will assume to be homogeneous), are the ones most frequently encountered for nondegenerate elliptic equations.

The Dirichlet problem, or *first boundary-value problem:*

$$u|_S = 0. \tag{3.62}$$

Neumann's problem, or the *second boundary-value problem:*

$$\left[\sum_{i,j=1}^{m} A_{ij} \frac{\partial u}{\partial x_j} \cos(\nu, x_i) \right]_S = 0. \tag{3.63}$$

The third-boundary value problem:

$$\left[\sum_{i,j=1}^{m} A_{ij} \frac{\partial u}{\partial x_j} \cos(\nu, x_i) + \sigma u \right]_S = 0. \tag{3.64}$$

Here ν is the exterior normal to the surface S and σ is some nonnegative and not identically zero function defined on the surface S.

If the coefficient $C(x) \geqslant 0$, the operator A contained in the left-hand side of nondegenerate Equation (3.59) is positive definite when boundary conditions (3.62) and (3.64) hold. The Dirichlet problem reduces to the problem of minimizing the functional

$$\int_{\Omega} \left(\sum_{i,j=1}^{m} A_{ij} \frac{\partial u}{\partial x_i} \frac{\partial u}{\partial x_j} + Cu^2 - 2fu \right) dx \tag{3.65}$$

(dx is a volume element) on the set of functions satisfying condition (3.62); the third boundary-value problem reduces to the problem of minimizing the somewhat different functional

$$\int_{\Omega} \left(\sum_{i,j=1}^{m} A_{ij} \frac{\partial u}{\partial x_i} \frac{\partial u}{\partial x_j} + Cu^2 - 2fu \right) dx + \int_S \sigma u^2 \, dS \tag{3.66}$$

in the class of functions on which this functional takes finite values, i.e., in the class $W_2^{(1)}(\Omega)$ [See Section 1.4]. It is not necessary to subject these functions to boundary condition (3.64), because this condition is natural.

If the coefficient $C(x)$ is not only nonnegative, but not identically equal to zero, the operator A is also positive definite on the set of functions that satisfy boundary condition (3.63); Neumann's problem is equivalent to the variational problem of minimizing integral (3.65) over the functions in the class $W_2^{(1)}(\Omega)$. Boundary condition (3.63) is natural.

Neumann's problem for the case in which $C \equiv 0$ deserves special attention. Equation (3.61) takes the form

$$A_0 u = - \sum_{i,j=1}^{m} \frac{\partial}{\partial x_j} \left(A_{ij} \frac{\partial u}{\partial x_j} \right) = f(x). \tag{3.67}$$

In the general case, Neumann's problem for this equation is unsolvable; a necessary and sufficient condition for solvability is the equation

$$(f, 1) = \int_{\Omega} f(x) \, dx = 0. \tag{3.68}$$

On the other hand, if Neumann's problem is unsolvable, it has a denumerable set of solutions that differ only by a constant term. This term can be selected so that $(u, 1) = 0$. Now it is possible to consider the given function $f(x)$ and the unknown function $u(x)$ in (3.67) as elements of a space orthogonal to unity. In this space the operator A_0 is positive definite on the set of functions satisfying condition (3.63). Neumann's problem is equivalent to the problem of minimizing the integral

$$\int_{\Omega} \sum_{i,j=1}^{m} A_{ij} \frac{\partial u}{\partial x_i} \frac{\partial u}{\partial x_j} \, dx$$

on the set of functions in $W_2^{(1)}(\Omega)$ that satisfy the condition

$$(u, 1) = \int_{\Omega} u(x) \, dx = 0; \tag{3.69}$$

this variational problem is solvable and has a unique solution.

Sometimes boundary conditions of mixed type are considered: The boundary S is split into two sections S' and S'', and the desired solution is subject to the conditions

$$u|_{S'} = 0, \quad \left[\sum_{i,j=1}^{m} A_{ij} \frac{\partial u}{\partial x_i} \cos(\nu, x_j) + \sigma u \right]_{S''} = 0. \tag{3.70}$$

Here the operator A in Eq. (3.61) is positive definite and the "mixed" problem is equivalent to the problem of minimizing the functional

$$\int_{\Omega} \left(\sum_{i,j=1}^{m} A_{ij} \frac{\partial u}{\partial x_i} \frac{\partial u}{\partial x_j} + Cu^2 - 2uf \right) dx + \int_{S''} \sigma u^2 \, dS$$

on the set of functions satisfying the first of conditions (3.70); the second of these conditions is natural.

All of what we have said about elliptic equations is true also for the Poisson equation

$$-\Delta u = f(x), \tag{3.61'}$$

where Δ is the Laplace operator. The boundary conditions of the second and third boundary-value problems for this equation simplify and take the form

$$\frac{\partial u}{\partial v}\bigg|_S = 0 \qquad (3.63')$$

and

$$\left[\frac{\partial u}{\partial v} + \sigma u\right]_S = 0. \qquad (3.64')$$

For definiteness, we will write the following formulas under the assumption that u depends on the three coordinates x, y, and z. The Dirichlet and Neumann problems for the Poisson equation are equivalent to the problem of minimizing the integral

$$\iiint_\Omega \left[\left(\frac{\partial u}{\partial x}\right)^2 + \left(\frac{\partial u}{\partial y}\right)^2 + \left(\frac{\partial u}{\partial z}\right)^2 - 2fu\right] dx\, dy\, dz$$

on the set of functions in the class $W_2^{(1)}(\Omega)$ that, in the case of the Dirichlet problem, are subject to condition (3.62) and, in the case of Neumann's problem, are subject to condition (3.69); in this case the function $f(x)$ must satisfy condition (3.68).

In Section 2.6 we gave variational problems to which the fundamental boundary-value problems for the Poisson equation (or Laplace equation) reduced in the case of *inhomogeneous* boundary conditions. For the general elliptic equation, the results are similar:

1. Assume that it is required to integrate Eq. (3.61) under the boundary condition

$$u|_S = g(x). \qquad (3.62')$$

We assume (and this assumption is necessary) that there exists some function $\psi(x) \in W_2^{(1)}(\Omega)$ that satisfies this boundary condition, so that $\psi|_S = g(x)$. Then our problem reduces to finding a function that minimizes functional (3.65) in the set of those functions in $W_2^{(1)}(\Omega)$ that satisfy boundary condition (3.62').

If we apply the Ritz method, we represent the approximate solution in the form

$$u_n(x) = \psi(x) + \sum_{k=1}^{n} a_k \varphi_k(x),$$

where $\psi(x)$ is the above-noted function that satisfies condition (3.62') and the $\varphi_k(x)$ are functions in $W_2^{(1)}(\Omega)$ that vanish on the boundary S and satisfy the conditions given in Section 2.3 for coordinate functions.

2. Assume that it is required to integrate Eq. (3.61) under the boundary condition

$$\left[\sum_{i,j=1}^{m} A_{ij} \frac{\partial u}{\partial x_j} \cos(v, x_i) + \sigma u\right]_S = h(x). \qquad (3.64'')$$

This problem reduces to the problem of minimizing the functional

$$\int_\Omega \left[\sum_{i,j=1}^m A_{ij} \frac{\partial u}{\partial x_i} \frac{\partial u}{\partial x_j} + Cu^2 - 2uf \right] dx + \int_S (\sigma u^2 - 2uh)\, dS;$$

the minimum must be sought in the set of functions $W_2^{(1)}(\Omega)$; condition (3.64″) is natural.

EXAMPLE 10: To illustrate the method, we consider the problem of integrating the equation

$$-\Delta u = -\left(\frac{\partial^2 u}{\partial x^2} + \frac{\partial^2 u}{\partial y^2}\right) = 1 \tag{3.71}$$

in the square $-1 \leqslant x, y \leqslant 1$, under the condition that the desired integral vanishes on the contour:

$$u(x, \pm 1) = u(\pm 1, y) = 0. \tag{3.72}$$

The desired function $u(x, y)$ differs only by a constant from the stress function of the problem on bending of a rod with square cross section.

Conditions (3.72) are principal, and the coordinate functions must satisfy them. For the coordinate functions we take polynomials of the form

$$(x^2 - 1)(y^2 - 1)x^m y^n \qquad (m, n = 0, 1, 2, \ldots).$$

It is clear from the statement of the problem that the function $u(x, y)$ is even with respect to both x and y; moreover, it does not change when x and y are exchanged. Therefore, it is easy to see that for the coordinate functions it is sufficient to use functions such that

$$(x^2 - 1)(y^2 - 1)(x^{2m} y^{2n} + x^{2n} y^{2m}) \quad (m, n = 0, 1, 2, \ldots).$$

Here we will consider only the first two coordinate functions; the approximate solution given by the Ritz method is of the form

$$u_2(x, y) = (x^2 - 1)(y^2 - 1)[a_0 + a_1(x^2 + y^2)].$$

In this case, the energy product is given by the formula

$$[u, v] = \int_{-1}^{1} \int_{-1}^{1} \left(\frac{\partial u}{\partial x} \frac{\partial v}{\partial x} + \frac{\partial u}{\partial y} \frac{\partial v}{\partial y} \right) dx\, dy$$

and we obtain the following Ritz system [see Formula (3.24)]:

$$\frac{256}{45} a_1 + \frac{1024}{525} a_2 = \frac{16}{9};$$

$$\frac{1024}{525} a_1 + \frac{11264}{4725} a_2 = \frac{32}{45};$$

or

$$\frac{16}{15} a_1 + \frac{64}{175} a_2 = \frac{1}{3} \, ;$$

$$\frac{32}{35} a_1 + \frac{352}{315} a_2 = \frac{1}{3} \, .$$

It thus follows that

$$a_1 = \frac{1295}{4432} \approx 0.292, \qquad a_2 = \frac{525}{8864} \approx 0.0592$$

and, consequently,

$$u_2 = (x^2 - 1)(y^2 - 1)[0.292 + 0.0592(x^2 + y^2)]. \qquad (3.73)$$

Below (see Section 5.3) we will obtain further information about the accuracy of the approximation we have constructed.

3.5 Degenerate elliptic equations. Here we will limit the discussion to the Dirichlet problem for the very simple equation in two independent variables

$$-\frac{\partial}{\partial x}\left(\varphi(x, y) \frac{\partial u}{\partial x}\right) - \frac{\partial}{\partial y}\left(\omega(x, y) \frac{\partial u}{\partial y}\right) = f(x, y), \qquad (3.74)$$

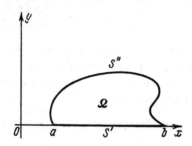

Fig. 15.

where the continuous functions $\varphi(x, y)$ and $\omega(x, y)$ are positive when $y > 0$, but one vanishes when $y = 0$. Equation (3.74) is elliptic in the upper half-plane and degenerates on the x axis.

Assume that the region Ω is of the form shown in Fig. 15; the boundary S consists of two sections: S', which is a segment of the x axis, and S'', which is located in the upper half-plane.

Assume that $\varphi(x, y) > 0$ when $y > 0$, $\varphi(x, 0) = 0$, and $\omega(x, y) > k$, where k is a positive constant. Then the ordinary condition (3.62) of the Dirichlet problem can be stated for Eq. (3.71); on the set of functions satisfying this condition, the operator

$$-\frac{\partial}{\partial x}\left(\varphi(x, y) \frac{\partial u}{\partial x}\right) - \left(\omega(x, y) \frac{\partial u}{\partial y}\right)$$

is positive definite and our problem reduces to the problem of minimizing the integral

$$\iint_{\Omega} \left[\varphi(x, y)\left(\frac{\partial u}{\partial x}\right)^2 + \omega(x, y)\left(\frac{\partial u}{\partial y}\right)^2 - 2f(x, y)u \right] dx\,dy \qquad (3.75)$$

over the set of functions satisfying condition (3.62).

We will now consider the case in which $\varphi(x, y)$ is positive when $y \geqslant 0$ but $\omega(x, 0) = 0$. In this case, the solvability of the problem depends on the rate with which the function ω decreases as $y \to 0$.

Assume that $\omega(x, y) = y^\alpha \omega_1(x, y)$, where $\omega_1(x, y) \geqslant k_1$, while α and k_1 are positive constants. If $\alpha < 1$, the ordinary condition (3.62) can be stated. The Dirichlet problem is equivalent to the above problem of minimizing functional (3.75). If $1 \leqslant \alpha \leqslant 2$, nothing can be given on the line of degeneration S': The operator in the left-hand side of Eq. (3.74) is positive definite on the set of functions satisfying the single condition

$$u\big|_{S''} = 0, \qquad (3.76)$$

and Eq. (3.74) under boundary condition (3.76) has a unique solution that can be obtained by minimizing integral (3.75) under condition (3.76). If $\alpha > 2$, the operator in (3.74) is positive when condition (3.76) is satisfied, but not positive definite; as before, the boundary-value problem is equivalent to the problem of minimizing integral (3.75) under condition (3.76), but, in the general case, this problem is unsolvable.

3.6 Higher-order equations.

Fourth-order elliptic equations are encountered in the theory of bending of plates, in plane problems in the theory of elasticity, in the theory of torsion of anisotropic rods, etc.; sixth-order equations are encountered in certain problems in the theory of elasticity of anisotropic media; eighth-order equations play a part in the theory of shells. And even higher-order equations are encountered in certain other problems.

In the general case, a self-adjoint partial differential equation of order $2n$ in a space of m independent variables $x_1, x_2, \ldots, x_m$ can be written in the form

$$L_{2n}u = \sum_{k=0}^{n} A_k u = f(x),$$

$$A_k u = \sum \frac{\partial^k}{\partial x_{i_1} \partial x_{i_2} \cdots \partial x_{i_k}} \left(A_{j_1,\ j_2,\ \ldots,\ j_k}^{i_1,\ i_2,\ \ldots,\ i_k}(x) \frac{\partial^k u}{\partial x_{j_1} \partial x_{j_2} \cdots \partial x_{j_k}} \right). \qquad (3.77)$$

In the expression for $A_k u$, summation is over all possible choices of indices $i_1, i_2, \ldots, i_k$ and $j_1, j_2, \ldots, j_k$, where each index independently runs through the index set $\{1, 2, \ldots, m\}$; the coefficients $A_{j_1,\ j_2,\ \ldots,\ j_M}^{i_1,\ i_2,\ \ldots,\ i_M}$ do not change upon permutation of upper and lower indices, nor do they change when the upper and lower indices are exchanged.

Equation (3.77) is said to be elliptic and nondegenerate in a given region Ω if the following condition is satisfied: Let $t_{i_1, i_2, \ldots, i_n}$ be real variables that do not change when the indices $i_1, i_2, \ldots, i_n$ are permuted; there exists a positive constant μ_n such that for any $x \in \Omega$ and for all $t_{i_1, i_2, \ldots, i_n}$ we have the inequality

$$\sum A^{i_1, i_2, \ldots, i_n}_{j_1, j_2, \ldots, j_n}(x) t_{i_1, i_2, \ldots, i_n} t_{j_1, j_2, \ldots, j_n} \geqslant \mu_n \sum t^2_{i_1, i_2, \ldots, i_n}. \qquad (3.78)$$

We will consider general equation (3.77) under the simple boundary conditions

$$u|_S = 0, \quad \frac{\partial u}{\partial x_{i_1}}\bigg|_S = 0, \quad \frac{\partial^2 u}{\partial x_{i_1}\, \partial x_{i_2}}\bigg|_S = 0, \ldots, \quad \frac{\partial^{n-1} u}{\partial x_{i_1}\, \partial x_{i_2} \cdots \partial x_{i_{n-1}}}\bigg|_S = 0,$$
$$(3.79)$$

where the indices $i_1, i_2, \ldots, i_{n-1}$ independently take on all values between 1 and m; conditions (3.79) mean that the function u and all of its derivatives of order up to $n - 1$ inclusive vanish on the boundary S.

On functions satisfying conditions (3.79), the operator $L_{2\bar{n}}$ is positive definite if for each operator A_k there exists a constant μ_k such that

$$\sum A^{j_1, j_2, \ldots, j_k}_{i_1, i_2, \ldots, i_k} t_{i_1, i_2, \ldots, i_k} t_{j_1, j_2, \ldots, j_k} \geqslant \mu_k \sum t^2_{i_1, i_2, \ldots, i_k}, \qquad (3.78')$$

where $\mu_n > 0$ and $\mu_k \geqslant 0$ when $0 \leqslant k \leqslant n - 1$. The variational problem corresponding to Eq. (3.78) and boundary conditions (3.79) consists in minimizing the integral

$$\int_\Omega \left[\sum_{k=0}^n \sum A^{i_1, i_2, \ldots, i_k}_{j_1, j_2, \ldots, j_k} \frac{\partial^k u}{\partial x_{i_1}\, \partial x_{i_2} \cdots \partial x_{i_k}} \frac{\partial^k u}{\partial x_{j_1}\, \partial x_{j_2} \cdots \partial x_{j_k}} - 2fu \right] dx \quad (3.80)$$

over the set of functions satisfying conditions (3.79).

Formulas (3.77) can also be used to write a system of partial differential equations if $u(x)$ and $f(x)$ are treated as s-component vector functions and the $A^{i_1, i_2, \ldots, i_k}_{j_1, j_2, \ldots, j_k}(x)$ are treated as $s \times s$ matrices. All of what we have said in the present paragraph about one equation extends verbatim to systems of equations; in this case $t_{i_1, i_2, \ldots, i_n}$ in inequality (3.78) need only be treated as an arbitrary s-component vector with real components.

3.7 Bending of a plate.

The equation for bending of thin elastic plates is written as

$$\Delta^2 w = \frac{q(x, y)}{D} \qquad (3.81)$$

or, in more detailed notation,

$$\frac{\partial^4 w}{\partial x^4} + 2 \frac{\partial^4 w}{\partial x^2\, \partial y^2} + \frac{\partial^4 w}{\partial y^4} = \frac{q(x, y)}{D}.$$

Here $w(x, y)$ is the normal deflection of the plate at the point with co-ordinates x and y, $q(x, y)$ is the intensity of the normal load, and $D = Eh^3/12(1 - \sigma^2)$, where E and σ are Young's modulus and the Poisson constant for the material of which the plate is made and $2h$ is its thickness. We denote the region covered by the plate in the (x, y) plane by Ω, and the contour of this region by S. Depending on the mounting of the plate edge, we obtain the following four boundary conditions which are most frequently encountered.

1. The edge of the plate is rigidly fixed:

$$w\bigg|_S = 0, \frac{\partial w}{\partial \nu}\bigg|_S = 0. \tag{3.82}$$

2. The edge of the plate is freely supported:

$$w|_S = 0, \quad \left[\Delta w - \frac{1 - \sigma}{\rho}\frac{\partial w}{\partial \nu}\right]\bigg|_S = 0. \tag{3.83}$$

3. The edge of the plate is elastically fixed:

$$w|_S = 0, \quad \left[\Delta w - \left(\frac{1 - \sigma}{\rho} - k\right)\frac{\partial w}{\partial \nu}\right]_S = 0. \tag{3.84}$$

4. The edge of the plate is free:

$$\left.\begin{array}{l}\left[\Delta w - (1 - \sigma)\left(\dfrac{\partial^2 w}{\partial s^2} - \dfrac{1}{\rho}\dfrac{\partial w}{\partial \nu}\right)\right]_S = 0, \\[3mm] \left[\dfrac{\partial \Delta w}{\partial \nu} - (1 - \sigma)\left(\dfrac{\partial}{\partial s}\dfrac{1}{\rho}\dfrac{\partial w}{\partial s} - \dfrac{\partial^2 w}{\partial s^2}\right)\right]_S = 0.\end{array}\right\} \tag{3.85}$$

In Formulas (3.82)–(3.85), ν is the exterior normal to S, s is the direction of the tangent to the contour, k is a positive constant, and ρ is the radius of curvature of the contour S. Different parts of the edge S may be fixed differently; accordingly, S can be split into several parts, where on each one or another of conditions (3.82)–(3.85) holds.

If at least one of conditions (3.82)–(3.84) holds on part of the contour S, the biharmonic operator Δ^2 proves to be positive definite. The problem of the bending of a plate is equivalent to the variational problem of minimizing the functional

$$\iint_\Omega \left[\left(\frac{\partial^2 w}{\partial x^2}\right)^2 + 2\sigma \frac{\partial^2 w}{\partial x^2}\frac{\partial^2 w}{\partial y^2} + \left(\frac{\partial^2 w}{\partial y^2}\right)^2 + 2(1 - \sigma)\left(\frac{\partial^2 w}{\partial x \partial y}\right)^2 - \frac{2q}{D}w\right]$$

$$\times dx\, dy + k\int_{S_3} \left(\frac{\partial w}{\partial \nu}\right)^2 ds, \tag{3.86}$$

where S_3 is the elastically fixed part of the edge S; if no part of the edge is elastically fixed, the contour integral drops out of expression (3.86). The minimum must be taken over the set of functions in the class $W_2^2(\Omega)$ that satisfy conditions (3.82) on the rigidly fixed part of the edge and the condition $w|_S = 0$ on the freely fixed and elastically fixed parts of the edge. The remaining boundary conditions (3.83)–(3.85) are natural and need not be satisfied beforehand.

If the entire edge of the plate is rigidly fixed, functional (3.86) can be represented in either of the two following simpler forms:

$$\iint\limits_{\Omega} \left[(\Delta w)^2 - \frac{2q}{D} w \right] dx\, dy$$

$$= \iint\limits_{\Omega} \left\{ \left[\left(\frac{\partial^2 w}{\partial x^2} \right)^2 + 2 \left(\frac{\partial^2 w}{\partial x\, \partial y} \right)^2 + \left(\frac{\partial^2 w}{\partial y^2} \right)^2 \right] - \frac{2q}{D} w \right\} dx\, dy. \quad (3.87)$$

Let $w_0(x, y)$ be the exact solution to a problem on the bending of a plate, and let $w_n(x, y)$ be the solution to the problem of minimizing functional (3.86) that is obtained, for example, with the Ritz method. Then the second derivatives of w_n converge to the corresponding derivatives of w_0 in mean with exponent 2. It follows from the embedding theorems (Section 1.5) that

$$\frac{\partial w_n}{\partial x} \to \frac{\partial w_0}{\partial x} \quad \text{and} \quad \frac{\partial w_n}{\partial y} \to \frac{\partial w_0}{\partial y}$$

in mean with any arbitrarily large exponent, while $w_n \to w_0$ uniformly in $\Omega + S$.

If the plate has variable thickness, then Eq. (3.81) is replaced by the following expressions:

$$\frac{\partial^2}{\partial x^2} \left(h^3 \frac{\partial^2 w}{\partial x^2} \right) + \sigma \frac{\partial^2}{\partial y^2} \left(h^3 \frac{\partial^2 w}{\partial x^2} \right) + \sigma \frac{\partial^2}{\partial x^2} \left(h^3 \frac{\partial^2 w}{\partial y^2} \right) + \frac{\partial^2}{\partial y^2} \left(h^3 \frac{\partial^2 w}{\partial y^2} \right)$$

$$+ 2(1 - \sigma) \frac{\partial^2}{\partial x\, \partial y} \left(h^3 \frac{\partial^2 w}{\partial x\, \partial y} \right) = \frac{q}{D'}, \quad D' = \frac{E}{12(1 - \sigma^2)}. \quad (3.88)$$

The boundary conditions on the fixed or freely supported part of the edge have the same form as for a plate of constant thickness. If the thickness $2h$ of the plate is always nonzero, the operator (3.88) is positive definite on the set of functions that satisfy conditions (3.82) and (3.83) on the fixed and freely supported edges, respectively; the corresponding variational problem consists in minimizing the integral

$$\iint\limits_{\Omega} \left\{ h^3 \left[\left(\frac{\partial^2 w}{\partial x^2} \right)^2 + 2\sigma \frac{\partial^2 w}{\partial x^2} \frac{\partial^2 w}{\partial y^2} + \left(\frac{\partial^2 w}{\partial y^2} \right)^2 \right. \right.$$

$$\left. \left. + 2(1 - \sigma) \left(\frac{\partial^2 w}{\partial x\, \partial y} \right)^2 \right] - \frac{2q}{D'} w \right\} dx\, dy \quad (3.89)$$

under conditions (3.82) on the rigidly fixed part of the edge and the condition $w|_S = 0$ on its freely supported part.

We will devote a special discussion to the case in which part of the edge of the plate is sharp, i.e., when the thickness $2h$ becomes zero at some part of the edge, limiting the discussion to the case in which the plan view of the plate is of the form shown in Fig. 15 and the thickness satisfies the inequality

$$c_1 y^\alpha \leqslant h(x, y) \leqslant c_2 y^\alpha, \qquad (3.90)$$

where c_1, c_2, and α are positive constants, so that the sharp edge of the plate coincides with S'. For simplicity, we will limit ourselves to the case in which the edge S'' is rigidly fixed.

If $0 < \alpha < \frac{1}{3}$, the following ordinary conditions for rigidly fixed boundaries can be given:

$$w|_{S'} = 0, \frac{\partial w}{\partial \nu}\bigg|_{S'} = 0.$$

If $\frac{1}{3} \leqslant \alpha < \frac{2}{3}$, only one condition can be given on S', and, in this case, we can require that $w = 0$ on S'.

If $\alpha \geqslant \frac{2}{3}$, no conditions can be given on S'. In all of the cases we have listed, the operator in Eq. (3.88) is positive, and the boundary-value problem under discussion has no more than one solution; if such a solution exists, it is also the solution of the variational problem of minimizing functional (3.89) under the same boundary conditions.

If $\alpha \leqslant \frac{4}{3}$ then, under the above-mentioned boundary conditions, operator (3.88) is positive definite and the corresponding variational problem has a solution.

3.8 Bending of a compressed plate. Assume that a plate of constant thickness $2h$ is subject to a normal load of intensity $q(x, y)$ and stresses T_{xx}, T_{xy}, and T_{yy} acting in the central plane of the plate; there are no body forces. We will denote the corresponding principal stresses in the central plane by T_1 and T_2. The equilibrium equation for such a plate is of the form

$$\Delta^2 w - \frac{h}{D}\left(T_{xx}\frac{\partial^2 w}{\partial x^2} + 2T_{xy}\frac{\partial^2 w}{\partial x\, \partial y} + T_{yy}\frac{\partial^2 w}{\partial y^2}\right) = \frac{q}{h}; \qquad (3.91)$$

as before, the boundary conditions are of the form (3.82)–(3.85), depending on the way in which the edge of the plate is mounted. Also, as before, we will assume that some of conditions (3.82)–(3.83) are satisfied on some part of the edge. Then there are two cases in which the operator in the left-hand side of Eq. (3.91) is positive definite: either $T_1 \geqslant 0$ and $T_2 \geqslant 0$, or T_1 and T_2 have sufficiently small absolute values. Both cases can be combined: We denote the smaller of the minima of T_1 and T_2 in Ω by T. Let A and B be the constants in the Poincaré and Friedrichs inequalities (Section 1.5), and let $C = B^{-1}$ if part of the boundary is rigidly fixed, or $C = (1 - \sigma)A^{-1}$ if there is no such section but, consequently, there is an edge region that is either freely supported or elastically fixed. Operator (3.91) is positive definite if $T > -CD/h$. The boundary-value problem for Eq. (3.91) is equivalent in this case to the problem of minimizing the functional

$$
\iint_\Omega \left\{ \left[\left(\frac{\partial^2 w}{\partial x^2} \right)^2 + 2\sigma \frac{\partial^2 w}{\partial x^2} \frac{\partial^2 w}{\partial y^2} + \left(\frac{\partial^2 w}{\partial y^2} \right)^2 + 2(1 - \sigma) \left(\frac{\partial^2 w}{\partial x \, \partial y} \right)^2 \right. \right.
$$
$$
\left. + \frac{h}{D} \left[T_{xx} \left(\frac{\partial w}{\partial x} \right)^2 + 2T_{xy} \frac{\partial w}{\partial x} \frac{\partial w}{\partial y} + T_{yy} \left(\frac{dw}{\partial y} \right)^2 \right] \right.
$$
$$
\left. - 2qw \right\} \, dx \, dy + k \int_{S_3} \left(\frac{\partial w}{\partial \nu} \right)^2 ds \quad (3.92)
$$

under the boundary conditions formulated in Section 3.7 for functional (3.86).

3.9 The principle of minimum potential energy in the static theory of elasticity.

The static elastic state of an object is described by a system of partial differential equations that does not enter the class considered in Section 3.6: This system does not satisfy inequality (3.78), but problems in the theory of elasticity nevertheless permit application of variational methods.

The relations given below are true for any inhomogeneous and anisotropic elastic medium if the deformation and rotation are small and the stress satisfies the linear Hooke's law.

Let $\mathbf{u}(u_1, u_2, u_2)$ denote the vector of elastic translations. We will denote the components of the stress and deformation tensors by $\tau_{ik} = \tau_{ki}$ and $2\varepsilon_{ik} = 2\varepsilon_{ki}$, respectively; in this case

$$
\varepsilon_{ik} = \frac{1}{2} \left(\frac{\partial u_i}{\partial x_k} + \frac{\partial u_k}{\partial x_i} \right). \quad (3.93)
$$

The linear Hooke's law is given by the formulas

$$
\tau_{ik} = \sum_{l,m=1}^{3} c_{iklm} \varepsilon_{lm}; \quad (3.94)
$$

the coefficients c_{iklm} satisfy the symmetry relations

$$
c_{iklm} = c_{limk} = c_{kilm},
$$

so that there are no more than 21 different coefficients.

If $\mathbf{K}(K_1, K_2, K_3)$ is the vector of body forces, the stresses satisfy the well-known equilibrium equations

$$
\sum_{k=1}^{3} \frac{\partial \tau_{ik}}{\partial x_k} + K_i = 0 \quad (i = 1, 2, 3).
$$

By using relations (3.94) to eliminate stresses, we obtain equilibrium equations in terms of translations; they can be written in the form of the single vector equation

$$\mathbf{Au} \equiv - \sum_{i,k,l,m=1} \frac{\partial^3}{\partial x_i} (c_{iklm}\varepsilon_{lm})\mathbf{X}_k^{(0)} = \mathbf{K}, \qquad (3.95)$$

where $\mathbf{x}_k^{(0)}$ is the unit vector along the x_k axis and A is a differential operator that transforms the vector of elastic translations into a vector of body forces.

The major boundary-value problems in the theory of elasticity are defined by the following boundary conditions, which we will, for the time being, assume to be homogeneous; as usual, we use S to denote the surface of the region Ω that is occupied by an elastic medium.

I. The problem with given translations (first problem):

$$\mathbf{u}|_S = 0. \qquad (3.96)$$

II. The problem with given stresses (second problem):

$$\mathbf{t}|_S = 0; \qquad (3.97)$$

here $\mathbf{t}$ is a vector of stresses acting on an elementary area of the surface S. If ν is the exterior normal to S, the Cauchy formula gives us

$$\mathbf{t} = \sum_{i,k=1}^{3} \tau_{ik} \cos{(\nu, x_i)}\mathbf{x}_k^{(0)}.$$

III. The problem on rigid contact (third problem):

$$u_{(\nu)}|_S = 0, \quad t_{(s)}|_S = 0. \qquad (3.98)$$

The indices (ν) and (s) denote the projection on the planes normal and tangent to S.

IV. The mixed (fourth) problem: The surface S is split into parts S_{I}, S_{II}, and S_{III}, on each of which the corresponding boundary conditions of Problems I, II and III are satisfied. It may occur that one of the sections S_{I}, S_{II}, or S_{III} is absent.

We introduce the Hilbert space $\mathbf{L}_2(\Omega)$ of vector functions whose absolute values are square summable in Ω. If $\mathbf{u}(u_1, u_2, u_3)$ and $\mathbf{v}(v_1, v_2, v_3)$ are two such functions, then, by definition,

$$(\mathbf{u}, \mathbf{v}) = \int_{\Omega} \sum_{i=1}^{3} u_i v_i \, dx, \quad \|\mathbf{u}\|^2 = \int_{\Omega} \sum_{i=1}^{3} u_i^2 \, dx = \int_{\Omega} |\mathbf{u}|^2 \, dx.$$

We will treat the operator $\mathbf{A}$ in the left-hand side of Eq. (3.95) as an operator in $L_2(\Omega)$, and we will also assume that $\mathbf{K} \in L_2(\Omega)$, i.e., the integral

$$\int_{\Omega} |\mathbf{K}|^2 \, dx$$

exists.

Under the conditions of any of Problems I–IV, the operator $\mathbf{A}$ is symmetric and we have

$$(\mathbf{Au}, \mathbf{u}) = 2 \int_\Omega W \, dx, \tag{3.99}$$

where

$$W = \frac{1}{2} \sum_{i,k=1}^{3} \tau_{ik} \varepsilon_{ik} = \frac{1}{2} \sum_{i,k,l,m=1}^{3} c_{iklm} \varepsilon_{ik} \varepsilon_{lm}$$

is the density of the potential energy of deformation. It is known that W is a positive definite quadratic form of the component deformations, so that $W \geqslant 0$ and $(Au, u) \geqslant 0$; if it is desirable, it can be asserted that under the conditions of Problems I–IV, the operator $\mathbf{A}$ is *nonnegative*.

We will now present some of the more important cases in which the operator $\mathbf{A}$ is positive definite.

1. $\mathbf{A}$ is positive definite in the space $L_2(\Omega)$ in the case of Problem I.

2. In the case of Problem II, the operator $\mathbf{A}$ is not positive definite in $L_2(\Omega)$, or even positive. However, it can be considered in some subspace in which it is positive definite. When there are no surface forces [Condition (3.97)], the principal vector and principal moments of body forces must both vanish:

$$\int_\Omega \mathbf{K} \, dx = 0, \quad \int_\Omega \mathbf{R} \times \mathbf{K} \, dx = 0, \tag{3.100}$$

where $\mathbf{R}$ is the radius vector of the point x. Under the conditions of Problem II, on the other hand, the vector of translations is defined only up to an arbitrarily small rigid translation. We can eliminate this arbitrariness by requiring that

$$\int_\Omega \mathbf{u} \, dx = 0, \quad \int_\Omega \mathbf{R} \times \mathbf{u} \, dx = 0. \tag{3.100'}$$

In the space $L_2(\Omega)$, Eqs. (3.100') separate a subspace in which, under conditions of Problem II, the operator $\mathbf{A}$ is positive definite.

In the following analysis of Problems III and IV, we will also occasionally select a subspace in which the operator $\mathbf{A}$ is positive definite. It turns out that $\mathbf{K}$ must belong to such a subspace, and u may, provided it satisfies appropriate conditions, be made an element of this subspace.

3. In Problem III, the operator $\mathbf{A}$ is positive definite in $L_2(\Omega)$ if S is not a surface or rotation.

If S has one axis of rotation, say, the x_3 axis, then A is positive definite in the subspace that is defined by the equation

$$\int_\Omega (x_1 u_2 - x_2 u_1) \, dx = 0. \tag{3.101}$$

If S has two axes of rotation, then S is a sphere or a set of two concentric spheres, and we place the coordinate origin at the center of these spheres. The operator A in this case is positive definite in the subspace in which

$$\int_\Omega \mathbf{R} \times \mathbf{u} \, dx = 0. \tag{3.102}$$

4. In Problem IV, the operator $\mathbf{A}$ is positive in $L_2(\Omega)$ if there is a boundary section S_I on which $u = 0$. If there is no such boundary section S_I, this operator is nonetheless positive definite in $L_2(\Omega)$, except in the following cases:

a. The surface S_{III} consists of sections of cylindrical surfaces with parallel generatrices. We direct the x_1 axis parallel to these generations, at which time the operator $\mathbf{A}$ becomes positive definite in the subspace in which

$$\int_\Omega u_i \, dx = 0. \tag{3.103}$$

It may occur that the cylindrical sections constituting S_{III} degenerate into sections of parallel planes. We direct the plane $x_3 = 0$ parallel to the indicated planes, at which time the operator $\mathbf{A}$ becomes positive definite in the subspace of $L_2(\Omega)$ in which

$$\int_\Omega u_1 \, dx = \int_\Omega u_2 \, dx = 0. \tag{3.104}$$

b. S_{III} is a surface of rotation (or consists of several sections of such surfaces) with one axis x_3 or with two axes. In this case, the operator $\mathbf{A}$ is positive definite in the subspace defined by Eq. (3.100) or Eq. (3.102).

c. S_{III} consists of one or more sections of the spiral surfaces

$$x_1 = \rho \cos \omega, \quad x_2 = \rho \sin \omega, \quad x_3 = f(\rho) + h\omega,$$

where ρ and ω are parameters determining the position of points on the surfaces and h is constant. The operator $\mathbf{A}$ is positive definite in the subspace in which

$$\int_\Omega (x_1 u_2 - x_2 u_1 + h u_3) \, dx = 0. \tag{3.105}$$

Thus, in all cases the operator $\mathbf{A}$ is positive definite either in the space $L_2(\Omega)$, or in some subspace. The four elasticity problems stated above reduce to the problem of minimizing the same integral

$$\int_\Omega (2W - 2\mathbf{K}\mathbf{u}) \, dx$$

over the set of vector functions that belong to the corresponding subspace and satisfy the principal boundary conditions of the corresponding problem.

In all of the elasticity theory problems discussed here, the energy norm is given by the formula

$$|\mathbf{u}|^2 = 2\int_\Omega W \, dx = \int_\Omega \sum_{i,k,l,m=1}^{3} c_{iklm}\varepsilon_{ik}\varepsilon_{lm} \, dx;$$

if the vectors $\mathbf{u}'$ and $\mathbf{u}''$ both belong to the corresponding subspace H_A, their energy product is

$$[\mathbf{u}', \mathbf{u}''] = \int_\Omega \sum_{i,k,l,m=1}^{3} c_{iklm}\varepsilon'_{ik}\varepsilon''_{lm} \, dx;$$

here ε'_{ik} and ε''_{ik} are the deformations corresponding to the translations $\mathbf{u}'$ and $\mathbf{u}''$.

In the case of an isotropic medium, which, in practice, is the most interesting case, the coefficients c_{iklm} are expressed in terms of the so-called Lamé constants λ and μ by the formulas

$$c_{iiii} = \lambda + 2\mu, \quad c_{iikk} = \lambda, \quad c_{ikik} = 2\mu, \quad i \neq k,$$

and the remaining coefficients $c_{iklm} = 0$. In this case

$$W = \frac{1}{2}\left(\lambda\varepsilon^2 + 2\mu \sum_{i,k=1}^{3} \varepsilon_{ik}^2\right), \qquad \varepsilon = \sum_{i=1}^{3} \varepsilon_{ii};$$

the expressions for the energy norm and energy product take the form

$$|\mathbf{u}|^2 = \int_\Omega \left(\lambda\varepsilon^2 + 2\mu \sum_{i,k=1}^{3} \varepsilon_{ik}^2\right) dx,$$

$$[\mathbf{u}', \mathbf{u}''] = \int_\Omega \left(\lambda\varepsilon'\varepsilon'' + 2\mu \sum_{i,k=1}^{3} \varepsilon'_{ik}\varepsilon''_{ik}\right) dx.$$

In the more commonly used notation in terms of x, y, and z coordinates,

$$|\mathbf{u}|^2 = \iiint_\Omega \{\lambda\varepsilon^2 + 2\mu(\varepsilon_{xx}^2 + \varepsilon_{yy}^2 + \varepsilon_{zz}^2 + 2\varepsilon_{xy}^2 + 2\varepsilon_{xz}^2 + 2\varepsilon_{yz}^2)\} \, dx \, dy \, dz,$$

$$[\mathbf{u}', \mathbf{u}''] = \iiint_\Omega \{\lambda\varepsilon'\varepsilon'' + 2\mu(\varepsilon'_{xx}\varepsilon''_{xx} + \varepsilon'_{yy}\varepsilon''_{yy} + \varepsilon'_{zz}\varepsilon''_{zz}$$

$$+ 2\varepsilon'_{xy}\varepsilon''_{xy} + 2\varepsilon'_{xz}\varepsilon''_{xz} + 2\varepsilon'_{yz}\varepsilon''_{yz})\} \, dx \, dy \, dz.$$

We will also state the variational problem corresponding to inhomogeneous boundary conditions, limiting our discussion to the mixed problem under the assumption that S_{III} is absent; we thus obtain Problems I and II as special cases.

Assume that the boundary conditions are of the form

$$\mathbf{u}\big|_{S_I} = \mathbf{f}, \quad \mathbf{t}\big|_{S_{II}} = \mathbf{g}. \tag{3.106}$$

The corresponding variational problem consists in minimizing the functional

$$\int_\Omega (2W - 2\mathbf{Ku})\,dx - \int_{S_{\mathrm{II}}} \mathbf{ug}\,dS \tag{3.107}$$

on the set of vector functions satisfying the condition

$$\mathbf{u}\big|_{S_{\mathrm{I}}} = \mathbf{f};$$

it is assumed that there exists at least one function on which the integral

$$\int_\Omega W\,dx$$

takes a finite value.

3.10 Boundary-value problems for infinite regions. In the case of an infinite region Ω, the differential operators usually encountered, for example, the Laplace operator with a minus sign or operator (3.95) of the theory of elasticity, most frequently, under the usual boundary conditions, proved to be positive, but not positive definite. If A is a positive operator defined on a Hilbert space H and f is a given element of this space, the equation $Au = f$ is generally unsolvable, i.e., there is no solution belonging to the space H. In particular, if A is a differential operator, H is the space $L_2(\Omega)$ of functions that are square summable in Ω, and $f(x) \in L_2(\Omega)$, it is far from never that the equation $Au = f(x)$ has a solution that is square summable in Ω. On the other hand, it is impossible to justify the requirement that such a solution exists. Thus, if a translation in an infinite region with a fixed boundary is sought, there is no reason to expect that the translation will vanish at infinity; all the more so there is no basis for expecting it to be square summable. At the same time, it is natural to give special attention to the case in which the potential energy of deformation corresponding to the desired solution remains finite.

Generalization of the considerations given for this special problem lead, in the case of a positive operator, to a situation in which, for the generalized solution of the equation $Au = f$, we can take an element u_0 (if it exists) belonging to the energy space H_A and minimizing the functional

$$F(u) = |u|^2 - 2(u, f).$$

In Section 2.6 we stated a necessary and sufficient condition for existence of such a "solution with finite energy"; this condition requires the scalar product (u, f) to be a functional that is bounded in the energy space H_A. Here we will state a concrete form of this condition for certain simple problems in mathematical physics.

We will say that a given vector $\mathbf{G}(x)$ has a generalized divergence div $\mathbf{G}(x) = g(x)$ if for any function $\varphi(x)$ that is continuously differentiable in Ω

and equal to zero close to the boundary S of the region Ω and at all points of this region that are sufficiently far from the coordinate origin, we have the identity

$$\int_\Omega \varphi(x)g(x)\,dx = -\int_\Omega \text{grad }\varphi \cdot \mathbf{G}(x)\,dx.$$

Under the boundary condition $u\,|_S = 0$, the Poisson equation

$$-\Delta u = f(x)$$

has a solution with finite energy if and only if $f(x)$ is the generalized divergence of a vector whose absolute value is square summable. If $\mathbf{F}(x)$ is such a vector and u_0 is a solution with finite energy, then

$$|u_0|^2 = \int_\Omega (\text{grad } u_0)^2\,dx \leqslant \int_\Omega |\mathbf{F}(x)|^2\,dx,$$

where $|\mathbf{F}|$ is the absolute value of the vector $\mathbf{F}$.

The same result holds for the more general elliptic equation

$$-\sum_{i,j=1}^m \frac{\partial}{\partial x_i}\left(A_{ij}\frac{\partial u}{\partial x_j}\right) = f(x)$$

if its coefficients satisfy the inequality

$$\mu_0 \sum_{i=1}^m t_i^2 \leqslant \sum_{i-j=1}^m A_{ij}(x)t_i t_j \leqslant \mu_1 \sum_{i=1}^m t_i^2,$$

where μ_0 and μ_1 are positive constants, t_i is an arbitrary real number, and x is any point in the region Ω. It is possible to prove the existence of a solution with finite energy for the case of the boundary conditions of the second or third problem by assuming that $f(x) = \text{div }\mathbf{F}(x)$, where $\mathbf{F}(x) \in L_2(\Omega)$ and, moreover, $\partial F_i/\partial x_j \in L_2(\Omega)$.

We now turn to the equations of elasticity theory. Assume that the region Ω is infinite, and that there exist positive numbers μ_0 and μ_1 such that for all ε_{ik} we have the inequality

$$\mu_0 \sum_{i,k=1}^3 \varepsilon_{ik}^2 \leqslant W \leqslant \mu_i \sum_{i,k=1}^3 \varepsilon_{ik}^2,$$

where W is defined by Formula (3.99); in any case, this inequality occurs if the elastic medium is homogeneous. Then Eq. (3.95) has, under boundary condition (3.96), a solution with finite energy if and only if there exists a symmetric tensor with components s_{ij} square summable in Ω that is such that the vector $\mathbf{K}$ of body forces is the generalized divergence of this tensor, so that

$$\mathbf{K} = \sum_{i,j=1}^3 \frac{\partial s_{ij}}{\partial x_i}\,\mathbf{x}_j^{(0)},$$

where $\mathbf{x}_j^{(0)}$ is the unit vector along the jth coordinate axis.

4. THE EIGENVALUE PROBLEM

4.1 Fundamental notions and theorems. The equation

$$Au - \lambda Bu = 0, \tag{3.108}$$

in which A and B are linear operators, and λ is a numerical parameter, has the obvious solution $u = 0$, which is called the *trivial solution*. It may, however, occur that for certain values of λ Eq. (3.108) has a nontrivial (i.e., not identically equal to zero) solution. Such a solution is called a *characteristic element* (*characteristic function* if u is a function of one or more numerical variables) of Eq. (3.108), and the corresponding value of λ is called an *eigenvalue* of this equation. If B is the identity operator, so that the equation takes the form

$$Au - \lambda u = 0, \tag{3.109}$$

we can also discuss the characteristic elements and eigenvalues of the operator A. The set of eigenvalues of an equation or an operator is called its *spectrum*.

If characteristic elements $u_1, u_2, \ldots, u_n$ of Eq. (3.108) correspond to a given eigenvalue λ, then any nonzero linear combination $c_1 u_1 + c_2 u_2 + \cdots + c_n u_n$, where $c_1, c_2, \ldots, c_n$ are arbitrary constants, is also a characteristic element corresponding to the same eigenvalue λ. Together with the zero element, therefore, the set of characteristic elements of a given equation corresponding to a given eigenvalue, forms a linear space.

Under certain very broad conditions, this set is a finite-dimensional space and is called the *characteristic space* [of Eq. (3.108)] corresponding to the eigenvalue λ; the dimension of this space is called the *multiplicity* of the corresponding eigenvalue.

Separation of variables in the Fourier method usually leads to the problem of finding the eigenvalues and characteristic elements of the equation in question. If, for example, the equation is of the form

$$AU - B\frac{\partial^k U}{\partial t^k} = 0,$$

where A and B are linear operators that do not depend on time, an attempt to find a solution of the form $U(x, t) = u(x)f(t)$ leads to Eq. (3.108) in the unknown $u(x)$. Stability problems lead to the same type of problem for eigenvalues and characteristic functions.

The most important applied problems are investigation of the spectra of symmetric and, especially, positive–definite operators.

The fundamental properties of the eigenvalues and characteristic elements of such operators are as follows.

1. The eigenvalues of a symmetric operator are real.

2. The characteristic elements of a symmetric operator corresponding to different eigenvalues are orthogonal.

3. If certain linearly independent characteristic elements correspond to a given eigenvalue, we can orthogonalize them. With this in view, we will assume that the set of all characteristic elements of a symmetric operator forms an orthogonal system.

4. A symmetric operator has either a finite or a countable set of eigenvalues, which can therefore be written in the form of a finite or countable sequence $\lambda_1, \lambda_2, \ldots, \lambda_n, \ldots$. Of course, it may also occur that a symmetric operator has no eigenvalues.

5. The characteristic elements of a positive-definite operator are orthogonal with respect to energy.

6. The eigenvalues of a positive-definite operator are positive.

If the system of characteristic elements of a self-adjoint operator is complete in the Hilbert space in which the given operator is defined and its eigenvalues $\lambda_n \underset{n \to \infty}{\to} \infty$, we will say that the given operator *has a discrete spectrum*.

We agree that in the sequence $\lambda_1, \lambda_2, \ldots$ of eigenvalues of an operator, each eigenvalue will appear as many times as its multiplicity. As a result, only one linearly independent characteristic element corresponds to each eigenvalue, but there may be equal eigenvalues.

For the remainder of the present section, we will consider only positive-definite operators.

If A is a positive-definite operator, then

$$\frac{(Au, u)}{(u, u)} \geqslant \gamma^2, \tag{3.110}$$

where γ^2 is a positive constant. In this case the left-hand side of the last inequality has a positive greatest lower bound, which we denote by λ_1.

Theorem 11. If there exists an element $u_1 \in D(A)$ such that

$$\frac{(Au_1, u_1)}{(u_1, u_1)} = \lambda_1,$$

then λ_1 is the smallest eigenvalue of the operator A and u_1 is the corresponding characteristic element.

Theorem 12. Let $\lambda_1 \leqslant \lambda_2 \leqslant \ldots \leqslant \lambda_n$ be the first n eigenvalues of an operator A, and let $u_1, u_2, \ldots, u_n$ be the corresponding orthonormal characteristic elements. Moreover, assume that λ_{n+1} is the greatest lower bound of the values that ratio (3.110) takes on the entire set of elements in

$D(A)$ that are orthogonal to $u_1, u_2, \ldots, u_n$. If this set contains an element u_{n+1} such that

$$\frac{(Au_{n+1}, u_{n+1})}{(u_{n+1}, u_{n+1})} = \lambda_{n+1},$$

then u_{n+1} is the characteristic element of the operator A that corresponds to the eigenvalue λ_{n+1}. This eigenvalue is the one immediately following λ_n.

Theorem 13. Assume that an operator is such that every set of elements whose energy norms taken together are bounded is compact in the metric of a given Hilbert space. Then the spectrum of the given operator is discrete, and its set of characteristic elements is complete with respect to energy (i.e., in the corresponding energy space).

The smallest eigenvalue of an operator A is equal to the minimum of $|u|_A^2$ under the condition $\|u\|^2 = 1$. If the first $n - 1$ eigenvalues $\lambda_1, \lambda_2, \ldots, \lambda_{n-1}$ and the corresponding characteristic elements $u_1, u_2, \ldots, u_{n-1}$ are known, the next eigenvalue can be determined as the minimum of $|u|_A^2$ under the conditions

$$\|u\|^2 = 1, \quad (u, u_k) = 0 \qquad (k = 1, 2, \ldots, n - 1).$$

4.2 The Rayleigh-Ritz method. Assume that an operator A has a discrete spectrum. We can determine the eigenvalues of this operator in the following manner. We choose a sequence of coordinate elements $\varphi_n \in H_A$ ($n = 1, 2, \ldots$), where H_A is the corresponding energy space, and we subject these coordinate elements to the same requirement as in Section 2.3, of this chapter. We then write the equation

$$\begin{vmatrix} [\varphi_1, \varphi_1] - \lambda(\varphi_1, \varphi_1) & [\varphi_2, \varphi_1] - \lambda(\varphi_2, \varphi_1) & \cdots & [\varphi_n, \varphi_1] - \lambda(\varphi_n, \varphi_1) \\ [\varphi_1, \varphi_2] - \lambda(\varphi_1, \varphi_2) & [\varphi_2, \varphi_2] - \lambda(\varphi_2, \varphi_2) & \cdots & [\varphi_n, \varphi_2] - \lambda(\varphi_n, \varphi_2) \\ \cdots\cdots\cdots\cdots\cdots & \cdots\cdots\cdots\cdots\cdots & \cdots & \cdots\cdots\cdots\cdots\cdots \\ [\varphi_1, \varphi_n] - \lambda(\varphi_1, \varphi_n) & [\varphi_2, \varphi_n] - \lambda(\varphi_2, \varphi_n) & \cdots & [\varphi_n, \varphi_n] - \lambda(\varphi_n, \varphi_n) \end{vmatrix} = 0.$$

$$(3.111)$$

This equation is of degree n, its roots are all positive, and we write them in increasing order: $\lambda_1^{(n)} \leqslant \lambda_2^{(n)} \leqslant \cdots \leqslant \lambda_n^{(n)}$. Each of these roots is an upper bound for the corresponding eigenvalue of the given operator, so that $\lambda_p^{(n)} \geqslant \lambda_p$ and $\lim_{n \to \infty} \lambda_p^{(n)} = \lambda_p$. Consequently, we must keep in mind that as p increases, the approximate equality $\lambda \approx \lambda_p^{(n)}$ deteriorates.

The approximate values of the normalized characteristic elements are of the form

$$u_p^{(n)} = \sum_{k=1}^{n} a_k \varphi_k; \qquad (3.112)$$

where the coefficients a_h are given by the equations

$$\sum_{k=1}^{n} a_k\{[\varphi_j, \varphi_k] - \lambda_p^{(n)}(\varphi_j, \varphi_k)\} = 0 \qquad (j = 1, 2, \ldots, n), \qquad (3.113)$$

$$\sum_{j,k=1}^{n} (\varphi_j, \varphi_k)a_j a_k = 1. \qquad (3.114)$$

The determinant of system (3.113) is equal to zero, and it is possible to solve this equation with accuracy up to an arbitrary factor whose value is determined by Eq. (3.114).

Equation (3.111) can be simplified somewhat if the coordinate elements are orthonormalized either in the metric of the given Hilbert space or in the metric of the energy space. In the first case

$$(\varphi_j, \varphi_k) = \begin{cases} 0, & j \neq k, \\ 1, & j = k, \end{cases}$$

and Eq. (3.111) takes the form

$$\begin{vmatrix} [\varphi_1, \varphi_1] - \lambda & [\varphi_2, \varphi_1] & \cdots & [\varphi_n, \varphi_1] \\ [\varphi_1, \varphi_2] & [\varphi_2, \varphi_2] - \lambda & \cdots & [\varphi_n, \varphi_2] \\ \cdots & \cdots & \cdots & \cdots \\ [\varphi_1, \varphi_n] & [\varphi_2, \varphi_n] & \cdots & [\varphi_n, \varphi_n] - \lambda \end{vmatrix} = 0;$$

in the second case

$$[\varphi_j, \varphi_k] = \begin{cases} 0, & j \neq k, \\ 1, & j = k, \end{cases}$$

and Eq. (3.114) reduces to the form

$$\begin{vmatrix} 1 - \lambda(\varphi_1, \varphi_1) & -\lambda(\varphi_2, \varphi_1) & \cdots & -\lambda(\varphi_n, \varphi_1) \\ -\lambda(\varphi_1, \varphi_2) & 1 - \lambda(\varphi_2, \varphi_2) & \cdots & -\lambda(\varphi_n, \varphi_2) \\ \cdots & \cdots & \cdots & \cdots \\ -\lambda(\varphi_1, \varphi_n) & -\lambda(\varphi_2, \varphi_n) & \cdots & 1 - \lambda(\varphi_n, \varphi_n) \end{vmatrix} = 0.$$

If the coordinate elements belong not only to the energy space, but to the domain of existence of the given operator* as well, Eq. (3.111) can also be represented in the form

$$\begin{vmatrix} (A\varphi_1, \varphi_1)-\lambda(\varphi_1, \varphi_1) & (A\varphi_2, \varphi_1)-\lambda(\varphi_2, \varphi_1) & \cdots & (A\varphi_n, \varphi_1)-\lambda(\varphi_n, \varphi_1) \\ (A\varphi_1, \varphi_2)-\lambda(\varphi_1, \varphi_2) & (A\varphi_2, \varphi_2)-\lambda(\varphi_2, \varphi_2) & \cdots & (A\varphi_n, \varphi_2)-\lambda(\varphi_n, \varphi_2) \\ \cdots & \cdots & \cdots & \cdots \\ (A\varphi_1, \varphi_n)-\lambda(\varphi_1, \varphi_n) & (A\varphi_2, \varphi_n)-\lambda(\varphi_2, \varphi_n) & \cdots & (A\varphi_n, \varphi_n)-\lambda(\varphi_n, \varphi_n) \end{vmatrix} = 0.$$

---

* If the operator is a differential operator, this means that the coordinate functions have derivatives of all the orders contained in the equation, and that these coordinate functions satisfy all, including the natural, boundary conditions of the problem.

4.3 Equations of the form $Au - \lambda Bu = 0$. We will assume that both of the operators A and B are positive definite and that the domain of existence of B is larger than the corresponding domain of existence A, i.e., $D(A) \subset D(B)$. Thus, for any element in $D(A)$, there are two ways of defining energy, the energy associated with the operator A, or the energy associated with the operator B. Accordingly, we will speak of the "energy of the operator A" or the "energy of the operator B."

Theorem 14. The eigenvalues of Eq. (3.108) are positive.

Theorem 15. The characteristic elements of Eq. (3.108) can be ortho-normalized relative to the energy of the operator B; in this case they are also orthogonal relative to the energy of the operator A.

Theorem 16. If there exists an element u_1 such that

$$\frac{(Au_1, u_1)}{(Bu_1, u_1)} = \lambda_1,$$

where

$$\lambda_1 = \mathrm{Inf}\,\frac{(Au, u)}{(Bu, u)},$$

then λ_1 is the smallest eigenvalue of Eq. (3.108) and u_1 is the corresponding characteristic element.

Theorem 17. Let $\lambda_1, \lambda_2, \ldots, \lambda_n$ be the first n eigenvalues of Eq. (3.108), written in increasing order, and let $u_1, u_2, \ldots, u_n$ be the corresponding characteristic elements. Moreover, let λ_{n+1} be the greatest lower bound of the functional

$$\frac{(Au, u)}{(u, u)}$$

under the conditions

$$(Bu, u_k) = 0 \qquad (k = 1, 2, \ldots, n),$$

If there exists an element u_{n+1} that satisfies these conditions and is such that

$$\frac{(Au_{n+1}, u_{n+1})}{(Bu_{n+1}, u_{n+1})} = \lambda_{n+1},$$

then λ_{n+1} is the eigenvalue of Eq. (3.108) immediately following λ_n and u_{n+1} is the corresponding characteristic element.

Theorem 18. Assume that the operators A and B are such that the set of elements whose norms with respect to the energy of the operator A are bounded as a group is compact with respect to the norm of the energy of the operator B. Then Eq. (3.108) has an infinite set of eigenvalues $0 < \lambda_1 \leqslant \lambda_2 \leqslant \ldots$, where $\lambda_n \to \infty$ as $n \to \infty$ and the corresponding characteristic elements form a system that is complete with respect to both the energy of the operator A and the energy of the operator B.

The smallest eigenvalue of Eq. (3.108) is equal to the minimum of $|u|_A^2$ when the additional condition $|u|_B^2 = 1$ is satisfied; we denote the energy norms of the element u in the spaces H_A and H_B by $|u|_A$ and $|u|_B$, respectively. We will use the symbols $[u, v]_A$ and $[u, v]_B$ to denote the energy products of the elements u and v in the corresponding spaces. If the first $n - 1$ eigenvalues and the corresponding characteristic elements $u_1, u_2, \ldots, u_{n-1}$ are known, the nth eigenvalue is the minimum of $|u|_A^2$ if the additional conditions $|u|_B^2 = 1$, $[u, u_k]_B = 0$ $(k = 1, 2, \ldots, n - 1)$ are satisfied.

Approximate values for the first n eigenvalues of Eq. (3.108) can be found as the roots of the equation

$$\begin{vmatrix} [\varphi_1, \varphi_1]_A - \lambda[\varphi_1, \varphi_1]_B & [\varphi_2, \varphi_1]_A - \lambda[\varphi_2, \varphi_1]_B & \cdots & [\varphi_n, \varphi_1]_A - \lambda[\varphi_n, \varphi_1]_B \\ [\varphi_1, \varphi_2]_A - \lambda[\varphi_1, \varphi_2]_B & [\varphi_2, \varphi_2]_A - \lambda[\varphi_2, \varphi_2]_B & \cdots & [\varphi_n, \varphi_2]_A - \lambda[\varphi_n, \varphi_2]_B \\ \cdots & \cdots & \cdots & \cdots \\ [\varphi_1, \varphi_n]_A - \lambda[\varphi_1, \varphi_n]_B & [\varphi_2, \varphi_n]_A - \lambda[\varphi_2, \varphi_n]_B & \cdots & [\varphi_n, \varphi_n]_A - \lambda[\varphi_n \; \varphi]_B \end{vmatrix} = 0;$$

$$(3.115)$$

the coordinate elements $\varphi_1, \varphi_2, \ldots$ must satisfy the following conditions:

1. $\varphi_n \in H_A$;

2. any finite number of elements forms a linearly independent set;

3. the set of coordinate elements is complete in H_A.

If $\varphi_n \in D(A)$, Eq. (3.115) can be written in the form

$$\begin{vmatrix} (A\varphi_1, \varphi_1) - \lambda(B\varphi_1, \varphi_1) & (A\varphi_2, \varphi_1) - \lambda(B\varphi_2, \varphi_1) & \cdots & (A\varphi_n, \varphi_1) - \lambda(B\varphi_n, \varphi_1) \\ (A\varphi_1, \varphi_2) - \lambda(B\varphi_1, \varphi_2) & (A\varphi_2, \varphi_2) - \lambda(B\varphi_2, \varphi_2) & \cdots & (A\varphi_n, \varphi_2) - \lambda(B\varphi_n, \varphi_2) \\ \cdots & \cdots & \cdots & \cdots \\ (A\varphi_1, \varphi_n) - \lambda(B\varphi_1, \varphi_n) & (A\varphi_2, \varphi_n) - \lambda(B\varphi_2, \varphi_n) & \cdots & (A\varphi_n, \varphi_n) - \lambda(B\varphi_n, \varphi_n) \end{vmatrix} = 0.$$

4.4 The spectrum of an ordinary differential operator. The operator

$$-\frac{d}{dx}\left(p(x)\frac{du}{dx}\right) + q(x)u \qquad (3.116)$$

under the boundary conditions

$$\alpha u'(a) - \beta u(a) = 0, \quad \gamma u'(b) + \delta u(b) = 0 \qquad (3.117)$$

has a discrete spectrum, and all of the eigenvalues are positive if the following conditions are satisfied:

1. $p(x) \geqslant p_0$, where p_0 is a positive constant;

2. $q(x) \geqslant 0$;

3. the constants α, β, γ, and δ are nonnegative and at least one of the constants β and δ is nonzero.

The spectrum of operator (3.116) remains discrete when the constants α, β, γ, and δ are chosen arbitrarily and $q(x)$ is not required to be nonnegative, but is required to satisfy the inequality $q(x) \geqslant -N$, where N is a nonnegative constant. It may now occur that the set of eigenvalues has a finite number of negative or zero members.

Under boundary conditions (3.117), the smallest eigenvalue of operator (3.116) is equal to the minimum of the functional

$$\int_a^b \left[p(x)\left(\frac{du}{dx}\right)^2 + q(x)u^2(x) \right] dx + \frac{\beta}{\alpha} p(a)u^2(a) + \frac{\delta}{\gamma} p(b)u^2(b) \quad (3.118)$$

under the additional condition

$$\int_a^b u^2(x)\, dx = 1. \quad (3.119)$$

In this case, if $\alpha \neq 0$ and $\gamma \neq 0$, conditions (3.117) are natural. However, if $\alpha = 0$, for example, the term containing α in functional (3.118) must be omitted, and the function $u(x)$ in this functional must satisfy not only condition (3.119), but the principal condition $u(a) = 0$ as well. If $\alpha = \gamma = 0$, the smallest eigenvalue is equal to the minimum of the functional

$$\int_a^b \left[p(x)\left(\frac{du}{dx}\right)^2 + q(x)u^2(x) \right] dx$$

under the additional conditions (3.119) and (3.117), which, in this case, take the form $u(a) = u(b) = 0$.

Similar conclusions hold for the eigenvalues of the equation

$$-\frac{d}{dx}\left(p(x)\frac{du}{dx} \right) + q(x)u - \lambda r(x)u = 0$$

if $r(x)$ lies between certain positive numbers r_0 and r_1. This time the smallest eigenvalue is equal to the minimum of functional (3.118) under the additional condition

$$\int_a^b r(x)u^2(x)\, dx = 1$$

and principal conditions (3.117), if there are any.

We will now consider the case in which $p(x)$ may vanish, assuming that $p(a) = 0$ and $p(x) > 0$ when $x > a$. We assume that the function $u(x)$ satisfies the boundary conditions stated in Section 3.1. Under these boundary conditions operator (3.116) has a discrete spectrum if the integral

$$\int_a^b \frac{(x - a)\, dx}{p(x)}.$$

converges. In particular, if $C_1(x - a)^\alpha \leqslant p(x) \leqslant C_2(x - a)^\alpha$, where C_1 and C_2 are positive constants, the spectrum of operator (3.116) is discrete when $\alpha < 2$, and not discrete when $\alpha \geqslant 2$.

We will now consider equations of order higher than two:

$$L_{2n}u - \lambda L_{2s}u = 0 \tag{3.120}$$

where $n > s$ and

$$L_{2n}u = \sum_{k=0}^{n} (-1)^k \frac{d^k}{dx^k} \left(p_k(x) \frac{d^k u}{dx^k} \right),$$

$$L_{2s}u = \sum_{k=0}^{s} (-1)^k \frac{d^k}{dx^k} \left(q_k(x) \frac{d^k u}{dx^k} \right),$$

while the function $u(x)$ satisfies the boundary conditions

$$\left. \begin{aligned} u(a) = u'(a) = \cdots = u^{(n-1)}(a) = 0, \\ u(b) = u'(b) = \cdots = u^{(n-1)}(b) = 0. \end{aligned} \right\} \tag{3.121}$$

We assume that $p_n(x) \geqslant C$, where C is a positive constant, and that, under boundary conditions (3.121), both of the operators L_{2n} and L_{2s} are positive definite; for this to occur, it is sufficient (but not necessary) that

$$p_k(x) \geqslant 0 \qquad (k = 1, 2, \ldots, n - 1)$$

and

$$q_k(x) \geqslant 0 \qquad (k = 1, 2, \ldots, s),$$

where at least one of the functions $q_k(x) \geqslant C'$, where C' is a positive constant. Under these conditions, the spectrum of Eq. (3.120) is discrete and all of its eigenvalues are positive. The smallest eigenvalue is the minimum of the functional

$$\int_a^b \sum_{k=0}^{n} p_k(x) \left(\frac{d^k u}{dx^k} \right)^2 dx \tag{3.122}$$

under the additional condition

$$\int_a^b \sum_{k=0}^{s} q_k(x) \left(\frac{d^k u}{\partial x^k} \right)^2 dx$$

and boundary conditions (3.121).

Now let $p_m(a) = 0$ but $p_m(x) > 0$ when $x > a$. More definitely, assume that $C_1(x - a)^\alpha \leqslant p_m(x) \leqslant C_2(x - a)^\alpha$, where C_1 and C_2 are positive constants, and consider the equation $L_{2n}u - \lambda u = 0$ under boundary conditions (3.51) and (3.54). The spectrum of this equation is discrete when $\alpha < 2n$, and not discrete when $\alpha \geqslant 2n$. If $\alpha < 2n$, the smallest eigenvalue is equal to the minimum of functional (3.122) under additional condition (3.119) and boundary conditions (3.51) and (3.54).

EXAMPLE 11: We will use the Rayleigh-Ritz method to find the approximate value of the smallest eigenvalue of the operator

$$-\frac{d}{dx}\left(\sqrt{1 + x}\,\frac{du}{dx}\right), \qquad u(0) = u(1) = 0. \qquad (3.123)$$

For the coordinate functions we take

$$\varphi_k(x) = (1 - x)x^k \qquad (k = 1, 2, \ldots).$$

We will limit the discussion to the first three coordinate equations. In this case Eq. (3.115) takes the form

$$\begin{vmatrix} 0.404757774 - \frac{1}{30}\lambda & 0.216156130 - \frac{1}{60}\lambda & 0.135002282 - \frac{1}{105}\lambda \\ 0.216156130 - \frac{1}{60}\lambda & 0.510789821 - \frac{1}{105}\lambda & 0.675363337 - \frac{1}{168}\lambda \\ 0.135002282 - \frac{1}{105}\lambda & 0.675363337 - \frac{1}{168}\lambda & 1.023822057 - \frac{1}{252}\lambda \end{vmatrix} = 0.$$

This equation can be solved with Newton's method; for the smallest eigenvalue of operator (3.123) we obtain a value

$$\lambda_1^{(3)} = 12.12255. \qquad (3.124)$$

4.5 The spectrum of elliptic operators. Consider the self-adjoint second-order equation

$$-\sum_{j,k=1}^{m} \frac{\partial}{\partial x_j}\left(A_{jk}(x)\,\frac{\partial u}{\partial x_k}\right) + C(x)u - \lambda r(x)u = 0 \qquad (3.125)$$

under any of boundary conditions (3.62)–(3.64), and assume the following:

1. in the finite region Ω under discussion, the operator

$$-\sum_{j,k=1}^{m} \frac{\partial}{\partial x_j}\left(A_{jk}\,\frac{\partial u}{\partial x_k}\right)$$

is elliptic and nondegenerate, so that we have the inequality

$$\sum_{j,k=1}^{m} A_{jk}t_j t_k \geqslant \mu_0 \sum_{j=1}^{m} t_j^2, \qquad \mu_0 = \text{const} > 0;$$

2. $C(x) \geqslant a$, where a is a constant of arbitrary sign;

3. $r_0 \leqslant r(x) \leqslant r_1$, where r_0 and r_1 are positive constants;

4. in the case of conditions (3.63) or (3.64), the region Ω satisfies the conditions of Section 1.5. *Under these conditions, operator* (3.125) *has a discrete spectrum.* Here all of the eigenvalues will be positive if the following conditions are satisfied:

a. In the case of boundary conditions (3.62) or (3.64), it is sufficient that $C(x) \geqslant 0$.

This requirement can be immediately weakened in the following manner: Let λ_1 be the smallest eigenvalue of the equation

$$-\sum_{j,k=1}^{m} \frac{\partial}{\partial x_j}\left(A_{jk}\frac{\partial u}{\partial x_j}\right) - \lambda r(x)u = 0$$

under boundary conditions (3.62) or (3.64); as we have just noted, $\lambda_1 > 0$. Under this boundary condition, the eigenvalues of Eq. (3.123) are positive if $C(x) > -\lambda_1$.

b. In the case of boundary condition (3.63), the eigenvalues of Eq. (3.123) are positive if the coefficient $C(x)$ is nonnegative and not identically equal to zero.

Under boundary condition (3.62), the smallest eigenvalue of Eq. (3.125) is equal to the minimum of the functional

$$\int_{\Omega}\left\{\sum_{j,k=1}^{m} A_{jk}\frac{\partial u}{\partial x_j}\frac{\partial u}{\partial x_k} + Cu^2\right\} dx$$

over the set of functions satisfying condition (3.62) and the additional condition

$$\int_{\Omega} ru^2 \, dx = 1. \tag{3.126}$$

In the case of condition (3.64) [when $\sigma \equiv 0$, condition (3.63) is a special case of this last condition], the smallest eigenvalue of Eq. (3.125) is the minimum of the functional

$$\int_{\Omega}\left\{\sum_{j,k=1}^{m} A_{jk}\frac{\partial u}{\partial x_j}\frac{\partial u}{\partial x_k} + Cu^2\right\} + \int_{S} \sigma u^2 \, dS$$

under the additional condition (3.126).

For Neumann's problem [condition (3.63)] for the case in which $C(x) \equiv 0$, the smallest eigenvalue is equal to zero; one linearly independent characteristic function, $u \equiv$ const, corresponds to it. The smallest positive eigenvalue for Neumann's problem in this case is the minimum of the integral

$$\int_{\Omega}\sum_{j,k=1}^{m} A_{ik}\frac{\partial u}{\partial x_j}\frac{\partial u}{\partial x_k} \, dx$$

under the additional conditions (3.126) and

$$(u, 1) = \int_\Omega u \, dx = 0.$$

We will now consider the higher-order equation

$$L_{2n}u - \lambda L_{2s}u = 0, \quad n > s, \tag{3.127}$$

where L_{2n} is defined by Formulas (3.77) and L_{2s} is defined by the analogous formulas

$$L_{2s}u = \sum_{k=0}^{s} B_k u,$$

$$B_k u = \sum \frac{\partial^k}{\partial x_{i_1} \partial x_{i_2} \cdots \partial x_{i_k}} \left(B_{j_1, j_2, \ldots, j_k}^{i_1, i_2, \ldots, i_k}(x) \frac{\partial^k u}{\partial x_{j_1} \partial x_{j_2} \cdots \partial x_{j_k}} \right).$$

We will consider Eq. (3.127) under boundary conditions (3.79), making the following assumptions:

1. inequality (3.78) is satisfied, so that the operator L_{2n} is elliptic and nondegenerate;
2. the coefficients of L_{2n} are bounded; and
3. the operator L_{2s} is positive definite.

Then Eq. (3.127) has a discrete spectrum. If, moreover, the operator L_{2n} is positive definite when conditions (3.79) are satisfied, the eigenvalues of Eq. (3.127) are positive. The smallest eigenvalue is equal to the minimum of the functional

$$(L_{2n}u, u) = \int_\Omega \sum_{k=0}^{n} \sum A_{j_1, j_2, \ldots, j_k}^{i_1, i_2, \ldots, i_k} \frac{\partial^k u}{\partial x_{i_1} \partial x_{i_2} \cdots \partial x_{i_k}} \frac{\partial^k u}{\partial x_{j_1} \partial x_{j_2} \cdots \partial x_{j_k}} \, dx$$

over the set of functions satisfying boundary conditions (3.79) and the additional condition

$$(L_{2s}u, u) = \int_\Omega \sum_{k=0}^{s} \sum B_{j_1, j_2, \ldots, j_k}^{i_1, i_2, \ldots, j_k} \frac{\partial^k u}{\partial x_{i_1} \partial x_{i_2} \cdots \partial x_{i_k}} \frac{\partial^k u}{\partial x_{j_1} \partial x_{j_2} \cdots \partial x_{j_k}} \, dx = 1.$$

The problem of the frequencies of the characteristic bending oscillations of a thin elastic plate deserves a special discussion. If the thickness of the plate is constant, this frequency is proportional to the eigenvalues of the biharmonic operator

$$\Delta^2 w = \frac{\partial^4 w}{\partial x^4} + 2 \frac{\partial^4 w}{\partial x^2 \partial y^2} + \frac{\partial^4 w}{\partial y^4}$$

under one of the boundary conditions considered in Section 3.6. We assume that we are dealing with the general case, in which the edge of the plate splits into four sections S_1, S_2, S_3, and S_4, on which conditions (3.82), (3.83),

(3.84), and (3.85), respectively, are satisfied. Under these conditions, the spectrum of the biharmonic operator is discrete.

The smallest eigenvalue of the biharmonic operator is the minimum of the functional

$$\iint_\Omega \left\{ \left(\frac{\partial^2 w}{\partial x^2}\right)^2 + 2\sigma \frac{\partial^2 w}{\partial x^2}\frac{\partial^2 w}{\partial y^2} + \left(\frac{\partial^2 w}{\partial y^2}\right)^2 + 2(1-\sigma)\left(\frac{\partial^2 w}{\partial x\,\partial y}\right)^2 \right\} dx\,dy$$
$$+ k\int_{S_3} \left(\frac{\partial w}{\partial \nu}\right)^2 ds; \quad (3.128)$$

this minimum is taken over the set of functions satisfying the equation

$$\iint_\Omega w^2\, dx\, dy = 1 \qquad (3.129)$$

and the boundary conditions

$$\mathbf{u}\big|_{S_1+S_2+S_3=0}, \qquad \frac{\partial u}{\partial \nu}\bigg|_{S_1} = 0. \qquad (3.130)$$

If the entire edge of the plate is rigidly fixed, the smallest eigenvalue of the biharmonic operator is also equal to the minimum of the integral

$$\iint_\Omega (\Delta w)^2\, dx\, dy,$$

where the function $w(x)$ satisfies Eq. (3.129) and the boundary conditions $w\big|_S = 0, \dfrac{\partial w}{\partial \nu}\bigg|_S = 0.$

The nth eigenvalue λ_n of the biharmonic operator is related to the nth characteristic frequency ω_n of the plate by the expression

$$\lambda_n = \frac{\gamma \omega_n^2}{D},$$

where γ is the density of the plate and $D = Eh^2/12(1-\sigma^2)$ is the resistance of the plate to bending.

If the thickness $2h$ of the plate varies, the equation for the characteristic oscillations of the plate takes the form

$$\frac{\partial^2}{\partial x^2}\left(h^3\frac{\partial^2 w}{\partial x^2}\right) + \sigma\frac{\partial^2}{\partial x^2}\left(h^3\frac{\partial^2 w}{\partial y^2}\right) + \sigma\frac{\partial}{\partial y^2}\left(h^3\frac{\partial^2 w}{\partial x^2}\right)$$
$$+ \frac{\partial^2}{\partial y^2}\left(h^3\frac{\partial^2 w}{\partial y^2}\right) + 2(1-\sigma)\frac{\partial^2}{\partial x\,\partial y}\left(h^3\frac{\partial^2 w}{\partial x\,\partial y}\right) = \lambda h w, \quad (3.131)$$

where, this time, the parameter λ is related to the frequency ω by the expression

$$\lambda = \frac{12(1 - \sigma^2)\gamma}{E} \omega^2.$$

The smallest eigenvalue λ_1 is the minimum of the functional

$$\iint_\Omega h^3 \left[\left(\frac{\partial^2 w}{\partial x^2} \right)^2 + 2\sigma \frac{\partial^2 w}{\partial x^2} \frac{\partial^2 w}{\partial y^2} + \left(\frac{\partial^2 w}{\partial y^2} \right)^2 \right.$$

$$\left. + 2(1 - \sigma) \left(\frac{\partial^2 w}{\partial x \, \partial y} \right)^2 \right] dx \, dy + k \int_{S_1} h^3 \left(\frac{\partial w}{\partial \nu} \right)^2 ds \quad (3.132)$$

under the additional condition

$$\iint_\Omega h w^2 \, dx \, dy = 1 \qquad (3.133)$$

and boundary conditions (3.130).

4.6 The stability of a compressed plate.   Assume that the stresses on a plate are proportional to some parameter λ and, consequently, are of the form λT_{xx}, λT_{xy}, and λT_{yy}. We also assume that there are no stress-free regions on the plate and, for simplicity, that the plate is of constant thickness. If at least one point of the plate is such that at least one of the principal stresses defined by the stress field T_{xx}, T_{xy}, T_{yy} is compressive, then, at certain positive values of λ, the plate becomes unstable. These values of λ ("critical values") and the corresponding deflections w are related by the equation

$$\Delta^2 w - \frac{\lambda h}{D} \left(T_{xx} \frac{\partial^2 w}{\partial x^2} + 2T_{xy} \frac{\partial^2 w}{\partial x \, \partial y} + T_{yy} \frac{\partial^2 w}{\partial y^2} \right) = 0;$$

moreover, w satisfies the corresponding conditions concerning the mounting of the plate. The smallest critical value is the minimum of functional (3.128) under boundary conditions (3.130) and the additional condition

$$-\iint_\Omega \left[T_{xx} \left(\frac{\partial w}{\partial x} \right)^2 + 2T_{xy} \frac{\partial w}{\partial x} \frac{\partial w}{\partial y} + T_{yy} \left(\frac{\partial w}{\partial y} \right)^2 \right] dx \, dy = 1.$$

4.7 The spectrum of a degenerate elliptic equation.   Here we will limit the discussion primarily to second-order equations, and we will consider the spectrum of the characteristic frequencies of a plate with a sharp edge. In both cases, we will assume that the boundary conditions given in Sections 3.4 and 3.6 are satisfied.

Consider the equation

$$\frac{\partial}{\partial x} \left(\varphi(x, y) \frac{\partial u}{\partial x} \right) + \frac{\partial}{\partial y} \left(\omega(x, y) \frac{\partial u}{\partial y} \right) + \lambda u = 0 \qquad (3.134)$$

under the boundary conditions just mentioned.

Under these conditions, the spectrum of Eq. (3.134) is discrete if $\varphi(x, y) > 0$ when $y > 0$, $\omega(x, y) = y^{\alpha}\omega_1(x, y)$, $\omega_1(x, y) \geqslant k$, where k is a positive constant and $0 \leqslant \alpha < 2$. The smallest eigenvalue of Eq. (3.134) is, as in the case of a nondegenerate equation, the minimum of the integral

$$\iint_{\Omega} \left[\varphi(x, y)\left(\frac{\partial u}{\partial x}\right)^2 + \omega(x, y)\left(\frac{\partial u}{\partial y}\right)^2 \right] dx\, dy$$

over the set of functions satisfying the boundary conditions of the problem, and, moreover, the equation

$$\iint_{\Omega} u^2\, dx\, dy = 1.$$

If $\alpha \geqslant 2$, the spectrum of Eq. (3.134) is not discrete.

The spectrum of characteristic frequencies of a plate of variable frequency is determined by Eq. (3.131) and the corresponding boundary conditions. Assume that $C_1 y^{\alpha} \leqslant h(x, y) \leqslant C_2 y^{\alpha}$, where C_1, C_2, and α are positive constants. Then the spectrum of characteristic frequencies is discrete if $\alpha < 2$, and otherwise not. As above, the smallest eigenvalue is equal to the minimum of functional (3.132) over the set of functions satisfying the boundary conditions of the problem and supplementary condition (3.133).

We should also note that the spectrum of the operator in the left-hand side of Eq. (3.131), i.e., the spectrum of the equation

$$\frac{\partial^2}{\partial x^2}\left(h^3\frac{\partial^2 w}{\partial x^2} \right) + \sigma\frac{\partial^2}{\partial x^2}\left(h^3\frac{\partial^2 w}{\partial y^2} \right) + \sigma\frac{\partial^2}{\partial y^2}\left(h^3\frac{\partial^2 w}{\partial x^2} \right)$$

$$+ \frac{\partial^2}{\partial y^2}\left(h^3\frac{\partial^2 w}{\partial y^2} \right) + 2(1 - \sigma)\frac{\partial^2}{\partial x\, \partial y}\left(h^3\frac{\partial^2 w}{\partial x\, \partial y} \right) = \lambda w,$$

is discrete only when $\alpha < \frac{4}{3}$.

4.8 Characteristic oscillations of elastic bodies. Under the boundary conditions given in Section 3.8, the operator

$$\mathbf{A}u = -\sum_{i,k,l,m=1}^{3} \frac{\partial}{\partial x_i}(c_{iklm}\varepsilon_{lm})\mathbf{x}_k^{(0)}$$

has a discrete spectrum. The eigenvalues of the operator $\mathbf{A}$ are positive when (see Section 3.8) this operator is positive definite; otherwise, the first several eigenvalues are equal to zero. The smallest eigenvalue of the operator $\mathbf{A}$ is equal to the minimum of twice the potential energy of deformation of the elastic body,

$$2\int_{\Omega} W\, dx = \int_{\Omega} \sum_{i,k,l,m=1}^{3} c_{iklm}\varepsilon_{ik}\varepsilon_{lm}\, dx$$

under the boundary conditions of the problem and the supplementary condition

$$\int_{\Omega} \sum_{i=1}^{3} u_i^2 \, dx = 1.$$

The eigenvalues λ_n of the operator $\mathbf{A}$ are related to the characteristic frequencies ω_n of the elastic body by the equation $\lambda_n = \gamma \omega_n^2$, where γ is the density of the elastic medium, which we assume to be constant.

EXAMPLE 12: We will find the smallest characteristic frequency of a homogeneous isotropic elastic circular cylinder with a free boundary, limiting the discussion to the case of radially symmetric oscillations. Let λ and μ be the Lamé constants, let R be the radius of the cylinder, and let h be its height. We introduce the cylindrical coordinates ρ, φ, and z, and let u_φ and u_z denote the components of the translation vector $\mathbf{u}$ along the directions of ρ and z, respectively; the component u_φ in the direction of φ is equal to zero because the translation is radially symmetric. In our case,

$$2\int_{\Omega} W \, dx = 2\pi \int_0^R \int_0^h \left\{ \lambda \left(\frac{\partial u_\rho}{\partial \rho} + \frac{u_\rho}{\rho} + \frac{\partial u_z}{\partial z} \right)^2 \right. $$

$$\left. + 2\mu \left[\left(\frac{\partial u_\rho}{\partial \rho} \right)^2 + \frac{u_\rho^2}{\rho^2} + \left(\frac{\partial u_z}{\partial z} \right)^2 \right] + \mu \left(\frac{\partial u_\rho}{\partial z} + \frac{\partial u_z}{\partial \rho} \right)^2 \right\} \rho \, d\rho \, dz.$$

The smallest characteristic frequency ω_2 of the cylinder is related to the smallest positive eigenvalue of the problem κ_1 by the equation $\kappa_1 = \gamma \omega_1^2$; however, κ_1 is not the smallest eigenvalue of the problem—it is equal to zero and the corresponding characteristic elements are small rigid translations. As a result, κ_1 can be constructed as the minimum of the integral described above, under the conditions

$$2\pi \int_0^R \int_0^h (u_\rho^2 + u_z^2) \rho \, d\rho \, dz = 1$$

and

$$\int_{\Omega} \mathbf{u} \, dx = 2\pi \int_0^R \int_0^h \mathbf{u} \rho \, d\rho \, dz = 0,$$

$$\int_{\Omega} \mathbf{r} \times \mathbf{u} \, dx = 2\pi \int_0^R \int_0^h \mathbf{r} \times \mathbf{u} \rho \, d\rho \, dz = 0,$$

of which, the last two are equivalent to the conditions required for orthogonality of the vector $\mathbf{u}$ and the vector of an arbitrary rigid translation.

The boundary conditions of this problem are natural and the vector $\mathbf{u}$ need not satisfy them.

It is clear from a symmetry considerations that $u_\rho = 0$ when $\rho = 0$. Applying the Rayleigh-Ritz method, we choose u_ρ / ρ and u_z in the form of polynomials in powers of ρ^2 and z; by limiting the polynomials to the terms, described below, we obtain

$$u_\rho = \rho(\alpha_0 + \alpha_1 z + \alpha_2 \rho^2 + \alpha_3 z^2),$$
$$u_z = \beta_0 + \beta_1 z + \beta_2 \rho^2 + \beta_3 z^2.$$

The above-mentioned conditions for orthogonality lead to the relations

$$\alpha_0 = -3\left(\frac{\alpha_1 h}{6} + \frac{\alpha_2 R^2}{5} + \frac{\alpha_3 h^2}{9}\right),$$

$$\beta_0 = -\left(\frac{\beta_1 h}{2} + \frac{\beta_2 R^2}{2} + \frac{\beta_3 h^2}{3}\right), \quad \alpha_1 = \frac{6}{h^2}\left(\frac{\beta_2 R^2}{5} - \frac{\alpha_3 h^3}{6}\right).$$

By eliminating the coefficients α_0, β_0, and α_1, we can see that u_t and u_z are components of the vector

$$\mathbf{u} = \sum_{k=1}^{5} \alpha_k \boldsymbol{\varphi}_k,$$

where

$$a_1 = \beta_1, \quad a_2 = \alpha_2, \quad a_3 = \beta_2, \quad a_4 = \alpha_3, \quad a_5 = \beta_3$$

and

$$\boldsymbol{\varphi}_1 = \left(0; \ z - \frac{h}{2}\right), \quad \boldsymbol{\varphi}_2 = \left(\rho^3 - \frac{3R^2}{5}\rho; \ 0\right),$$

$$\boldsymbol{\varphi}_3 = \left(\frac{6R^2}{5h^2}\rho z - \frac{3R^2}{5h}\rho; \ \rho^2 - \frac{R^2}{2}\right),$$

$$\boldsymbol{\varphi}_4 = \left(\frac{h^2}{6}\rho - h\rho z + z^2\rho; \ 0\right), \quad \boldsymbol{\varphi}_5 = \left(0; \ z^2 - \frac{h^2}{3}\right).$$

The main Hilbert space of the present problem is the space of radially symmetric vector functions that are square summable in the cylindrical region in question; in this space the scalar product of $\boldsymbol{\varphi}$ and $\boldsymbol{\psi}$ is given by the formula

$$(\boldsymbol{\varphi}, \boldsymbol{\psi}) = 2\pi \int_0^R \int_0^h (\varphi_\rho \psi_\rho + \varphi_z \psi_z)\rho \, d\rho \, dz;$$

the energy product is of the form

$$[\boldsymbol{\varphi}, \boldsymbol{\psi}] = 2\pi \int_0^R \int_0^h \left\{ \lambda \left(\frac{\partial \varphi_\rho}{\rho \, \partial} + \frac{\varphi_\rho}{\rho} + \frac{\partial \varphi_z}{\partial z}\right)\left(\frac{\partial \psi_\rho}{\partial \rho} + \frac{\psi_\rho}{\rho} + \frac{\partial \psi_z}{\partial z}\right) \right.$$

$$+ 2\mu \left(\frac{\partial \varphi_\rho}{\partial \rho}\frac{\partial \psi_\rho}{\partial \rho} + \frac{\varphi_\rho \psi_\rho}{\rho^2} + \frac{\partial \varphi_z}{\partial z}\frac{\partial \psi_z}{\partial z}\right)$$

$$\left. + \mu \left(\frac{\partial \varphi_\rho}{\partial z} + \frac{\partial \varphi_z}{\partial \rho}\right)\left(\frac{\partial \psi_\rho}{\partial z} + \frac{\partial \psi_z}{\partial \rho}\right)\right\}\rho \, d\rho \, dz.$$

Equation (3.115) can now be written, and we will substitute κ for λ, since λ already denotes one of the Lamé constants. In our case Eq. (3.115) is a fifth-degree equation, and splits into three:

$$\frac{(\lambda + \mu)R^2 h^2}{90} + \frac{\mu R^4 h^3}{12} - \frac{R^4 h^5}{720} \kappa = 0,$$

$$\begin{vmatrix} \dfrac{(\lambda + 2\mu)R^2 h}{2} - \dfrac{R^2 h^3}{24}\kappa & \dfrac{2\lambda R^4 h}{5} \\[3mm] \dfrac{2\lambda R^4 h}{5} & \dfrac{(74\lambda + 124\mu)R^6 h}{75} - \dfrac{3R^8 h}{200}\kappa \end{vmatrix} = 0.$$

$$\begin{vmatrix} \dfrac{6(\lambda + \mu)R^6}{25h} + \dfrac{\mu R^4 h}{4}\left(\dfrac{6R^2}{5h^2} + 2\right) - \left(\dfrac{3R^3}{100h} + \dfrac{R^6 h}{24}\right)\kappa & \lambda R^4 h \\[3mm] \lambda R^4 h & \dfrac{(\lambda + 2\mu)R^2 h^3}{6} - \dfrac{R^2 h^5}{360}\kappa \end{vmatrix} = 0.$$

For the sake of definiteness, we will consider the case $\lambda = 2\mu$, which corresponds to a Poisson constant of $\sigma = 1/3$. Moreover, we set $R = 2$ and $h = 4$, so that the axial cross section of the cylinder is a square. The smallest of the roots of the equations written above is $\kappa_1 = 2.722808\mu$, as a result of which

$$\omega_1 = 0.1650051\sqrt{\frac{\mu}{\gamma}}.$$

4.9 More general conditions for positive definiteness of differential operators.
We will limit the discussion to one example, since extension to other cases presents no difficulty. In Section 3.3 we showed that under the boundary condition $u|_S = 0$, the nondegenerate elliptic operator

$$Au = -\sum_{j,k=1}^{m} \frac{\partial}{\partial x_j}\left(A_{jk}\frac{\partial u}{\partial x_k}\right) + C(x)u$$

is positive definite if $C(x) \geqslant 0$. This condition, however, is not necessary. Under the boundary condition $u|_S = 0$, the smallest eigenvalue λ_1 of the operator

$$A_1 u = -\sum_{j,k=1}^{m} \frac{\partial}{\partial x_j}\left(A_{jk}\frac{\partial u}{\partial x_j}\right)$$

is positive. But

$$\lambda_1 = \text{Inf}\,\frac{(A_1 u, u)}{(u, u)} = \text{Inf}\,\frac{(A_1 u, u)}{\|u\|^2},$$

and for any function $u \in D(A_1)$, i.e., for any function $u \in W_2^2(\Omega)$, that is equal to zero on S,

$$(A_1 u, u) \geqslant \lambda_1 \|u\|^2.$$

It is now clear that the operator A is positive definite if $C(x) > -\mu$, where the constant $\mu < \lambda_1$. Indeed,

$$(Au, u) = (A_1 u, u) + (Cu, u) > \lambda_1(u, u) - \mu(u, u) = (\lambda_1 - \mu)\|u\|^2.$$

EXAMPLE 13: Let

$$Au = -\Delta u - a(x^2 + y^2)u = -\left(\frac{\partial^2 u}{\partial x^2} + \frac{\partial^2 u}{\partial y^2}\right) - a(x^2 + y^2)u, \quad u|_S = 0,$$

where a is a positive constant and the region Ω is the square $0 \leqslant x, y \leqslant 1$; as always, S denotes the boundary of this square. In this case $A_1 u = -\Delta u$, $u|_S = 0$. For the first boundary-value problem, the eigenvalues of the Laplace operator in the unit square are given by the well-known formula $\lambda_{mn} = \pi^2(m^2 + n^2)$ $(m, n = 1, 2, \ldots)$; the smallest one is $\lambda_1 = \lambda_{11} = 2\pi^2$. It is clear that in the square Ω we have $-a(x^2 + y^2) \geqslant -2a$, and the operator A is positive definite if $-2a > -2\pi^2$ or $a < \pi^2$.

4.10 The minimax principle. Let A be a positive-definite operator with discrete spectrum, and let $\lambda_1 \leqslant \lambda_2 \leqslant \cdots \leqslant \lambda_n \leqslant \cdots$ be its eigenvalues. The following method makes it possible to compute the nth eigenvalue without knowing the characteristic elements $u_1, u_2, \ldots, u_{n-1}$ corresponding to the preceding eigenvalues $\lambda_1, \lambda_2, \ldots, \lambda_{n-1}$. In the energy space H_A we take arbitrary elements $v_1, v_2, \ldots, v_{n-1}$ and find the minimum of $|u|_A^2$ under the supplementary conditions

$$\|u\|^2 = 1, \quad (u, v_k) = 0 \quad (k = 1, 2, \ldots, n - 1);$$

we denote this minimum by $\lambda(v_1, v_2, \ldots, v_{n-1})$. It turns out that

$$\lambda_n = \text{Max } \lambda(v_1, v_2, \ldots, v_{n-1}); \tag{3.135}$$

where the maximum is taken over all possible sets of elements $v_1, v_2, \ldots, v_{n-1}$ in the energy space H_A. Equation (3.135) is called the *minimax principle*.

Under certain conditions, the minimax principle makes it possible to compare the eigenvalues of different operators. Let A and B be two positive operators. We will say that A is *no smaller than* the operator B, $A \geqslant B$, if the space H_B contains all of the elements of H_A and for each $u \in H_A$ we have the inequality $|u|_A \geqslant |u|_B$. It turns out that if $A \geqslant B$ and B has a discrete spectrum, A also has a discrete spectrum; if λ_n and μ_n $(n = 1, 2, \ldots)$ are the eigenvalues of the operators A and B, respectively, then $\lambda_n \geqslant \mu_n$ for all n.

The following simple cases should be noted:

1. Let two membranes (or plates) with rigidly fixed edges be made of the same material, and assume that one membrane is completely covered by the other. Then the characteristic frequencies of the oscillations of the smaller membrane are larger than the corresponding characteristic frequencies of the larger membrane;

2. A plate with a rigidly fixed edge has higher characteristic frequencies than a plate whose edge is elastically fixed; in turn, the frequency in this last case is larger than the frequency for the case of a freely supported or free edge.

5. OTHER VARIATIONAL METHODS AND ERROR ESTIMATES

5.1 Error estimates and approximate solutions. Let u_0 and u_n, respectively, be the exact and approximate solutions of the equation

$$Au = f, \tag{3.136}$$

where the operator A is assumed to be positive definite,

$$(Au, u) \geqslant \gamma^2 \|u\|^2, \quad \gamma^2 = \text{const} > 0. \tag{3.137}$$

The problem consists in estimating the error $u_0 - u_n$ under the assumption that the approximate solution is known and the exact solution is unknown. It is desirable to characterize this error in terms of its norm in one space or other, but it is simplest to use the norm $\|u_0 - u_n\|$ in the Hilbert space H in which A is defined, or the norm $|u_0 - u_n|_A$ in the energy space H_A.

If $u_n \in D(A)$, we have the following simple formula for error estimation:

$$\|u_0 - u_n\| \leqslant \frac{1}{\gamma^2} \|Au_n - f\|. \tag{3.138}$$

Formula (3.138) can, for example, be used if u_n is constructed with the Ritz method and members of the region $D(A)$ are used as the coordinate functions. If the operator A is a differential operator, the coordinate functions satisfy all of the boundary conditions of the problem. It should be remembered that estimate (3.138) is rather crude.

Another estimate that is more practical in practice is obtained as follows. Let $F(u)$ denote the functional of the energy method,

$$F(u) = (Au, u) - 2(u, f) = |u|^2 - 2(u, f),$$

and let d denote its minimum. If δ is any number smaller than d,

$$|u_0 - u_n| \leqslant \sqrt{F(u_n) - \delta}; \tag{3.139}$$

as a corollary, we obtain still one more estimate:

$$\|u_0 - u_n\| \leqslant \frac{1}{\gamma} \sqrt{F(u_n) - \delta}. \tag{3.140}$$

Application of Formula (3.139) or (3.140) does not require the assumption that $u_n \in D(A)$; it is sufficient for $u_n \in H_A$ (in particular, u_n need not satisfy the natural boundary conditions), which always occurs when u_n is constructed with the Ritz method. Here a convenient formula can be given for computing $F(u_n)$, i.e., if

$$u_n = \sum_{k=1}^{n} a_k \varphi_k,$$

where the φ_k are the coordinate elements and a_k is the solution of the corresponding Ritz system, we have

$$F(u_n) = -\sum_{k=1}^{n} a_k(f, \varphi_k). \tag{3.141}$$

A general method for constructing $\delta < d$ proceeds as follows, It is known that

$$d = \min F(u) = -|u_0|^2.$$

We now assume that we can find a functional $\Phi(v)$ with the property that

$$\min \Phi(v) = -d = -\min F(u). \tag{3.142}$$

If v is any member of the domain of existence of the functional Φ, then $\Phi(v) \geqslant -d$ or $-\Phi(v) \leqslant d$, and thus we can set $\delta = -\Phi(v)$. For the functional $\Phi(v)$ we construct a minimizing sequence, i.e., a sequence v_m $(m = 1, 2, \ldots)$ such that

$$\lim_{m \to \infty} \Phi(v_m) = -d,$$

and setting $\delta = -\Phi(v_m)$ in Formula (3.139), we obtain an error estimate that approaches the actual error when m is sufficiently large. We should note that the sequence v_m can be constructed with the Ritz method. The problem reduces to constructing a functional Φ that satisfies condition (3.142). The most important methods of carrying out this construction are the *method of orthogonal projections* and the *Trefftz method*. We should also note that each of these methods makes it possible to construct approximate solutions for Eq. (3.136).

5.2 The method of orthogonal projections.   Again consider Eq. (3.136), and assume that the positive operator A in this equation can be represented in the form of the product of two conjugate operators T^* and T such that $A = T^*T$. Here it is not necessary for the operators T^* and T to be defined in the same space H as the operator A; it can be assumed that T maps members of the space H into members of some Hilbert space $\mathfrak{H}$, and, conversely, that T^* maps members of the space $\mathfrak{H}$ into members of the space H.

If we set $Tu = v$ in Eq. (3.136), we find that

$$T^*v = f. \tag{3.143}$$

In what follows, we will be interested only in the case in which the equation $T^*w = 0$ has a nontrivial solution. The set of nontrivial solutions forms some subspace of the space $\mathfrak{H}$, which we denote by $\mathfrak{H}$. We denote the orthogonal complement of $\mathfrak{H}_2$ by $\mathfrak{H}_1$, so that $\mathfrak{H} = \mathfrak{H}_1 \oplus \mathfrak{H}_2$. It can easily be shown that the desired element $v_0 = Tu_0 \in \mathfrak{H}_1$ and that $\|v_0\|_{\mathfrak{H}} = |u_0|_A$; here u_0 is a solution of Eq. (3.136).

We find some element $v \in \mathfrak{H}$ that satisfies Eq. (3.143), assuming that it is not difficult to do so. Then the *desired element v_0 is the projection of V in the subspace $\mathfrak{H}_1$*; as a result, the difference $V - v_0$ is the projection of the same element V in the subspace $\mathfrak{H}_2$.

It is known from the properties of projections that

$$\|v_0\|_{\mathfrak{H}} = \text{Min} \ \|V - w\|_{\mathfrak{H}},$$

where the minimum is taken over all w that belong to $\mathfrak{H}_2$, and it is clear that for the functional Φ we can take

$$\Phi(w) = \|V - w\|_{\mathfrak{H}}^2. \tag{3.144}$$

We solve the problem of minimizing functional (3.144), say, with the Ritz method, and assume that w_m is the approximate solution of this problem. If we set $v_m = V - w_m$, Formula (3.139) now gives us

$$|u_0 - u_n| \leqslant \sqrt{F(u_n) + \|v_m\|_{\mathfrak{H}}^2}. \tag{3.145}$$

The element v_m can be treated as the approximate value of $v_0 = Tu_0$, and we have the estimate

$$\|v_0 - v_m\|_{\mathfrak{H}}^2 \leqslant \sqrt{F(u_n) + \|v_m\|_{\mathfrak{H}}^2}. \tag{3.146}$$

In Formulas (3.145) and (3.146), u_n denotes the approximate solution of Eq. (3.136) given by the energy method.

If the arithmetic mean $(Tu_n + v_m)/2$ is taken for the approximate value of v_0, we obtain an *exact formula for the error:*

$$\|v_0 - \tfrac{1}{2}(Tu_n + v_m)\|_{\mathfrak{H}}^2 = \tfrac{1}{2}\sqrt{F(u_n) + \|v_m\|_{\mathfrak{H}}^2}. \tag{3.147}$$

This formula was obtained by Synge [126].

5.3 Applications to particular problems. For the Poisson equation in three-dimensional space

$$-\Delta u = -\left(\frac{\partial^2 u}{\partial x^2} + \frac{\partial^2 u}{\partial y^2} + \frac{\partial^2 u}{\partial z^2}\right) = f(x, y, z) \tag{3.148}$$

the Dirichlet problem is as follows: Find the integral of this equation that satisfies boundary condition (3.62):

$$u|_S = 0.$$

As we know, $\Delta u = \text{div grad } u$, and we can set $Tu = -\text{grad } u$, assuming that the operator T is defined not only on functions that satisfy condition (3.62). In our case $H = L_2(\Omega)$, and for the space $\mathfrak{H}$ we can take the space $L_2(\Omega)$ of vectors whose absolute value is square summable in Ω. The conjugate operator $T^*\mathbf{v} = \text{div } \mathbf{v}$ so $-\Delta = T^*T$. In the case under discussion, the subspace $\mathfrak{H}$ consists of vectors with zero divergence (solenoidal vectors), and the subspace $\mathfrak{H}$ consists of the gradients of scalar functions that vanish on the boundary S. For $\mathbf{V}$ we can take any solution of the equation

$$\operatorname{div} \mathbf{V} = f(x, y, z),$$

and we can, for example, set

$$\mathbf{V} = \left(0, 0, -\int_a^z f(x, y, z) \, dz\right),$$

where a is any fixed number for which the last integral is meaningful. The method of orthogonal projections requires us to find the minimum of the integral

$$\|\mathbf{V} - \mathbf{w}\|^2 = \iiint_\Omega [(V_x - w_x)^2 + (V_y - w_y)^2 + (V_z - w_z)^2] \, dx \, dy \, dz,$$

where V_x, V_y, V_z and w_x, w_y, w_z are the projections of the vectors V and w on the coordinate axes; the minimum is taken over the set of vectors $\mathbf{w}$ that satisfy the equation $\operatorname{div} \mathbf{w} = 0$. If the Ritz method is applied to this problem, it is necessary to construct a system of vectors φ_n $(n = 1, 2, \ldots)$ that is complete in $\mathfrak{H}_2$ and set

$$\mathbf{w}_m = \sum_{k=1}^m \alpha_k \varphi_k;$$

in order to determine the coefficients α_k, we obtain the system of equations*

$$\left.\begin{array}{l} (\varphi_1, \varphi_1)\alpha_1 + (\varphi_2, \varphi_1)\alpha_2 + \cdots + (\varphi_m, \varphi_1)\alpha_m = (V, \varphi_1), \\ (\varphi_1, \varphi_2)\alpha_1 + (\varphi_2, \varphi_2)\alpha_2 + \cdots + (\varphi_m, \varphi_2)\alpha_m = (V, \varphi_2), \\ \cdots \cdots \cdots \cdots \cdots \cdots \cdots \cdots \cdots \cdots \cdots \cdots \\ (\varphi_1, \varphi_m)\alpha_1 + (\varphi_2, \varphi_m)\alpha_2 + \cdots + (\varphi_m, \varphi_m)\alpha_m = (V, \varphi_n); \end{array}\right\} \quad (3.149)$$

here the scalar product (φ, ψ) of two vectors φ and ψ is given by the formula

$$(\varphi, \psi) = \iiint_\Omega (\varphi_x \psi_x + \varphi_y \psi_y + \varphi_z \psi_z) \, dx \, dy \, dz.$$

If Neumann's problem with boundary condition

$$\left. \frac{\partial u}{\partial v} \right|_S = 0$$

is stated for Eq. (3.147), we take, for T, the operator $Tu = \operatorname{grad} u$, this time defined on all scalar functions $u(x, y, z)$ for which $\operatorname{grad} u \in L_2(\Omega)$, i.e., on all functions for which

$$\iiint_\Omega (\operatorname{grad} u)^2 \, dx \, dy \, dz < \infty;$$

---

* We should note that system (3.149) is applicable whenever the method of orthogonal projections is used, and not only to Problem (3.148), (3.62).

these functions are subject to no boundary conditions. Here it turns out that $T^*\mathbf{v} = - \text{div } \mathbf{v}$, where the vector $\mathbf{v}$ must satisfy the condition that its normal component be equal to zero on the boundary S: $v_\nu|_S = 0$. We now proceed as in the Dirichlet problem, with the difference that the coordinate vectors $\boldsymbol{\varphi}_k$ must satisfy the boundary condition $\boldsymbol{\varphi}_{k\nu}|_S = 0$; this circumstance causes certain difficulties in applying the method of orthogonal projections to Neumann's problem. The fact that Eq. (3.147) contains three independent variables is not important.

In application to fundamental problems in the theory of elasticity, the method of orthogonal projections leads to the well-known Castigliano principle.

EXAMPLE 14: We will use the method of orthogonal projections to solve Problem (3.71)–(3.72). Set grad $u = \mathbf{v}$, where $\mathbf{v}$ is a two-dimensional vector with components $v_x = -\dfrac{\partial u}{\partial x}$, $v_y = -\dfrac{\partial u}{\partial y}$. Equation (3.72) takes the form

$$\text{div } v = 1.$$

It is easy to construct a vector $\mathbf{V}$ satisfying this last equation, for it is sufficient, for example, to set $V_x = x$, $V_y = 0$. We now select a complete system of vectors $\boldsymbol{\varphi}_n$ that satisfies the equation div $\boldsymbol{\varphi}_n = 0$. Such a system can be constructed by choosing the components of $\boldsymbol{\varphi}_n$ to be products of powers of x and y, but, in so doing, we must recall that we will not need all such vectors. The fact is that a function $u(x, y)$ providing a solution to Problem (3.71)–(3.72) is even with respect to both x and y, so the component $v_x = -\partial u/\partial x$ must be odd with respect to x and even with respect to y, while the component $v_y = -\partial u/\partial y$ must be odd with respect to y and even with respect to x. The components of the vector $\mathbf{v} = \mathbf{V} - \mathbf{v}$ must satisfy the same conditions. Since the vectors $\mathbf{w}_n$ are necessary only for approximation of the vector $\mathbf{w}$, we can subject them to the same evenness conditions and set

$$\boldsymbol{\varphi}_1 = (x, -y), \quad \boldsymbol{\varphi}_2 = (x^3, -3x^2y), \quad \boldsymbol{\varphi}_3 = (3xy^2, -y^3), \ldots$$

Limiting the discussion to the terms we have written, we set

$$\mathbf{w} \approx \mathbf{w}_3 = \alpha_1\boldsymbol{\varphi}_1 + \alpha_2\boldsymbol{\varphi}_2 + \alpha_3\boldsymbol{\varphi}_3$$

or, in more detail,

$$w_x \approx w_{3x} = \alpha_1 x + \alpha_2 x^3 + 3\alpha_3 xy^2,$$
$$w_y \approx w_{3y} = -\alpha_1 y - 3\alpha_2 x^2 y - \alpha_3 y^3.$$

The coefficients α_1, α_2, and α_3 must be determined from system (3.149), which, in this case, takes the form

$$\tfrac{8}{3}\alpha_1 + \tfrac{32}{15}\alpha_2 + \tfrac{32}{15}\alpha_3 = \tfrac{4}{3},$$
$$\tfrac{32}{15}\alpha_1 + \tfrac{104}{35}\alpha_2 + \tfrac{8}{5}\alpha_3 = \tfrac{4}{5},$$
$$\tfrac{32}{15}\alpha_1 + \tfrac{8}{5}\alpha_2 + \tfrac{104}{35}\alpha_3 = \tfrac{4}{3}.$$

It follows that $\alpha_1 = 0.5000$, $\alpha_2 = -\frac{7}{36} \approx 0.1944$, $\alpha_3 = \frac{7}{36} \approx 0.1944$, and, consequently,

$$w_3 = 0.5000\varphi_1 - 0.1944\varphi_2 + 0.1944\varphi_3.$$

The approximate solution given by the method of orthogonal projections is of the form

$$v_{3x} = x - (0.5000x - 0.1944x^3 + 0.5832xy^2),$$

$$v_{3y} = -(0.5000y - 0.5832xy^2 + 0.1944y^3).$$

Given this solution, we can estimate the error in the approximate solution (3.73) obtained with the energy method. In Formula (3.145), which provides an error estimate, the quantity $F(u_3)$ can be computed with Formula (3.141); for $\|v_3\|^2$, we can use the same method to obtain the analogous formula

$$\|v_3\|^2 = \|\mathbf{V}\|^2 - \sum_{k=1}^{3} \alpha_k(\mathbf{V}, \varphi_k).$$

By carrying out the necessary computations, we find that

$$F(u)_2 = -0.5616, \quad \|\mathbf{v}_2\|^2 = 0.5630$$

and, consequently,

$$|u - u_2| \leqslant \sqrt{0.5630 - 0.5616} = \sqrt{0.0014} = 0.0374,$$

which yields a relative error in energy of the order of 6%.

In virtue of Formula (3.146), the same quantity 0.0374 yields an upper bound for the error in the approximate solution v_3 given by the method of orthogonal projections.

If we take

$$\tilde{\mathbf{v}} = \tfrac{1}{2}(-\operatorname{grad} u_3 + \mathbf{v}_3)$$

for the approximate value of the vector $\mathbf{v} = -\operatorname{grad} u$, then, by Formula (3.147), we have the exact equation

$$\|\mathbf{v} - \tilde{\mathbf{v}}\| = \tfrac{1}{2}\sqrt{0.0014} = 0.0187.$$

5.4 Trefftz' method. In a region Ω, assume that it is required to integrate the linear differential equation

$$Lu = f(x) \qquad (3.150)$$

under certain, say, homogeneous, boundary conditions

$$G_k u|_S = 0 \qquad (k = 1, 2, \ldots, r),$$

and assume that an operator A coinciding with L on the set of functions satisfying these boundary conditions is positive definite.

In order to state Trefftz' method, we must first introduce the notions of bilinear and homogeneous quadratic functionals. A functional $\Phi(u, v)$ that depends on two variables u and v is said to be *bilinear* if it is linear with respect to each of the variables u and v separately, i.e., if for all constants a_1 and a_2 we have the equations

$$\Phi(a_1 u_1 + a_2 u_2, v) = a_1 \Phi(u_1, v) + a_2 \Phi(u_2, v),$$

$$\Phi(u, a_1 v_1 + a_2 v_2) = a_1 \Phi(u, v_1) + a_2 \Phi(u, v_2).$$

A *homogeneous quadratic functional* is obtained from a bilinear quadratic functional if we set $u = v$: $\Phi(v) = \Phi(v, v)$.

Let u_0 denote the solution to the problem stated at the beginning of Section 5.4. Trefftz' method consists in constructing some nonnegative homogeneous quadratic functional Φ that is defined on the solutions of Eq. (3.150) and, on these solutions, satisfies the inequality $\Phi(v) \geqslant \Phi(u_0)$ and the equation $\Phi(u_0) = |u_0|^2$. As soon as this functional is stated, we consider the problem of finding the solution of Eq. (3.150) that minimizes this functional on the set of all possible solutions of this equation. If we have some particular solution of Eq. (3.150) at our disposal, along with the complete system of linearly independent solutions of the homogeneous equation $Lp = 0$, the problem of minimizing $\Phi(v)$ can be solved by means of the Ritz method; here the above-noted solutions of the homogeneous equation are taken for the coordinate functions.

A general method for constructing "Trefftz' functional" can be given (see the bibliographic comments at the end of this chapter); here we will limit the discussion to giving these functionals for several simple problems.

1. For the problem of integrating the Poisson equation $-\Delta u = f(x)$ under the boundary conditions

$$u|_{S_1} = 0, \quad \left[\frac{\partial u}{\partial v} + \sigma u\right]_{S_2} = 0, \sigma \geqslant \sigma_0 = \text{const}, S_1 + S_2 = S,$$

we can take

$$\Phi(v) = \int_\Omega (\text{grad } v)^2 \, dx + \int_S \tilde{\sigma} v^2 \, dS + \int_{S_2} \frac{1}{\sigma - \tilde{\sigma}} \left(\frac{\partial v}{\partial v} + \tilde{\sigma} v\right)^2 dS, \quad (3.151')$$

where $\tilde{\sigma}$ is any function that satisfies the inequality $0 \leqslant \tilde{\sigma} \leqslant \sigma$,

In the case of the Dirichlet problem the surface S_2 is absent and we can take

$$\Phi(v) = \int_\Omega (\text{grad } v)^2 \, dx + \int_S \tilde{\sigma} v^2 \, ds, \quad (3.151'')$$

where $\tilde{\sigma}$ is any nonnegative function; in particular, we can set $\tilde{\sigma} = 0$.

In the case of Neumann's problem we can take

$$\Phi(v) = \int_\Omega (\text{grad })v^2 \, dx - \alpha \int_S v^2 \, ds + \frac{1}{\alpha} \int_S \left(\frac{\partial v}{\partial v} - \alpha v\right)^2 ds, \quad (3.151''')$$

where α is a sufficiently small constant. Functional (3.151) must be minimized over the solutions of the Poisson equation $-\Delta v = f(x)$.

2. Consider the equation for bending of a plate,

$$\Delta^2 w = \frac{\partial^4 w}{\partial x^4} + 2\frac{\partial^4 w}{\partial x^2 \partial y^2} + \frac{\partial^4 w}{\partial y^4} = f(x, y), \qquad (3.152)$$

under the boundary conditions $w|_S = 0$, $\partial w/\partial \nu |_S = 0$. In this case the functional Φ has the extremely simple form

$$\Phi(v) = \iint_\Omega (\Delta v)^2 \, dx \, dy, \qquad (2.153')$$

where Ω is the region covered by the plate and $v(x, y)$ is any solution of Eq. (3.152). This functional can be simplified even more by setting $\Delta v = q(x, y)$. Then the problem reduces to minimizing the functional

$$\Phi_1(q) = \iint_\Omega q^2 \, dx \, dy \qquad (3.153'')$$

over the set of solutions of the equation $\Delta q = f(x, y)$.

3. In the case of a freely supported plate, the Trefftz functional has a different form, depending on whether or not the contour S of the plate is convex or contains nonconvex regions. If the contour is convex, we can set

$$\Phi(v) = \iint_\Omega \left\{ \left(\frac{\partial^2 v}{\partial x^2}\right)^2 + 2\left(\frac{\partial^2 v}{\partial x \partial y}\right)^2 + \left(\frac{\partial^2 v}{\partial y^2}\right)^2 \right\} dx \, dy$$

$$+ \frac{1}{\sigma} \int_S \rho \left[\Delta v - \left(\frac{\partial^2 v}{\partial s^2} + \frac{1}{\rho}\frac{\partial v}{\partial \nu}\right)^2 \right] ds. \qquad (3.153''')$$

Here σ is the Poisson constant, ρ is the radius of curvature of the contour, and s is its arc length. If the contour contains nonconvex sections, we can set

$$\Phi(v) = \iint_\Omega \left\{ \left(\frac{\partial^2 v}{\partial x^2}\right)^2 + 2\sigma \frac{\partial^2 v}{\partial x^2}\frac{\partial^2 v}{\partial y^2} + \left(\frac{\partial^2 v}{\partial y^2}\right)^2 \right.$$

$$+ 2(1 - \sigma)\left(\frac{\partial^2 v}{\partial x \partial y}\right)^2 \right\} dx \, dy + \int_S \left\{ \beta v^2 - \alpha\left(\frac{\partial v}{\partial \nu}\right)^2 \right.$$

$$+ \frac{1}{\alpha}\left[\Delta v - (1 - \sigma)\left(\frac{\partial^2 v}{\partial s^2} + \frac{1}{\rho}\frac{\partial v}{\partial \nu}\right)\right]^2 \right\} ds. \qquad (3.153^{IV})$$

Here α and β are positive constants and α is sufficiently small.

Functionals (3.153) must be minimized over the set of solutions of Eq. (3.152).

We will now consider minimizing the Trefftz' functional $\Phi(v)$ in more detail. Let ψ be some particular solution of Eq. (3.150), and let p be an arbitrary solution of the homogeneous equation $Lp = 0$. Any solution of Eq. (3.150) can be represented in the form $v = \psi + p$. As we know, under certain very general conditions, the solution of the equation $Lp = 0$ is square summable in a given finite region Ω and forms some subspace in $L_2(\Omega)$. Assume that a sequence $\{p_n(x)\}$ of members of this subspace (in other words, solutions of the homogeneous equation that are square summable in Ω) is complete in it, and assume that the functions $p_n(x)$ are such that the functional Φ vanishes on no linear combination of them if the coefficients of the linear combination are not all simultaneously equal to zero. We take the functions $p_n(x)$ for coordinate functions, and we attempt to find an approximate solution to the problem of minimizing $\Phi(v)$ in the form

$$v_m(x) = \psi(x) + \sum_{k=1}^{m} \alpha_k p_k(x);$$

the coefficients α_k are determined from the linear system

$$\sum_{k=1}^{m} \Phi(p_k, p_j)\alpha_k = -\Phi(\psi, p_j) \quad (j = 1, 2, \ldots, m), \qquad (3.154)$$

which has a unique solution. It is clear that $\Phi(v_m) \geqslant \Phi(u_0)$, so we can set $\delta = -\Phi(v_m)$ in Formula (3.62) and obtain a new error estimate for the approximate solution given by the energy method:

$$|u_0 - u_n| \leqslant \sqrt{F(u_n) + \Phi(v_m)}. \qquad (3.155)$$

If the functional Φ is also defined on the solutions of the homogeneous equation $Lp = 0$, the formula

$$\sqrt{\Phi(u_0 - v_m)} \leqslant \sqrt{F(u_n) + \Phi(v_m)} \qquad (3.155')$$

yields some idea of the error of the approximate solution v_m given by Trefftz' method.

Concerning the convergence of the Trefftz method, see [63].

EXAMPLE 15: Consider the problem of the bending of a square rod, which we have already discussed in Sections 3.4 and 5.3. The solutions of the equation $-\Delta v = 1$ are of the form $v = -\dfrac{x^2}{2} + p(x, y)$, where p is a harmonic function. We choose a Trefftz functional in the form (3.151''), and set $\sigma \equiv 0$; the problem now reduces to constructing a function $p(x, y)$ that is harmonic in the square $-1 \leqslant x, y \leqslant 1$, and minimizes the integral

$$\Phi(v) = \int_{-1}^{1} \int_{-1}^{1} \left(\mathrm{grad}\left(p(x, y) - \frac{x^2}{2} \right) \right)^2 dx\, dy$$

$$= \int_{-1}^{1} \int_{-1}^{1} \left[\left(\frac{\partial p}{\partial x} - x \right)^2 + \left(\frac{\partial p}{\partial y} \right)^2 \right] dx\, dy.$$

It can be shown that the system of harmonic functions

$$\frac{\cos}{\sin}\frac{(2m-1)\pi x}{2}\frac{\cosh}{\sinh}\frac{(2m-1)\pi y}{2} \qquad (m = 1, 2, \ldots)$$

satisfies the requirements listed above. In virtue of the symmetry properties of the desired solution, it is sufficient to take

$$p_m(x, y) = \cos\frac{(2m-1)\pi x}{2}\cosh\frac{(2m-1)\pi x}{2} \qquad (m = 1, 2, \ldots)$$

for the coordinate functions. It is not difficult to show that the functions p_m satisfy an "orthogonality" relation:

$$\Phi(p_k, p_m) = \int_{-1}^{1}\int_{-1}^{1}\left(\frac{\partial p_k}{\partial x}\frac{\partial p_m}{\partial x} + \frac{\partial p_k}{\partial y}\frac{\partial p_m}{\partial y}\right) dx\, dy = 0, \quad k \neq m.$$

As a result, the only terms remaining on the left of the jth equation of system (3.154) contain a_j, and this quantity is easily calculated:

$$a_j = \frac{(-1)^j \cdot 16}{(2j-1)^3\pi^3 \cosh\dfrac{(2j-1)\pi}{2}}.$$

By using the same "orthogonality" relationship, we can easily show that

$$\Phi(v_m) = \frac{4}{3} - \frac{256}{\pi^5}\sum_{k=1}^{m}\frac{\tanh\dfrac{2k-1}{2}\pi}{(2k-1)^5}.$$

The terms of this last sum decrease rather rapidly and can be limited to a small value of m. Taking $m = 3$, we find that $\Phi(v_3) = 0.5620$. Above (see Section 5.3) we found $F(u_2) = -0.5616$; Formula (3.154) now yields

$$|u_0 - u_2| \leqslant \sqrt{0.5620 - 0.5616} = 0.02.$$

Thus, solution (3.73) is more accurate than the estimate of Section 5.3 implies.

EXAMPLE 16: Consider the problem of the bending of an elastic square plate covering the region $-1 \leqslant x, y \leqslant 1$, rigidly fixed at its edge, and under the influence of a uniformly distributed normal load. When the units of measurement are appropriately chosen, the problem reduces to integration of the equation

$$\frac{\partial^4 w}{\partial x^4} + 2\frac{\partial^4 w}{\partial x^2\,\partial y^2} + \frac{\partial^4 w}{\partial y^4} = 1$$

under the boundary conditions

$$w(x, \pm1) = w(\pm1, y) = w_x(\pm1, y) = w_y(x, \pm1) = 0.$$

If we use the energy method to solve this problem, we must approximately compute a function that satisfies the boundary conditions just formulated and minimizes the integral

$$F(w) = \int_{-1}^{1}\int_{-1}^{1}[(\Delta w)^2 - 2w] \, dx \, dy.$$

We choose coordinate functions in the form

$$(x^2 - 1)^2(y^2 - 1)^2(x^{2k}y^{2m} + x^{2m}y^{2k}) \qquad (k, m = 0, 1, 2, \ldots);$$

this type of coordinate function takes the symmetry of the problem into account. Limiting the discussion to the first two functions, we can write an approximate solution in the form

$$w_2 = (x^2 - 1)^2(y^2 - 1)^2[a_1 + a_2(x^2 + y^2)].$$

In our case system (3.24) takes the form

$$\tfrac{18}{7}a_1 + \tfrac{36}{77}a_2 = \tfrac{7}{128},$$

$$\tfrac{36}{77}a_1 + \tfrac{96}{91}a_2 = \tfrac{1}{64}.$$

By solving this system, we find that

$$w_2 = (x^2 - 1)^2(y^2 - 1)^2[0.02067 + 0.0038(x^2 + y^2)].$$

The corresponding value of F is $F(w_2) = -0.02486$.

We will now use Trefftz' method to find an approximate solution, for which we must know the solutions of the equation $\Delta q = 1$; these solutions can be written in the form $q(x, y) = \dfrac{x^2 + y^2}{4} + p(x, y)$, where $\Delta p = 0$. For the coordinate functions we take harmonic polynomials that account for the symmetry of the problem and are orthonormal in the square under discussion. The first three of them are

$$p_1(x, y) = \tfrac{1}{2}, \quad p_2(x, y) = \tfrac{1}{2}\sqrt{\tfrac{7}{13}}[\tfrac{1}{2} + \tfrac{15}{8}(x^4 - 6x^2y^2 + y^4)],$$

$$p_3(x, y) = 0.356359(p_1 - \sqrt{\tfrac{7}{13}} \cdot 4.76724p_2 - 1.40625N_3),$$

where

$$N_3 = x_8 - 28x^6y^2 + 70x^4y^4 - 28x^2y^6 + y^8.$$

We will attempt to find an approximate solution of the problem of minimizing functional (3.153″) in the form

$$q_3 = \frac{x^2 + y^2}{4} + \alpha_1 p_1(x, y) + \alpha_2 p_2(x, y) + \alpha_3 p_3(x, y).$$

Because the polynomials p_k are orthonormal, system (3.154), in which Φ_1 must be substituted for Φ, takes the particularly simple form

$$a_1 = \tfrac{1}{3}, \quad a_2 = -0.1397, \quad a_3 = 0.0014.$$

Without determining the function v_3 (which is associated with difficult computations), we can nonetheless assert that $\Phi(v_3) = \Phi_1(q_3) = 0.02491$. Now, by Formula (3.155),

$$|w_0 - w_2| \leqslant \sqrt{0.02491 - 0.02486} = 0.0071,$$

where w_0 is the exact solution of the problem. Because we have an estimate in the energy norm, we can estimate the difference $w_0 - w_2$ (see [63]); this estimate is of the form $|w_0 - w_2| \leqslant 0.005$.

5.5 Two-sided functional estimates.

Very often it is important to find not only the solution of the equation $Au_0 = f$, but some functional of the form (u_0, g), where g is a given element in the Hilbert space under discussion. The simplest and crudest method of doing this consists in finding an approximate solution u_n of the given equation and setting

$$(u_0, g) \approx (u_n, g). \tag{3.156}$$

The error of this approximation is given by the formula

$$|(u_0, g) - (u_n, g)| \leqslant \|g\| \, \|u_0 - u_n\|.$$

If A is positive definite and $u_n \in H_A$, the quantity $\|u_0 - u_n\|$ can be estimated by using the method of orthogonal projections or the Trefftz method. Generally speaking, approximate solutions, more accurate than Formula (3.156), can be constructed. We can, for example, set

$$(u_0, g) \approx b_n = (u_n, g) + (f - f_n, v_n), \tag{3.156'}$$

where $f_n = Au_n$ and v_n is an approximate solution of the equation $Av_0 = g$. The error of Formula (3.156') is given by the inequality

$$|(u_0, g) - b_n| \leqslant |u_0 - u_n| \cdot |v_0 - v_n|. \tag{3.156''}$$

The right-hand side of Formula (3.156'') can be estimated by the method of orthogonal projections or the Trefftz method.

One more approximate formula can be constructed in the following manner. Let, as in Section 5.2, $A = T^*T$. Now, let u and v be arbitrary members of the domain of existence of the operator T, and let u' and v' be arbitrary solutions of the equations $T^*u' = f$ and $T^*v' = g$. Set

$$\alpha = (u, g) + (v, f) - (Tu, Tv), \qquad \beta = (u', v').$$

The error of the approximate equation

$$(u_0, g) \approx \tfrac{1}{2}(\alpha + \beta)$$

is no greater than

$$\tfrac{1}{2}\|Tu - u'\| \, \|Tv - v'\|.$$

5.6 Two-sided eigenvalue estimates. The energy method provides an over-sized approximate value for the eigenvalues of a positive-definite operator. The important problem of determining undersized approximate values cannot yet be assumed to be satisfactorily solved. Here we will present two methods of solving this problem, although each has a rather limited field of application.

1. Assume that we are given a positive-definite differential operator. If we know its Green's function $G(x, y)$, its eigenvalues coincide with the characteristic roots of the integral equation

$$u(x) - \lambda \int_\Omega G(x, y)u(y)\, dy = 0. \tag{3.157}$$

Because it is Green's function of a positive-definite operator, $G(x, y)$ is symmetric. We also assume that the "double" integral

$$\int_\Omega \int_\Omega |G(x, y)|^2\, dx\, dy$$

is finite. Let $G_m(x, y)$ denote the mth iterated kernel of Eq. (3.157), and let a_m denote the trace of this kernel:

$$a_m = \int_\Omega G_m(x, x)\, dx.$$

If the smallest characteristic root λ_1 has multiplicity p, we have the approximate equation*

$$\lambda_1 \approx {}^{2m}\!\!\sqrt{\frac{p}{a_{2m}}}, \tag{3.158}$$

which yields an undersized value of λ_1.

For $m \to \infty$, we have the exact equation

$$\lambda_1 = \lim_{m \to \infty} \frac{1}{{}^{2m}\!\!\sqrt{a_{2m}}}.$$

When m is sufficiently large, therefore, the error of Formula (3.158) is arbitrarily small. If the characteristic roots λ_1 and λ_2 of Eq. (3.157) are both simple and an exact or oversized value of λ_1 is available, the formula

$$\lambda_2 \approx \frac{1}{\lambda_1} {}^{2m}\!\!\sqrt{\frac{2}{a_{2m}^2 - a_{4m}}}$$

yields an undersized value of λ_2. Analogous formulas can also be constructed for the case of multiple characteristic roots λ_1 and λ_2, as well as for subsequent characteristic roots.

---

* For more details concerning this, see Chapter IV of the present book, Section 1.5.

The above method yields a satisfactory result for certain types of differential equations, provided that it is relatively simple to construct Green's function and its iterations.

EXAMPLE 17: We return to Example 11. It is easy to construct Green's function of operator (2.123): when $x \leqslant y$, it is

$$G(x, y) = \frac{2(\sqrt{1 + x} - 1)(\sqrt{2} - \sqrt{1 + y})}{\sqrt{2} - 1};$$

its value for $x > y$ is obtained by exchanging x and y. The value of the second iterated kernel for $x \leqslant y$ is

$$G_2(x, y) = \frac{4}{3(3 - 2\sqrt{2})}\left\{(\sqrt{2} - \sqrt{1 + y})\left[(\sqrt{2} - 1)\left(-2 - x - \frac{x^2}{2}\right.\right.\right.$$
$$\left.\left. - 2\sqrt{1 + x} + x\sqrt{1 + x}\right) + 4(\sqrt{2} - \sqrt{1 + x})\right]$$
$$+ (\sqrt{1 + x} - 1)\left[(\sqrt{2} - 1)\left(2 + y + \frac{y^2}{2} + 2\sqrt{2}\sqrt{1 + y}\right.\right.$$
$$\left.\left.\left. - \sqrt{2}\,y\sqrt{1 + y}\right) - \frac{11}{2}(\sqrt{1 + y} - 1)\right]\right\};$$

for $x > y$, the value of $G_2(x, y)$ is again obtained by exchanging x and y. By the general rule for computing iterated kernels,

$$G_4(x, y) = \int_0^1 G_2(x, s)G_2(s, y)\, ds = \int_0^1 G_2(x, s)G_2(y, s)\, ds.$$

It follows that

$$a_4 = \int_0^1 G_4(x, x)\, dx = \int_0^1\int_0^1 G_2^2(x, s)\, dx\, ds = 2\int_0^1 ds\int_0^s G_2^2(x, s)\, dx$$
$$= 0.50092905 \cdot 10^{-4}.$$

It is well known that the eigenvalues of the first boundary-value problem for a second-order ordinary differential equation are simple. Thus $p = 1$, and by Formula (3.158),

$$\lambda_1 \geqslant \frac{1}{\sqrt[4]{a_4}} = 11.88655.$$

By Formula (3.124),

$$11.88655 \leqslant \lambda_1 \leqslant 12.12255.$$

The average of the two approximate values yields a new approximate value

$$\lambda_1 \approx 12.00455,$$

which has an error less than 1%.

2. Another method was developed for a special case by Weinstein, and extended to the general case by Aronszajn. A different exposition of what is essentially the same method was later given by Svirskiy. Here we will present only the latter variant, since it is simpler.

In addition to a given operator A, assume that we are given a smaller operator A_0 with domain of existence $D(A_0) \supset D(A)$, and suppose that we know all of the eigenvalues of A_0. If λ_n and $\lambda_n^{(0)}$ are the eigenvalues of A and A_0, respectively, then $\lambda_n \geqslant \lambda_n^{(0)}$, and we immediately obtain an undersized value of λ_n, although values obtained in this way are generally extremely crude. To refine them, we construct a sequence of operators $A_k (k = 1, 2, \ldots)$ such that $A_0 \leqslant A_1 \leqslant A_2 \leqslant \cdots \leqslant A$. For any k we have $\lambda_n^{(0)} \leqslant \lambda_n^{(k)} \leqslant \lambda_n$, where the $\lambda_n^{(k)}$ are the eigenvalues of A_k.

The operators A_k are constructed in the following manner. We set $A - A_0 = C$, where the operator C is nonnegative, and we select k elements $f_r \in D(A)$ satisfying the relations

$$(Cf_r, f_s) = \begin{cases} 0, & r \neq s, \\ 1, & r = s. \end{cases}$$

We can now set

$$A_k u = A_0 u + \sum_{r=1}^{k} (Cu, f_r)Cf_r.$$

It is desirable to construct operators A_k so that the inequality $\lambda_1^{(0)} \leqslant \lambda_1^{(k)}$ is strict, which occurs if, no matter what the characteristic element $\tilde{\varphi}$ (of the operator A_0) corresponding to the eigenvalue λ_0, there exists an f_r such that $(Cf_r, \tilde{\varphi}) \neq 0$. In turn, this occurs if k is larger than or equal to the multiplicity of the eigenvalue $\lambda_1^{(0)}$.

Certain lower bounds for the smallest eigenvalue can be obtained on the basis of the following considerations. Let A be a positive-definite operator with a discrete spectrum, and assume that u is an arbitrary element in the domain of existence of A such that $\|u\| = 1$. Now, set $(Au, u) = \eta$ and $\|Au - \eta u\|^2 = \|Au\|^2 - \eta^2 = \varepsilon^2$. It is known that then the interval $\eta - \varepsilon \leqslant \lambda \leqslant \eta + \varepsilon$ contains at least one eigenvalue of the operator A. We now assume that we have at least a crude estimate of the second eigenvalue $\lambda_2 > \beta$, and that $\eta + \varepsilon < \beta$. Then the first eigenvalue λ_1 lies in the interval $\eta - \varepsilon \leqslant \lambda_1 \leqslant \eta$ and, consequently, $\eta - \varepsilon$ is an undersized approximate value of λ_1.

If the eigenvalue λ_1 is simple (of multiplicity one), the following expression gives a generally more accurate undersized approximation of λ_1:

$$\lambda_1 \geqslant \eta - \frac{\varepsilon^2}{\beta - \eta}.$$

5.7 Solution errors due to errors in equations. To simplify a problem, a given equation $Au = f$ is frequently replaced by another equation $Bu = f$ that contains a simpler operator B. This leads to a certain error that can be estimated in the following manner.

Assume that both operators A and B are positive definite, and that the corresponding energy spaces H_A and H_B contain the same elements. Then there exist positive constants α_1 and α_2 such that

$$\alpha_1 |u|_B^2 \leqslant |u|_A^2 \leqslant \alpha_2 |u|_B^2 .$$

Now, let u_0 and u_1 satisfy the equations $Au_0 = f$ and $Bu_1 = f$. We have the inequality

$$|u_0 - u_1|_B \leqslant \eta |u_1|_B,$$

where

$$\eta = \text{Max} \left(\frac{|\alpha_1 - 1|}{\alpha_1}, \frac{|\alpha_2 - 1|}{\alpha_2} \right).$$

Slobodyanskiy [92] showed that the constant η can be reduced by substituting $u_2 = \frac{1}{2} \left(\frac{1}{\alpha_1} + \frac{1}{\alpha_2} \right) u_1$ for u_0. Then

$$|u_1 - u_2|_B \leqslant \frac{\alpha_2 - \alpha_1}{\alpha_2 + \alpha_1} |u_2|_B.$$

6. THE METHOD OF LEAST SQUARES

6.1 General comments. Let A be a linear operator defined in some Hilbert space; it is to be emphasized that the operator A is not assumed to be symmetric or positive definite. Now, assume that the equation

$$Au = f \qquad (3.159)$$

is solvable. Then an element u_0 that satisfies this equation, clearly will minimize the functional

$$\|Au - f\|^2. \qquad (3.160)$$

The method of least squares consists in replacing Eq. (3.159) by the variational problem of minimizing functional (3.160). This problem can be solved with the Ritz method. We choose a sequence of coordinate elements φ_n ($n = 1, 2, \ldots$) that belong to the domain of existence of A, and set

$$u_n = \sum_{k=1}^{n} a_k \varphi_n. \qquad (3.161)$$

Then we choose the constants a_k so that $\|Au_n - f\|^2$ is minimal. This leads to the following system of linear algebraic equations:

$$\left.\begin{array}{l}
(A\varphi_1, A\varphi_1)a_1 + (A\varphi_2, A\varphi_1)a_2 + \cdots + (A\varphi_n, A\varphi_1)a_n = (f, A\varphi_1), \\
(A\varphi_1, A\varphi_2)a_1 + (A\varphi_2, A\varphi_2)a_2 + \cdots + (A\varphi_n, A\varphi_2)a_n = (f, A\varphi_2), \\
\cdots \cdots \cdots \cdots \cdots \cdots \cdots \cdots \cdots \cdots \cdots \cdots \cdots \cdots \\
(A\varphi_1, A\varphi_n)a_1 + (A\varphi_2, A\varphi_n)a_2 + \cdots + (A\varphi_n, A\varphi_n)a_n = (f, A\varphi_n).
\end{array}\right\} \qquad (3.162)$$

Theorem 19. Assume that: 1. the sequence $A\varphi_n$ $(n = 1, 2, \ldots)$ is complete in the Hilbert space under discussion; 2. Eq. (3.159) is solvable; 3. there exists a bounded inverse operator A^{-1}, i.e., there exists a positive constant K such that for all $u \in D(A)$ we have

$$\|u\| \leqslant K \|Au\|. \tag{3.163}$$

Then system (3.162) has one and only one solution for all n, and if u_n is constructed with Formula (3.161) and u_0 is the exact solution of Eq. (3.159), then

$$\|u_0 - u_n\| \underset{n \to \infty}{\to} 0, \qquad \|Au_n - f\| \underset{n \to \infty}{\to} 0.$$

We have the inequality

$$\|u_0 - u_n\| \leqslant K \|Au_n - f\|, \tag{3.164}$$

which provides an estimate of the error in the method of least squares.

If A is positive definite, we have the inequality

$$|u_0 - u_n|_A \leqslant \sqrt{K} \|Au_n - f\|; \tag{3.165}$$

here the approximate solutions constructed with the method of least squares also converge in energy, but this convergence is slower than for approximate solutions constructed with the energy method with the same coordinate elements φ_k. The advantage of the method of least squares for this case consists in the fact that $Au_n \to f$, so that the *approximate solution approximately satisfies the given equation;* as we know, this relationship generally does not hold when u_n is constructed with the energy method.

In practice, it is desirable to use the following form of the method of least squares. Assume that the problem consists in finding one or more functions $u^{(1)}, u^{(2)}, \ldots, u^{(m)}$ that satisfy two systems of linear equations: a homogeneous system

$$L_j(u^{(1)}, u^{(2)}, \ldots, u^{(m)}) = 0 \quad (j = 1, 2, \ldots, m), \tag{3.166}$$

and an inhomogeneous system

$$G_j(u^{(1)}, u^{(2)}, \ldots, u^{(m)}) = f^{(j)} \quad (j = 1, 2, \ldots, m). \tag{3.167}$$

We will treat the sets $(u^{(1)}, u^{(2)}, \ldots, u^{(m)})$ and $(f^{(1)}, f^{(2)}, \ldots, f^{(m)})$ as members of some Hilbert space H, and it should be noted that there is a considerable amount of arbitrariness in the choice of this space, an arbitrariness that can be used to simplify and refine computations. The coordinate elements $\varphi_n = \{\varphi_n^{(1)}, \varphi_n^{(2)}, \ldots, \varphi_n^{(m)}\}$ $(n = 1, 2, \ldots)$ are chosen so that they satisfy the homogeneous system (3.166), and we set

$$u_n = \sum_{k=1}^{n} a_k \varphi_k$$

'or, more accurately,

$$u_n^{(j)} = \sum_{k=1}^{n} a_k \varphi_k^{(j)} \quad (j = 1, 2, \ldots, m),$$

where the coefficients a_k are determined from the condition $\|Gu_n - f\|^2 = $ min; G denotes the operator generated in H by the set of operators G_j.

6.2 Relationship to the energy method. Let A^* be the conjugate of A. If Eq. (3.159) is solvable and $f \in D(A^*)$, Eq. (3.159) is equivalent to the equation

$$A^*Au = A^*f. \tag{3.168}$$

Moreover, if inequality (3.163) is satisfied, the operator A^*A is positive definite:

$$(A^*Au) \geqslant K^{-2} \|u\|^2.$$

The solution of Eq. (3.168) minimizes the functional

$$(A^*Au, u) - 2(A^*f, u) = \|Au - f\|^2 - \|f\|^2,$$

which differs only in the constant term $-\|f\|^2$ from the functional $\|Au - f\|^2$. Under the conditions given above, therefore, the method of least squares for Eq. (3.159) coincides with the energy method for Eq. (3.168).

On the other hand, if the operator A is positive definite, the energy method for Eq. (3.159) coincides with the method of least squares for the equation

$$A^{1/2}u = A^{-1/2}f,$$

which is equivalent to Eq. (3.159).

6.3 Application to problems in the theory of potentials on a plane. Let D be a finite singly-connected region in the complex plane $z = x + iy$, and let S be the boundary of this region. We assume that S is sufficiently smooth, i.e., we assume that the angle between the normal to S and the x axis has at least $r + 2$ derivatives with respect to arc length, where r is defined below. Let $L_2(S)$ denote the *complex* Hilbert space of functions that are square summable along S, and let $L_2^{(r)}(S)$, $r > 0$, be the complex Hilbert space of functions that are continuous on S together with their derivatives of order up to $r - 1$ with respect to the complex coordinate of a variable point on the contour S, and have their (generalized) rth derivatives square summable along S. We define a scalar product and norm in $L_2^{(r)}(S)$ by means of the formulas

$$(\varphi, \psi)_r = \int_S [\varphi(z)\overline{\psi(z)} + \varphi^{(r)}(z)\overline{\psi^{(r)}(z)}] \, ds,$$

$$\|\varphi\|_r^2 = \int_S [|\varphi(z)|^2 + |\varphi^{(r)}(z)|^2] \, ds.$$

Here z is the complex coordinate of a variable point on the contour L and $ds = |dz|$. The scalar product and norm in $L_2(S)$ are given by the usual formulas,

$$(\varphi, \psi) = \int_S \varphi(z)\overline{\psi(z)} \, ds, \qquad \|\varphi\|^2 = \int_S |\varphi(z)|^2 \, ds.$$

The Dirichlet problem for the region D is stated as follows: Find a function $u(x, y)$ that is harmonic in D and coincides on S with a given real-valued function $f(z)$ defined on S. As we know, $u(x, y) = \text{Re } \{\omega(z)\}$, where $\omega(z)$ is a holomorphic (in D) function of the variable $z = x + iy$. The function $\omega(z)$ is defined up to a purely imaginary constant, which we normalize by placing the coordinate origin inside D and requiring that

$$\text{Im } \{\omega(0)\} = 0. \tag{3.169}$$

For the coordinate functions we take integral nonnegative powers of z, and accordingly attempt to find an approximate solution to this Dirichlet problem in the form of a polynomial

$$\omega_n(z) = u_n(x, y) + iv_n(x, y) = \sum_{k=1}^{n} a_k z^k$$

with complex coefficients $a_k = \alpha_k + i\beta_k$. To ensure that condition (3.169) is satisfied, we set $\beta_0 = 0$. We determine the coefficients $\alpha_0, \alpha_1, \ldots, \alpha_n$, $\beta_1, \ldots, \beta_n$ from the condition $\|u_n - f\|^2 = \min$, and system (3.162) now takes the following form ($\varphi_0 = 1$, $\varphi_k = \text{Re } (z^k)$, $\psi_k = \text{Im } (z^k)$):

$$\left.\begin{aligned}
&(\varphi_0, \varphi_0)\alpha_0 + (\varphi_1, \varphi_0)\alpha_1 + \cdots + (\varphi_n, \varphi_0)\alpha_n \\
&\quad - (\psi_0, \varphi_0)\beta_1 - (\psi_2, \varphi_0)\beta_2 - \cdots - (\psi_n, \varphi_0)\beta_n = (f, \varphi_0), \\[4pt]
&(\varphi_0, \varphi_1)\alpha_0 + (\varphi_1, \varphi_1)\alpha_1 + \cdots + (\varphi_n, \varphi_1)\alpha_n \\
&\quad - (\psi_1, \varphi_1)\beta_1 - (\psi_2, \varphi_1)\beta_2 - \cdots - (\psi_n, \varphi_1)\beta_n = (f, \varphi_1), \\[2pt]
&\cdots \cdots \cdots \cdots \cdots \cdots \cdots \cdots \cdots \cdots \cdots \cdots \cdots \\[2pt]
&(\varphi_0, \varphi_n)\alpha_0 + (\varphi_1, \varphi_n)\alpha_1 + \cdots + (\varphi_n, \varphi_n)\alpha_n \\
&\quad - (\psi_1, \varphi_n)\beta_1 - (\psi_2, \varphi_n)\beta_2 - \cdots - (\psi_n, \varphi_n)\beta_n = (f, \varphi_n), \\[4pt]
&(\varphi_0, \psi_1)\alpha_0 + (\varphi_1, \psi_1)\alpha_1 + \cdots + (\varphi_n, \psi_1)\alpha_n \\
&\quad - (\psi_1, \psi_1)\beta_1 - (\psi_2, \psi_1)\beta_2 - \cdots - (\psi_n, \psi_1)\beta_n = (f, \psi_1), \\[2pt]
&\cdots \cdots \cdots \cdots \cdots \cdots \cdots \cdots \cdots \cdots \cdots \cdots \cdots \\[2pt]
&(\varphi_0, \psi_n)\alpha_0 + (\varphi_1, \psi_n)\alpha_1 + \cdots + (\varphi_n, \psi_n)\alpha_n \\
&\quad - (\psi_1, \psi_n)\beta_1 - (\psi_2, \psi_n)\beta_2 - \cdots - (\psi_n, \psi_n)\beta_2 = (f, \psi_n).
\end{aligned}\right\} \tag{3.170}$$

If the coefficients satisfy system (3.170), then $\|u_n - f\| \to 0$ and $\omega_n(z) \to \omega(z)$ uniformly in any interior subregion of D; it thus follows, as we know, that in any interior subregion the derivatives $\omega_n^{(k)}(z)$ uniformly approach $\omega^{(k)}(z)$ for all k.

The coefficients a_k can also be determined from the condition $\|u_n - f\|_r^2 = \min$. This leads to a system of the form (3.170) in which all of the scalar products have index r. If the a_k satisfy such a system, then $\omega_n^{(k)}(z) \to \omega^{(k)}(z)$ uniformly in the closed region $\bar{D} = D + S$ when $0 \leqslant k \leqslant r - 1$.

Neumann's problem can be stated as a problem of constructing a function that is harmonic in D and has normal derivative on S coincident with a given real function $h(z)$; the problem is solvable if and only if

$$\int_S h(z)\, ds = 0.$$

In our case, the holomorphic (in D) function $\omega(z)$ is defined up to a constant term, which we normalize by means of the condition $\omega(0) = 0$. We write an approximate solution in the form

$$\omega_n(z) = u_n(x, y) + iv_n(x, y) = \sum_{k=1}^{n} a_k z^k, \qquad a_k = \alpha_k + i\beta_k$$

and we set

$$\rho_k(z) = \frac{\partial}{\partial v} \operatorname{Re}(z^k),$$

$$\sigma_k(z) = \frac{\partial}{\partial v} \operatorname{Im}(z^k);$$

where v is the exterior normal to S. If the coefficients a_k are determined from the condition $\left\| \dfrac{\partial u_n}{\partial v} - h(z) \right\|_r = \min$, we obtain the system

$$\left.
\begin{aligned}
&(\rho_1, \rho_1)_r \alpha_1 + (\rho_2, \rho_1)_r \alpha_2 + \cdots + (\rho_n, \rho_1)_r \alpha_n \\
&\quad - (\sigma_1, \rho_1)_r \beta_1 - (\sigma_2, \rho_1)_r \beta_2 - \cdots - (\sigma_n, \rho_1)_r \beta_n = (h, \rho_1)_r, \\
&\cdot \cdot \cdot \cdot \cdot \cdot \cdot \cdot \cdot \cdot \cdot \cdot \cdot \cdot \cdot \cdot \cdot \cdot \cdot \cdot \cdot \cdot \cdot \cdot \cdot \cdot \cdot \cdot \cdot \\
&(\rho_1, \rho_n)_r \alpha_1 + (\rho_2, \rho_n)_r \alpha_2 + \cdots + (\rho_n, \rho_n)_r \alpha_n \\
&\quad - (\sigma_1, \rho_n)_r \beta_1 - (\sigma_2, \rho_n)_r \beta_2 - \cdots - (\sigma_n, \rho_n)_r \beta_n = (h, \rho_n)_r, \\
&(\rho_1, \sigma_1)_r \alpha_1 + (\rho_2, \sigma_1)_r \alpha_2 + \cdots + (\rho_n, \sigma_1)_r \alpha_n \\
&\quad - (\sigma_1, \sigma_1)_r \beta_1 - (\sigma_2, \sigma_1)_r \beta_2 - \cdots - (\sigma_n, \sigma_1)_r \beta_n = (h, \sigma_1)_r, \\
&\cdot \cdot \cdot \cdot \cdot \cdot \cdot \cdot \cdot \cdot \cdot \cdot \cdot \cdot \cdot \cdot \cdot \cdot \cdot \cdot \cdot \cdot \cdot \cdot \cdot \cdot \cdot \cdot \\
&(\rho_1, \sigma_n)_r \alpha_1 + (\rho_2, \sigma_n)_r \alpha_2 + \cdots + (\rho_n, \sigma_n)_r \alpha_n \\
&\quad - (\sigma_1, \sigma_n)_r \beta_1 - (\sigma_2, \sigma_n)_r \beta_2 - \cdots - (\sigma_n, \sigma_n)_r \beta_n = (h, \sigma_n)_r.
\end{aligned}
\right\} \quad (3.171)$$

In particular, we can set $r = 0$, at which time the scalar product $(,)_r$ becomes the ordinary scalar product $(,)$.

If the coefficients α_k and β_k are obtained from system (3.171) then $\omega_n^{(k)}(z) \to \omega^{(k)}(z)$ uniformly in the closed region.

6.4 Application to plane problems in elasticity theory.

We will consider the case of displacements given on the boundary; the same technique, with slight modifications, also applies to the case of given stresses. We will assume that there are no body forces, that D is a finite, singly connected region, and that its contour S is sufficiently smooth. As we know, the problem reduces to finding functions $\varphi(z)$ and $\psi(z)$ that are homomorphic in D and, on S, satisfy the relationship

$$(3 - 4\sigma)\varphi(z) - \overline{z\varphi'(z)} - \overline{\psi(z)} = g(z),$$

where σ is the Poisson constant and $g(z)$ is a function given on the contour. The function $\varphi(z)$ is determined up to a constant term, which we normalize by the condition $\varphi(0) = 0$; as in Section 6.3, we locate the coordinate origin inside D. We will attempt to find approximate values of the functions $\varphi(z)$ and $\psi(z)$ in the form of polynomials

$$\varphi_n(z) = \sum_{k=1}^{n} a_k z^k, \qquad \psi(z) = \sum_{k=1}^{n} b_k z^k$$

and we require that

$$\|(3 - 4\sigma)\varphi(z) - \overline{z\varphi'(z)} - \overline{\psi(z)} - g(z)\|_r^2 = \min. \tag{3.172}$$

We thus obtain a system of equations for the unknown coefficients; we will present its structure. Notation:

$$a_k = \alpha_k + i\alpha_{n+k}, \quad b_k = \alpha_{2n+k+1} + i\alpha_{3n+k+2},$$

$$\Phi_{2k-1}(z) = z^{(k)}, \quad \Phi_{2k}(z) = iz^k, \quad 1 \leqslant k \leqslant n,$$

$$\Phi_m(z) \equiv 0, \quad m > 2n,$$

$$\Psi'_m(z) \equiv 0, \quad m \leqslant 2n,$$

$$\Psi'_{2k+2n+1}(z) = z^{(k)}, \quad \Psi'_{2k+2n+2}(z) = iz^k, \quad 0 \leqslant k \leqslant n,$$

$$g_k(z) = (3 - 4\sigma)\Phi_k(z) - z\overline{\Phi'_k(z)} - \overline{\Psi_k(z)}.$$

Condition (3.172) gives us the following system for the coefficients α_k:

$$\sum_{k=1}^{4n+2} \mathrm{Re}\,(g_k, g_j)\alpha_k = \mathrm{Re}\,(g, g_j) \qquad (j = 1, 2, \ldots, 4n + 2),$$

This system is solvable and has a unique solution. If $r \geqslant 2$, then

$$\varphi_n(z) \to \varphi(z), \qquad \varphi'_n(z) \to \varphi'(z) \quad \text{and} \quad \psi_n(z) \to \psi(z)$$

uniformly in the closed region. If $r < 2$, uniform convergence occurs in any closed subregion.

7. STABILITY OF THE RITZ METHOD

7.1 General comments. If the coordinate system satisfies the requirements given in Section 2.3, the approximate solution given by the Ritz method approaches the exact solution as the index increases. This is true if the approximate solution is computed without error, but in practice, as a rule, the situation is different: Usually, we can assume that only the coordinate elements are given exactly, and that the coefficients of the approximate solution are determined from the Ritz system, which is constructed and solved with some error. These errors, which we assume to be small, are not very important if the order of the Ritz system is small, i.e., if the Ritz method is used to find only a crude approximation; here any coordinate system satisfying the conditions given above can be used. If, however, it is desired to construct a more exact approximation, it is necessary to use higher-order Ritz systems, and here the errors accumulated during computation of the matrices of the Ritz systems and its columns of free terms, as well as in solving this system, can reach appreciable proportions whenever the coordinate system is chosen arbitrarily. This raises the problem of determining whether the Ritz method is stable with respect to this kind of small error. The fundamental results pertaining to this problem are discussed in the following paragraphs of the present section.

7.2 Minimal and strongly minimal systems. Consider a Hilbert space $\mathfrak{H}$. We will call a sequence (finite or infinite) of elements $\varphi_k \in \mathfrak{H}$ minimal in $\mathfrak{H}$ if elimination of any element from this space restricts the subspace spanned by the sequence.* The term "minimal system" is frequently used instead of "minimal sequence."

EXAMPLE 18:   A finite system of linearly independent elements is minimal: The fact that a member φ_1 of the sequence cannot be expressed as a linear combination of $\varphi_2, \varphi_3, \ldots, \varphi_n$ indicates that φ_1 does not belong to the subspace spanned by $\varphi_2, \varphi_3, \ldots, \varphi_n$; when we eliminate φ_1, we therefore contract the subspace spanned by the given elements.

EXAMPLE 19:   A finite system of linearly dependent elements is not minimal: If φ_1 can be expressed as a linear combination of $\varphi_2, \varphi_3, \ldots, \varphi_n$, then φ_1 belongs to the subspace spanned by $\varphi_2, \varphi_3, \ldots, \varphi_n$ and elimination of the element φ_1 does not contract the subspace in question.

EXAMPLE 20:   Any orthonormal system is minimal.

EXAMPLE 21:   In the space $\mathfrak{H} = L_2(0, 1)$ the system

$$x, \sin \pi x, \sin 2\pi x, \ldots, \sin n\pi x, \ldots$$

is not minimal. Indeed, if we eliminate x, we obtain the system

$$\sin \pi x, \sin 2\pi x, \ldots, \sin n\pi x, \ldots,$$

which is complete in $L_2(0, \pi)$; the subspace spanned by this complete system is, in virtue of completeness, $L_2(0, \pi)$, and the eliminated element x therefore does not restrict the subspace.

---

* The definition of a minimal sequence also holds when the Hilbert space is replaced by any Banach Space.

EXAMPLE 22: The sequence $\{x^k\}$ $(k = 0, 1, 2, \ldots)$ is not minimal in $L_2(0, 1)$. This follows from Müntz' theorem that states that any system of functions of the form x^{μ_k} $(= 0, 1, 2, \ldots)$, $\mu = 0$, is complete in $L_2(0, 1)$ if the series

$$\sum_{k=1}^{\infty} \frac{1}{\mu_k}.$$

diverges.

A system $\{\varphi_k\}$ is minimal in a given space $\mathfrak{H}$ if, and only if, this space contains a system $\{\psi_k\}$ that is biorthogonal to the system $\{\varphi_k\}$ and such that

$$(\varphi_j, \psi_k)_{\mathfrak{H}} = \begin{cases} 0, & j \neq k, \\ 1, & j = k. \end{cases} \tag{3.173}$$

Any basis of a space $\mathfrak{H}$ is minimal in this space.

An infinite system $\{\varphi_k\}$, $\varphi_k \in \mathfrak{H}$ is said to be strongly minimal in $\mathfrak{H}$ if the smallest eigenvalue of the matrix

$$R_n = ||(\varphi_j, \varphi_k)|_{\mathfrak{H}}|_{j,k=1}^{j,k=n} \tag{3.174}$$

is bounded below by a positive number that is independent of n. Any system that is strongly minimal in some space is minimal.

Any orthonormal system in a space $\mathfrak{H}$ is strongly minimal. In this case all of the eigenvalues of R_n are equal to one for all n.

Theorem 20. Let A and B be operators that are self-adjoint and positive definite in some Hilbert space H, and assume that every member of H_A belongs to H_B. If $\varphi_k \in H_A$ $(k = 1, 2, \ldots)$ and the system $\{\varphi_k\}$ is minimal (strongly minimal) in H_B, then it is minimal (strongly minimal) in H_A.

Corollary 1. Under the conditions of Theorem 20, a system that is orthonormal in H_B is strongly minimal in H_A.

Corollary 2. If A is a positive definite operator, a system that is minimal (strongly minimal) in H is also minimal (strongly minimal) in H_A. In particular, a system that is orthonormal in H is strongly minimal in H_A.

7.3 Limit properties of the Ritz coefficients. In the formula (see Section 2.3)

$$u_n = \sum_{k=1}^{n} a_k \varphi_k,$$

which expresses the nth approximate solution given by the Ritz method, the coefficients a_k do, in fact, depend on n; accordingly, we will denote these coefficients by $a_k^{(n)}$ and write

$$u_n = \sum_{k=1}^{n} a_k^{(n)} \varphi_k. \tag{3.175}$$

Theorem 21. If a coordinate system is minimal in H_A, then the limits

$$a_k = \lim_{n \to \infty} a_k^{(n)} \tag{3.176}$$

exist. Moreover, if a system that is biorthogonal in H_A to a coordinate system is bounded in the metric of H_A, the convergence of Formula (3.176) is uniform with respect to k.

Theorem 22. Assume that a coordinate system is strongly minimal in H_A, and let a_k $(k = 1, 2, \ldots)$ be the limits of (3.176). The series

$$\sum_{k=1}^{\infty} |a_k|^2$$

converges, so that the sequence

$$a = (a_1, a_2, \ldots, a_n, a_{n+1}, \ldots)$$

is a member of l_2; if we set

$$a^{(n)} = (a_1^{(n)}, a_2^{(n)}, \ldots, a_n^{(n)}, 0, 0, \ldots),$$

we find that

$$\lim_{n \to \infty} \|a^{(n)} - a\|_{l_2} = 0.$$

The last inequality implies that

$$\lim_{n \to \infty} \left\{ \sum_{k=1}^{n} |a_k^{(n)} - a_k|^2 + \sum_{k=n+1}^{\infty} |a_k|^2 \right\} = 0.$$

7.4 Stability of the Ritz method. We assume that when the Ritz system (3.124) is written, each energy product $[\varphi_k, \varphi_j]$ is computed with some small error $\gamma_{kj} = \bar{\gamma}_{jk}$, and that the constant terms (f, φ_j) of this system are also computed with some small error δ_j. Instead of system (3.124), we obtain

$$\sum_{k=1}^{n} \{[\varphi_k, \varphi_j] + \gamma_{kj}\} a_k^{(n)'} = (f, \varphi_j) + \delta_j \qquad (j = 1, 2, \ldots, n). \tag{3.177}$$

Notation: $a^{(n)}$, $a^{(n)'}$, and $\delta^{(n)}$ are the vectors whose components are equal, respectively, to

$$a_1^{(n)}, \quad a_2^{(n)}, \ldots, a_n^{(n)};$$
$$a_1^{(n)'}, \quad a_2^{(n)'}, \ldots, a_n^{(n)'};$$
$$\delta_1, \quad \delta_2, \quad \ldots, \delta_n;$$

Γ_n is the matrix with entries γ_{kj} $(j, k = 1, 2, \ldots, n)$. In an n-dimensional unitary space, the matrix Γ_n defines an operator whose norm we will denote by $\|\Gamma_n\|$; as we know,*

$$\|\Gamma_n\|^2 \leqslant \sum_{j,k=1}^{n} |\gamma_{kj}|^2.$$

* In the terminology of [94], the quantity $\|\Gamma_n\|$ is the "third norm" of the matrix Γ_n.

We will say that a Ritz system is stable with respect to small variations in its matrix and column of free terms if there exist constants q and p that do not depend on n and are such that for small $\|\Gamma_n\|$ and $\|\delta^{(n)}\|$ we have the estimate

$$\|a^{(n)\prime} - a^{(n)}\| \leqslant p \|\Gamma_n\| + q \|\delta^{(n)}\|;$$

recall that the norm of any vector $t = (t_1, t_2, \ldots, t_n)$ in an n-dimensional unitary space is given by the formula

$$\|t\|^2 = \sum_{k=1}^{n} |t_k|^2.$$

Assume that the coordinate system is strongly minimal in H_A, and let $\tilde{\lambda} > 0$ be the lower bound of the eigenvalues of the Ritz matrix.

If the error γ_{kj} is so small that $\|\Gamma_n\| \leqslant \tilde{\lambda}\beta$, $\beta < 1$, then

$$\|a^{(n)\prime} - a^{(n)}\| \leqslant \frac{\tilde{\lambda}^{-3/2} |u_0| \|\Gamma_n\| + \tilde{\lambda}^{-1} \|\delta^{(n)}\|}{1 - \beta}. \tag{3.178}$$

Estimate (3.178) implies that the following theorem holds:

Theorem 23. *If the coordinate system is strongly minimal in H_A, the solution of the Ritz system is stable with respect to small variations in its matrix and column of free terms.*

Theorem 24 [109]. If the coordinate system is strongly minimal in H_A, the approximate solution given by the Ritz method is stable with respect to small variations in the matrix of the Ritz system and its column of free terms.

The assertion of this theorem can be clarified in the following manner. Let

$$u_n' = \sum_{k=1}^{n} a_k^{(n)\prime} \varphi_k,$$

where the coefficients $a_k^{(n)\prime}$ satisfy system (3.177). If the coordinate system is strongly minimal in H_A and $\|\Gamma_n\|$ and $\|\delta^{(n)}\|$ are sufficiently small, there exist constants p_1 and q_1 that do not depend on n and are such that $|u_n' - u_n| \leqslant p_1 \|\Gamma_n\| + q_1 \|\delta^{(n)}\|$.

EXAMPLE 23 [62]:   We consider an elastic plate in the form of an annular sector; the quantities characterizing the dimensions of the plate are shown in Fig. 16. The plate is subjected to a real uniform pressure q, and the interior arc of the plate edge is rigidly fixed, while the remaining part of the edge is free. Let r and θ denote polar coordinates, and set

$$\rho = \frac{r - b}{a}, \qquad \vartheta = \frac{\theta - \frac{1}{2}\theta_0}{\theta_0}.$$

$$0 \leqslant \rho \leqslant \rho_0 = \frac{a - b}{a}, \qquad -\tfrac{1}{2} \leqslant \vartheta \leqslant \tfrac{1}{2}.$$

In addition, let w denote the sag of the plate, let D denote its rigidity, and let $\tilde{w}$ denote the dimensionless quantity

$$\tilde{w} = \frac{Dw}{qa^2};$$

the function $\tilde{w}$ minimizes the functional

$$\iint \left[\left(\frac{\partial^2 \tilde{w}}{\partial x^2}\right)^2 + \left(\frac{\partial^2 \tilde{w}}{\partial y^2}\right)^2 + 2(1-\sigma)\left(\frac{\partial^2 \tilde{w}}{\partial x\, \partial y}\right)^2 + 2\sigma \frac{\partial^2 \tilde{w}}{\partial x^2} \frac{\partial^2 \tilde{w}}{\partial y^2} - \frac{2}{a^2}\, \tilde{w} \right] dx\, dy$$

over the set of functions that vanish when $\rho = 0$; this function was determined

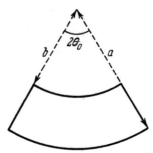

Fig. 16

with the Ritz method, the computations being carried out twice with two systems of coordinate functions. The functions of the first system were of the form

$$w_{ij} = \rho^{i+2}\vartheta^{2j} \qquad (i, j = 0, 1, 2, \ldots);$$

and the second system was obtained from the first by the following orthogonalization process. The functions $\varphi_i(\rho) = \rho^{i+2}$ and $\psi_j(\vartheta) = \vartheta^{2j}$ were separately orthogonalized in the intervals $0 \leqslant \rho \leqslant \rho_0$ and $-\frac{1}{2} \leqslant \vartheta \leqslant \frac{1}{2}$, respectively.

The orthonormal functions thus obtained were denoted by $\bar{\varphi}_i(\rho)$ and $\bar{\psi}_j(\vartheta)$; the functions of the second coordinate system were of the form

$$\bar{w}_{ij} = \bar{\varphi}_i(\rho)\bar{\psi}_i(\vartheta) \qquad (i, j = 0, 1, 2, \ldots).$$

It can be shown that the functions of the first coordinate system are not strongly minimal in the energy space of our problem, but that the functions of the second system are.

The computations were carried out for a plate with $\rho_0 = 1.82$, $\theta_0 = 48°$. Twelve coordinate functions for each coordinate system were used, i.e., the functions wi_j with indices $i = 0, 1, 2, 3$ and $j = 0, 1, 2$ were used for the first coordinate system, while the above-described orthogonalization process yielded the functions w_{ij} for the second coordinate system. The corresponding values of $\bar{\varphi}_i(\rho)$ and $\bar{\psi}_j(\vartheta)$ are

$$\bar{\varphi}_0(\rho) = \sqrt{5}\rho^2, \quad \bar{\varphi}_1(\rho) = 6\sqrt{7}(\rho^3 - \tfrac{5}{6}\rho^2),$$

$$\bar{\varphi}_2(\rho) = 84(\rho^4 - \tfrac{3}{2}\rho^3 + \tfrac{15}{28}\rho^2),$$

$$\bar{\varphi}_3(\rho) = 120\sqrt{11}(\rho^5 - \tfrac{21}{10}\rho^4 + \tfrac{7}{5}\rho^3 - \tfrac{7}{24}\rho^2),$$

$$\bar{\psi}_0(\vartheta) = 1, \quad \bar{\psi}_1(\vartheta) = 6\sqrt{5}(\vartheta^2 - \tfrac{1}{12}),$$

$$\bar{\psi}_2(\vartheta) = 210(\vartheta^4 - \tfrac{3}{14}\vartheta^2 + \tfrac{3}{560}).$$

The computations were carried out with a "Strela" computer, which has a word-length of nine decimal digits. The program was written so that it was possible to substitute zeros for the last, third from the last, and fifth from the last digits, thus introducing an error into the Ritz matrix. Actually, we only substituted zeros for the ninth decimal digit. Both the exact and incorrect solutions of the Ritz system provided sufficient accuracy, so that round-off errors apparently could be neglected in this case.

Below are certain results of the computation. Let δ_a, δ_w, and δ_M denote the relative error in the Ritz coefficients, the sag, and the moments for the first coordinate system; for the second coordinate system, denote the analogous quantities by $\bar{\delta}_a$, $\bar{\delta}_w$, and $\bar{\delta}_M$. The following table shows the ratios δ_a/δ_0 and

i, j	0.0	1.0	0.1	1.1	2.0	0.2
δ_a/δ_0	875	3930	54,400	126,800	10,900	13,000
$\bar{\delta}_a/\delta_0$	0.195	0.692	0.550	0.314	0.521	2.82

i, j	2.1	1.2	2.2	3.0	3.1	3.2
δ_a/δ_0	34,700	16,900	20,200	23,600	58,000	22,900
$\bar{\delta}_a/\delta_0$	0.67	0.47	0.595	39.7	2.13	0.957

$\bar{\delta}_a/\delta_0$, where $\delta_0 = 10^{-7}$ is the upper bound of the relative error in the entries of the Ritz matrix with the ninth decimal digit replaced by a zero.

Thus, when the first coordinate system, which is not strongly minimal, is used, the error in the Ritz coefficients is extremely large in comparison with the error of the entries in the Ritz matrix—the ratio of these errors is of the order of 10^4–10^5. When we use the second coordinate system, which is strongly minimal, the ratio under discussion drops to a low value—less than one, with the exception of two cases, in which $2 < \bar{\delta}_a/\delta_0 < 3$, and one case in which $\bar{\delta}_a/\delta_0 = 39.7$.

It is clear from the results given in [62] that, for example, the ratio δ_w/δ_0 oscillates between 35.9 and 82.4 on the outer edge of the plate, while the ratio δ_M/δ_0 oscillates between 272 and 1520; the ratios $\bar{\delta}_w/\delta_0$ and $\bar{\delta}_M/\delta_0$, however, vary from 0.10 to 0.23 and from 1.37 to 2.95, respectively.

The results given here demonstrate the great advantage of using strongly minimal coordinate systems.

7.5 The condition number of the Ritz matrix. In the preceding paragraphs of the present section we have assumed that the Ritz system is solved exactly, so that the error appears only when this system is set up. However, a round-off error is inevitable in solution of the system. If the coordinate system is strongly minimal in H_A, the condition number of the Ritz matrix, which is the ratio of the largest eigenvalue to the smallest, can increase without bound as n increases, and the solution of the Ritz system may prove to be unstable with respect to the round-off error. It is clear that the condition number of the Ritz matrix will be bounded independently of n if its eigenvalues are bounded from above and below by positive numbers.

We will now state a condition under which the property just formulated holds. Together with a given operator A, we consider another positive-definite operator B, assuming that both operators are such that the spaces H_A and H_B contain the same members. This occurs if, and only if, there exist constants $c_1 > 0$ and $c_2 < \infty$ such that

$$c_1 |u|_B \leqslant |u|_A \leqslant c_2 |u|_B.$$

If any orthonormal system that is complete in H_B is taken for the coordinate system during solution of the equation $Au = f$, the eigenvalues of the Ritz matrix will be bounded from above and below by the constants c_1 and c_2; the condition number of the Ritz matrix is then the bounded quantity c_2/c_1.

7.6 Convergence of residuals to zero. If the equation $Au = f$, where A is a positive-definite operator defined in a given Hilbert space H, is solved with the Ritz method, and u_n is the approximate solution given by the Ritz method, Au_n generally does not approach f as $n \to \infty$. At worst, this is clear from the fact that the coordinate elements, and with them the approximate solution u_n, are not necessarily numbers of the domain of existence of the operator A, at which point the expression Au_n becomes meaningless. But even when the coordinate elements $\varphi_k \in D(A)$, the equation $\lim_{n \to \infty} Au_n = f$ generally does not hold. It can be shown that if, for any selection of coordinate system with members in the domain of existence $D(A)$ of the operator A, the above equation holds, so that the "residual" $Au_n - f$ approaches zero as $n \to \infty$, then the operator A must be bounded.

However, when the coordinate system is appropriately selected, the residual may approach zero even when the operator A is not bounded.

One method of making such a choice is given by

Theorem 25 [69], [98a]. Let A and B be positive definite self-adjoint operators such that $D(A) = D(B)$, and assume that we have the inequality

$$|(Au, Bu)| \geqslant m \, \|Au\|^2, \quad m = \text{const} > 0;$$

moreover, assume that the sequence of characteristic elements of the operator B is complete in the initial space H. If the characteristic elements of the operator B are taken for the coordinate functions for construction of the approximate solution of the equation $Au = f$, then the residual $Au_n - f$ approaches zero as $n \to \infty$.

8. SELECTION OF COORDINATE FUNCTIONS

8.1 Construction of complete coordinate systems. In selecting a coordinate system, we must first show that it is complete in the energy space. The following theorem is useful for this purpose.

Theorem 26. Let $\varphi_n \in D(A)$ $(n = 1, 2, \ldots)$, where A is a positive-definite operator, and suppose that the sequence $\{A\varphi_n\}$ is complete in the given Hilbert space H. Then the sequence $\{\varphi_n\}$ is complete in the energy space H_A.

The following remark is also useful for proving completeness of a system of coordinate functions: If A and B are positive definite operators and the spaces H_A and H_B contain the same members, any system that is complete in H_B is complete in H_A, and conversely.

EXAMPLE 24: Consider the equation

$$Au = -\frac{d}{dx}\left(p(x)\frac{du}{dx}\right) + q(x)u = f(x), \quad u(0) = u(1) = 0,$$

where $p(x) \geqslant p_0 = \text{const} > 0$, $q(x) \geqslant 0$.
Set

$$Bu = -\frac{d^2u}{dx^2}, \quad u(0) = u(1) = 0.$$

The spaces H_A and H_B consist of the same elements, namely, the functions for which $u(0) = u(1) = 0$ and

$$\int_0^1 u'^2(x) \, dx < \infty;$$

it is therefore sufficient to verify completeness in H_B. But completeness of the system $\{\varphi_n(x)\}$ in H_B implies completeness of the system of derivatives

$\{\varphi'_n(x)\}$ in the subspace of $L_2(0, 1)$ that is orthogonal to unity. We can therefore conclude that the functions

$$\varphi_n(x) = x^n(1 - x) \qquad (n = 1, 2, \ldots)$$

form a complete system in H_A.

EXAMPLE 25:   Consider the problem

$$Au = \sum_{k=0}^{s}(-1)^k \frac{d^k}{dx^k}\left(p_k(x) \frac{d^k u}{dx^k}\right) = f(x),$$

$$u(0) = u'(0) = \cdots = u^{(s-1)}(0) = 0,$$

$$u(1) = u'(1) = \cdots = u^{(s-1)}(1) = 0.$$

Assume that $p_s(x) \geqslant p_0 = \text{const} > 0$, and that the remaining coefficients
$p_x(x)$ are such that the operator A is positive definite under the boundary
conditions of the problem.
   The system of coordinate functions

$$\varphi_n(x) = x^{n+s}(1 - x)^s \qquad (n = 0, 1, 2, \ldots)$$

is complete in H_A.

EXAMPLE 26:   Let $\omega(x_1, x_2, \ldots, x_m) = 0$ be the equation of the boundary
S of a region Ω, and assume that $\omega > 0$ inside Ω and has continuous first
derivatives in $\Omega + S$. The system of coordinate functions

$$\omega(x_1, x_2, \ldots, x_m)x_1^{n_1} x_2^{n_2} \cdots x_m^{n_m},$$

in which $n_1, n_2, \ldots, n_m$ independently take all integral values between zero
and infinity, is complete in H_A, where

$$Au = -\sum_{j,k=1}^{m} \frac{\partial}{\partial x_j}\left(A_{jk} \frac{\partial u}{\partial x_k}\right) + Cu, \qquad u\big|_S = 0,$$

is a nondegenerate positive-definite elliptic operator.

EXAMPLE 27:   In Example 24 the eigenfunctions of the operator

$$Bu = -\frac{d^2u}{dx^2}; \qquad u(0) = u(1) = 0$$

can be taken for the coordinate functions. They are $\sin n\pi x$ $(n = 1, 2, \ldots)$.
   The eigenfunctions of the Laplace operator for Ω can be taken for the
coordinate functions in Example 26.

8.2 Requirements toward rational selection of coordinate systems. The
assertions of Section 8.2 are based on the results of Section 7.
   If it is necessary only to construct a crude approximation with the Ritz

method and a small number of coordinate elements, it is sufficient to subject the coordinate system to the following requirements.

1. All members of the coordinate system must belong to the energy space of the problem. In particular, if the problem is a boundary-value problem for a differential equation or system of differential equations, the coordinate functions must:

    a. have all generalized derivatives of order $\leqslant k$, where k is the order of the highest-order derivative in the energy integral (or, equivalently, in the expression for the square of the energy norm);

    b. be such that the energy integral has a finite value;

    c. satisfy all of the principal boundary conditions of the problem.

2. Any finite number of coordinate elements must be linearly independent.

3. The coordinate system must be complete in the energy space of the problem.

The above requirements are not adequate for construction of a Ritz approximation with a small error. This requires a large number of coordinate elements which, in turn, makes it necessary to prove that both the process of solving the Ritz system and the approximate solution are stable. If possible, it is also desirable to improve the convergence of the approximate solution to the exact; for example, it is desirable to arrange for the residual of the approximate solution to approach zero. As far as possible, therefore, it is desirable to have the coordinate elements possess the following properties:

4a. The coordinate system should be strongly minimal in the energy space H_A; in this case the solution of the Ritz system for the equation $Au = f$ and the approximate solution itself are stable.

4b. We will say that two positive-definite operators A and B are semi-consistent if their energy spaces H_A and H_B consist of the same elements. Suppose that the sequence $\{\varphi_n\}$ is complete and orthonormal in H_B; if the sequence is taken as a coordinate sequence for the equation $Au = f$ then the solution of the Ritz system and the approximate solution given by the Ritz system are stable, while the condition number of the Ritz matrix is bounded, no matter how large n becomes.

4c. We will say that two self-adjoint positive-definite operators A and B are similar if their domains of existence coincide, so that $D(A) = D(B)$. Suppose that

$$|(Au, Bu)| \geqslant m \, \|Au\|^2, \qquad m = \text{const} > 0,$$

and that the system of characteristic elements of the operator B, which we assume to be normalized in H_B, is complete in H_B. This system is then also complete in H_A, and if we take it as the coordinate system for the equation $Au = f$, then both the solution of the Ritz system and the approximate solution given by the Ritz method are stable, the condition number of the

Ritz matrix is bounded for all n, and the residual $Au_n - f$ approaches zero as $n \to \infty$.

8.3 One-dimensional boundary-value problems. In this Section we will present several examples of choices of coordinate systems for solution of boundary-value problems associated with ordinary differential equations; of course, these examples do not exhaust all possible cases. We assume that the initial Hilbert space for all of the examples in Section 8.3 is $L_2(0, 1)$.

EXAMPLE 28: Consider the second-order differential equation

$$-\frac{d}{dx}\left(p(x)\frac{du}{dx}\right) + q(x)u = f(x) \tag{3.179}$$

with the boundary conditions

$$u(0) = u(1) = 0. \tag{3.180}$$

Suppose that the functions $p(x)$, $p'(x)$, and $q(x)$ are continuous on the segment $[0, 1]$, $p(x) \geqslant p = \text{const} > 0$, $q(x) > -\lambda_1$, where λ_1 is the smallest eigenvalue of operator (3.179), (3.180) with $q(x) \equiv 0$. The operator $B = -d^2/dx^2$ under boundary condition (3.180) is similar to the operator of this problem. Now, assume that the eigenfunctions (normalized in H_B) are

$$\varphi_n(x) = \frac{\sqrt{2}}{n\pi} \sin n\pi x \qquad (n = 1, 2, \ldots); \tag{3.181}$$

if these functions are taken for the coordinate function of Problem (3.179)–(3.180), Statement 4c of Section 8.2 holds.

EXAMPLE 29: We now consider Eq. (3.179) with the boundary conditions

$$u(0) = 0, \quad u'(1) = 0. \tag{3.182}$$

The differential operator $-d^2/dx^2$ with boundary conditions (3.182) is similar to the operator of Problem (3.179), (3.182); normalized in the metric of the corresponding energy space, the eigenfunctions of this operator are

$$\varphi_n(x) = \frac{2\sqrt{2}}{(2n-1)\pi} \sin \frac{(2n-1)\pi x}{2} \qquad (n = 1, 2, \ldots); \tag{3.183}$$

use of these functions as the coordinate functions guarantees that Statement 4c of Section 8.2 holds.

EXAMPLE 30: Consider Eq. (3.179) with the boundary conditions

$$u'(0) = u'(1) = 0; \tag{3.184}$$

we assume that the coefficients $q(x)$ are such that the operator of Problem (3.179), (3.184) is positive definite; this occurs, for example, if $q(x)$ is strictly positive. An operator similar to that in question is the positive-definite operator $-(d^2/dx^2) + I$ (I is the identity operator) with boundary conditions (3.184). Normalized in the appropriate energy space, the eigenfunctions of this operator are

$$\varphi_1(x) = 1, \quad \varphi_n(x) = \sqrt{\frac{2}{n^2\pi^2 + 1}} \cos n\pi x \qquad (n = 1, 2, \ldots); \quad (3.185)$$

their use in Problem (3.179), (3.185) guarantees that Statement 4c of Section 8.2 holds.

EXAMPLE 31: Assume that differential equation (3.179) is to be solved under the boundary conditions

$$u'(0) - \alpha u(0) = 0, \quad u'(1) + \beta u(1) = 0, \quad \alpha > 0, \quad \beta > 0. \quad (3.186)$$

A similar operator for this case is $-d^2/dx^2$ under the conditions (3.186). Construction of the eigenfunctions of the similar operator, however, is associated with solution of some transcendental equation, and is therefore rather difficult. Even if this difficulty cannot be overcome, it is not difficult to construct an operator that is semisimilar to operator (3.179), (3.186). Such an operator, for example, is the operator $-(d^2/dx^2) + I$ under boundary conditions (3.184) [see Example 30]; if its system of eigenfunctions (3.185) is taken for the coordinate functions for solution of Problem (3.179), (3.186), Statement 4b of Section 8.2 is true. Another operator semisimilar to operator (3.179), (3.186) is

$$Bu = -\frac{d^2u}{dx^2}, \quad u'(0) - u(0) = 0, \quad u'(1) = 0, \quad (3.187)$$

which has the energy product and norm

$$[u, v]_B = u(0)\overline{v(0)} + \int_0^1 u'(x)\overline{v'(x)}\, dx, \left.\begin{array}{c}\\ \\ \\ \end{array}\right\}$$

$$|u|_B = |u(0)|^2 + \int_0^1 |u'(x)|^2\, dx. \qquad (3.188)$$

It is not difficult to construct a sequence of functions that is orthonormal and complete in the metric (3.188); such a sequence, for example, is provided by the system

$$1, x, \frac{\sqrt{2} \sin \pi x}{\pi}, \frac{\sqrt{2} \sin 2\pi x}{2\pi}, \ldots, \frac{\sqrt{2} \sin n\pi x}{n\pi}, \ldots \qquad (3.189)$$

If functions (3.189) are used as the coordinate functions for solution of Problem (3.179), (3.186), Statement 4b of Section 8.2 is true.

EXAMPLE 32: In practice, the case in which the function $p(x)$ is discontinuous (most frequently, piecewise-continuous) is of interest. Suppose that the function $p(x)$, which we assume to be discontinuous, satisfies the inequalities $\tilde{p} \leqslant p(x) \leqslant p_1$, where $\tilde{p}$ and p_1 are positive constants. Use of the coordinate functions given in Examples 23–31 guarantees the validity of Statement 4b of Section 8.2.

EXAMPLE 33:   Here we will consider the case of a degenerate equation. In Eq. (3.179) assume that

$$p(x) = x^\alpha p_1(x), \tag{3.190}$$

where $0 < \alpha < 2$, and that the function $p_1(x)$ is bounded above and below by positive constants. We will solve Eq. (3.179) under the boundary conditions

$$\left.\begin{array}{ll} u(0) = u(1) = 0, & 0 < \alpha < 1, \\ u(1) = 0, & 1 \leqslant \alpha < 2. \end{array}\right\} \tag{3.191}$$

An operator similar to operator (3.179), (3.191) is the operator defined by the differential expression

$$Bu = -\frac{d}{dx}\left(x^\alpha \frac{du}{dx}\right)$$

with boundary conditions (3.191); the eigenfunctions of this operator are

$$\varphi_n(x) = c_n x^{(1-\alpha)/2} J_\nu(\gamma_{\nu,n} x^{1-(\alpha/2)}), \quad \nu = \left|\frac{1-\alpha}{2-\alpha}\right| \quad (n = 1, 2, \ldots), \tag{3.192}$$

where $\gamma_{\nu,n}$ is the nth positive root of the Bessel function $J_\nu(x)$ and the constant c_n is chosen so that $|\varphi_n|_B = 1$. We choose this constant so that

$$c_n = \sqrt{\frac{2}{2-\alpha}}\left\{\int_0^1 z^{\alpha/(2-\alpha)}\left[\frac{d}{dz}(z \pm \nu J_\nu(\gamma_{\nu,n} z))\right]^2 dz\right\}^{-1/2};$$

where the plus sign is taken when $\alpha < 1$, and the minus sign is taken when $\alpha > 1$.

8.4 Two-dimensional boundary-value problems.   Those eigenfunctions of the operator $B = -\Delta$ (Δ is the Laplace operator) on the unit disk that vanish on the boundary of the disk are of the form

$$\varphi_{k,n}(x, y) = c_{k,n} J_k(\gamma_{k,n} r)\genfrac{}{}{0pt}{}{\cos}{\sin} k\theta$$

$$(k = 0, 1, 2, \ldots; \quad n = 1, 2, 3, \ldots)x = r\cos\theta, \quad y = r\sin\theta; \tag{3.193}$$

the coefficients $c_{k,n}$ are such that $|\varphi_{k,n}|_B = 1$.

Consider the problem

$$-\sum_{j,k=1}^{2} \frac{\partial}{\partial x_j}\left(A_{jk}\frac{\partial u}{\partial x_k}\right) + Cu = f(x_1, x_2), \qquad x_1 = x, \qquad x_2 = y, \quad (3.194)$$

$$u|_S = 0. \tag{3.195}$$

Here S is the boundary of a finite region Ω. We assume that this boundary is sufficiently smooth, so that the angle between the normal and the x axis has at least two continuous derivatives. We also assume that A_{jk} and C are functions of x and y such that differential operator (3.194) is nondegenerate and elliptic and the operator of Problem (3.194), (3.195) is positive definite. Finally, we assume that the function C is continuous, and that the functions A_{jk} are continuously differentiable in the closed region $\bar{\Omega} = \Omega + S$.

Suppose that the transformation

$$x = \varphi(x', y'), \qquad y = \psi(x', y') \tag{3.196}$$

is a one-to-one mapping of the unit disk K of the (x', y') plane into the region Ω of the (x, y) plane, where the functions (3.196) are twice continuously differentiable and their Jacobian

$$J = \frac{D(x, y)}{D(x', y')}$$

is bounded above and below by positive constants.

Transformation (3.196) transforms Problem (3.194), (3.195) into the problem

$$-\sum_{j,k=1}^{2} \frac{\partial}{\partial x_j'}\left(A_{jk}'\frac{\partial u}{\partial x_k'}\right) + CJu = Jf, \quad x_1' = x', \quad x_2' = y', \quad (3.197)$$

$$u|_\Gamma = 0. \tag{3.198}$$

Here Γ is the unit circle in the (x', y') plane and

$$A_{jk}' = J\sum_{r,s=1}^{2} A_{rs}\frac{\partial x_j'}{\partial x_r}\frac{\partial x_k'}{\partial x_s}.$$

The operator of Problem (3.197), (3.198) is similar to the operator $B = -\Delta$ mentioned at the beginning of Section 8.4; use of functions (3.193) as the coordinate functions guarantees the validity of Statement 4c of Section 8.2.

In the following cases, it is easy to construct transformation (3.196):

1. A conformal transformation of the disk onto the region Ω is known.
2. Assume that Ω is such that lines parallel to the x axis intersect the boundary S no more than twice. Place the x axis midway between the two lines parallel to the x axis that are most distant from it and still intersect the

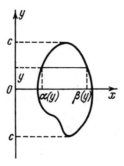

Fig. 17

region Ω (Fig. 17); denote the distance between these two lines by $2c$. The line $y = y_0$, $|y_0| < c$, intersects the contour S at points whose abscissas we denote by $\alpha(y)$ and $\beta(y)$. Set

$$x' = x\mu(y) - \nu(y), \qquad y' = \frac{1}{c}\, y, \qquad (3.199)$$

where

$$\mu(y) = \frac{2\sqrt{c^2 - y^2}}{c[\beta(y) - \alpha(y)]}, \qquad \nu(y) = \frac{\beta(y) + \alpha(y)}{\beta(y) - \alpha(y)}\, \frac{\sqrt{c^2 - y^2}}{c}. \qquad (3.200)$$

Assume that the contour S is such that functions (3.200) have continuous second derivatives when $|y| \geqslant c$; then the function (3.199) is a one-to-one twice continuously differentiable mapping of the region Ω onto the unit disk.

EXAMPLE 34: If Ω is the interior of the ellipse

$$\frac{x^2}{a^2} + \frac{y^2}{b^2} = 1,$$

then $\mu(y) = 1/a$, $\nu(y) = 0$, and the transformation is of the form $x' = x/a$, $y' = y/b$.

Assume that the contour S is piecewise smooth. In this case the operator of Problem (3.194)–(3.195) is at least semisimilar to the operator of the Dirichlet problem; thus, if, for the coordinate functions, we take the eigenfunctions of the Dirichlet problem for the Laplace operator and the appropriate region, we guarantee that Statement 4c of Section 8.2 holds. As above, for the operator A we take the operator of Problem (3.194)–(3.195) for the corresponding transformed region, and for the operator B we take the operator $-\Delta$ for the same region.

3. Assume that the region Ω is of the form shown in Fig. 18. Then transformation (3.199)–(3.200) [we assume that the functions (3.200) have continuous second derivatives] transforms the region into half a disk, for which

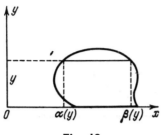

Fig. 18

the eigenfunctions of the Laplace operator are

$$c_{k,n}J_k(\gamma_{k,n}r)\sin k\theta \qquad (k = 1, 2, \ldots), \qquad (3.201)$$

where the $c_{k,n}$ are normalizing factors.

4. Under certain conditions, the region shown in Fig. 19 can be mapped onto a sector of a circle with central angle β. We assume that $0 < \beta < \pi/2$

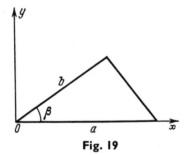

Fig. 19

and that the line $y = $ const intersects the boundary of Ω only at the two points $x = ky$ and $x = \alpha(y)$, $k = \cotan \beta$. The transformation

$$x' = \frac{1}{b}\left\{ky + (x - ky)\frac{\sqrt{b^2 - y^2} - ky}{\alpha(y) - ky}\right\}, \qquad y' = \frac{1}{b}y \qquad (3.202)$$

maps Ω into the sector shown in Fig. 20; here we assume that the ratio

$$\frac{\sqrt{b^2 - y^2} - ky}{\alpha(y) - ky} \qquad (3.203)$$

is continuously differentiable when $0 \leqslant y \leqslant b \sin \beta$. The eigenfunctions of the

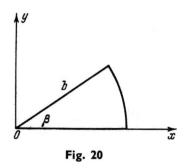

Fig. 20

Laplace operator for the sector shown in Fig. 20 are

$$c_{k,n} \frac{J_{k\pi}}{\beta} \left(\frac{\gamma_{k\pi}}{\beta}, {}_n r \right) \sin \frac{k\pi\theta}{\beta}$$

$$(k = 1, 2, \ldots; \quad n = 1, 2, \ldots). \tag{3.204}$$

EXAMPLE 35: For a right triangle (Fig. 21) with acute angle β

$$\alpha(y) = a + \frac{b \cos \beta - a}{b \sin \beta} y;$$

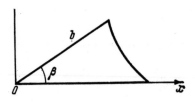

Fig. 21

ratio (3.203) takes the form

$$\frac{b \sin \beta}{a} \frac{\sqrt{b^2 - y^2} - y \cot \beta}{b \sin \beta - y}$$

and is infinitely differentiable when $0 \leqslant y \leqslant b \sin \beta$.

5. Sometimes it is desirable to map the region Ω onto a rectangle, for which the eigenfunctions of the Laplace are well known: If the rectangle is given by the inequalities $0 \leqslant x' \leqslant a, 0 \leqslant y' \leqslant b$, the eigenfunctions, normalized in the

metric of the Dirichlet integral, are of the form

$$\frac{2}{\pi} \frac{1}{\sqrt{\dfrac{k^2}{a^2} + \dfrac{n^2}{b^2}}} \sin \frac{k\pi x'}{a} \sin \frac{n\pi y'}{b} \qquad (k, n = 1, 2, \ldots). \qquad (3.205)$$

Thus, assume that Ω is trapezoidal (Fig. 22) with each "lateral side" intersecting the line $y = $ const only once; let $\alpha(y)$ and $\beta(y)$ be the abscissas of

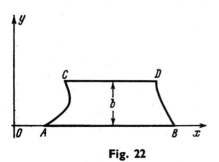

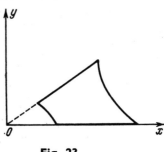

Fig. 22   **Fig. 23**

the intersection points. We also assume that these two functions are twice continuously differentiable. The transformation

$$x' = \frac{x - a(y)}{\beta(y) - \alpha(y)}, \qquad y' = \frac{1}{b} y \qquad (3.206)$$

maps the region of Fig. 22 onto the square $0 \leqslant x, y \leqslant 1$.

The region of Fig. 23 may first be mapped onto the region of Fig. 22 by introducing coordinates x_1 and y_1 with $y_1 = $ arc tan y/x.

EXAMPLE 36:   In the square $0 \leqslant x, y \leqslant 1$, consider the equation

$$-\Delta u - 9(x^2 + y^2)u = -\left(\frac{\partial^2 u}{\partial x^2} + \frac{\partial^2 u}{\partial y^2}\right) - 9(x^2 + y^2)u = f(x, y)$$

under the boundary condition $u|_S = 0$, where S is the contour of the square. The operator of this problem is positive definite (see Section 4.9) and is similar to the operator $-\Delta u, u|_S = 0$. Here the inequality of Theorem 25 is satisfied, and for the coordinate functions it is desirable to take the eigenfunctions of the latter operator, the eigenfunctions being normalized in the energy metric; by formula (3.205), the eigenfunctions are

$$\frac{2}{\pi\sqrt{k^2 + n^2}} \sin k\pi x \sin n\pi y$$

$$(k, n = 1, 2, \ldots).$$

The condition number of the Ritz matrix with this selection of coordinate functions is bounded, no matter what the order (see Section 7.5). To estimate the bound of the condition number, we will estimate the constants c_1 and c_2 of the inequality of Section 7.5.

Let A denote the operator of the present problem, and B denote the operator $-\Delta$ with the boundary condition $u|_S = 0$. We have

$$|u|_A^2 = \int_0^1 \int_0^1 \left[\left(\frac{\partial u}{\partial x} \right)^2 + \left(\frac{\partial u}{\partial y} \right)^2 \right] dx\, dy - 9 \int_0^1 \int_0^1 (x^2 + y^2) u^2 \, dx\, dy,$$

$$|u|_B^2 = \int_0^1 \int_0^1 \left[\left(\frac{\partial u}{\partial x} \right)^2 + \left(\frac{\partial u}{\partial y} \right)^2 \right] dx\, dy.$$

Thus, $|u|_A \leqslant |u|_B$ and, consequently, we can set $c_2 = 1$. Moreover, it is well known that the smallest eigenvalue of the operator B is $2\pi^2$, so if $u \in H_B$, we have $\dfrac{|u|_B}{\|u\|^2} \geqslant 2\pi^2$, or

$$\int_0^1 \int_0^1 u^2 \, dx\, dy \leqslant \frac{1}{2\pi^2} |u|_B^2.$$

Now,

$$9 \int_0^1 \int_0^1 (x^2 + y^2) u^2 \, dx\, dy \leqslant 18 \int_0^1 \int_0^1 u^2 \, dx\, dy \leqslant \frac{9}{\pi^2} |u|_B^2,$$

so

$$|u|_A^2 \geqslant \left(1 - \frac{9}{\pi^2} \right) |u|_B^2$$

and we can set $c_1 = (1/\pi)\sqrt{\pi^2 - 9}$. The condition number of the Ritz matrix is no greater than

$$\frac{c_2}{c_1} = \frac{\pi}{\sqrt{\pi^2 - 9}} < 4 \cdot 5.$$

The image of the Ritz system under transformation (3.33) can be solved by iteration, which, no matter what the order of the system, converges, for it is a progression with mean

$$\frac{\pi - \sqrt{\pi^2 - 9}}{\pi + \sqrt{\pi^2 - 9}} < 0 \cdot 55.$$

For specific Ritz matrices, the results may be even better. For instance, consider the sixth-order matrix, which is obtained by considering only the coordinate functions

$$\varphi_1 = \frac{2}{\pi\sqrt{2}} \sin \pi x \sin \pi y, \qquad \varphi_2 = \frac{2}{\pi\sqrt{5}} \sin \pi x \sin 2\pi y,$$

$$\varphi_3 = \frac{2}{\pi\sqrt{5}} \sin 2\pi x \sin \pi y, \qquad \varphi_4 = \frac{2}{\pi\sqrt{10}} \sin \pi x \sin 3\pi y,$$

$$\varphi_5 = \frac{1}{\pi\sqrt{2}} \sin 2\pi x \sin 2\pi y, \qquad \varphi_6 = \frac{2}{\pi\sqrt{10}} \sin 3\pi x \sin \pi y,$$

for which $k + n \leqslant 4$. The Ritz matrix then takes the form

$$
\begin{bmatrix}
1+\left(\dfrac{1}{6}-\dfrac{1}{4\pi^2}\right)\dfrac{2(-9)}{\pi^2} & \dfrac{16}{\sqrt{10}\,\pi^4} & \dfrac{16}{\sqrt{10}\,\pi^4} & \dfrac{-27}{32\sqrt{5}\,\pi^4} & 0 & \dfrac{-27}{32\sqrt{5}\,\pi^4} \\[3ex]
\dfrac{16}{\sqrt{10}\,\pi^4} & 1+\left(\dfrac{1}{6}-\dfrac{5}{32\pi^2}\right)\dfrac{4}{5\pi^2}(-9) & 0 & -\dfrac{48(-9)}{125\sqrt{2}\,\pi^4} & \dfrac{8}{\sqrt{10}\,\pi^4} & 0 \\[3ex]
\dfrac{16}{\sqrt{10}\,\pi^4} & 0 & 1+\left(\dfrac{1}{6}-\dfrac{5}{32\pi^2}\right)\dfrac{4}{5\pi^2}(-9) & 0 & \dfrac{8}{\sqrt{10}\,\pi^4} & -\dfrac{48(-9)}{125\sqrt{2}\,\pi^4} \\[3ex]
\dfrac{3(-9)}{32\sqrt{5}\,\pi^4} & -\dfrac{48(-9)}{125\sqrt{2}\,\pi^4} & 0 & 1+\left(\dfrac{1}{6}-\dfrac{5}{36\pi^2}\right)\dfrac{2}{5\pi^2}(-9) & 0 & 0 \\[3ex]
0 & \dfrac{8}{\sqrt{10}\,\pi^4} & \dfrac{8}{\sqrt{10}\,\pi^4} & 0 & 1+\left(\dfrac{1}{6}-\dfrac{1}{16\pi^2}\right)\dfrac{1}{2\pi^2}(-9) & 0 \\[3ex]
\dfrac{3(-9)}{32\sqrt{5}\,\pi^4} & 0 & -\dfrac{48(-9)}{125\sqrt{2}\,\pi^4} & 0 & 0 & 1+\left(\dfrac{1}{6}-\dfrac{5}{36\pi^2}\right)\dfrac{2(-9)}{5\pi^2}
\end{bmatrix}
$$

It is not difficult to see that here the iteration also converges for the untransformed Ritz system; indeed, it converges rather rapidly. As a matter of fact, the diagonal elements of the Ritz matrix are greater than $\frac{2}{3}$ (and the sum of the absolute values of the remaining elements in any row is no greater than $11/\pi^4 < 0.1133$). Therefore if Ritz's system is solved with respect to its diagonal members and the method of iteration is applied, the iterations will converge no slower than a progression with ratio $.1133/(\frac{2}{3}) = 0.17$.

9. THE BUBNOV-GALERKIN METHOD

9.1 Basis of the method.   Assume that we are given an equation $Au - f = 0$, where A is a linear operator defined in some Hilbert space H, where no assumption is made about A except that it is linear.

The Bubnov-Galerkin method requires us to select a sequence of elements $\varphi_n \in D(A)$ and to attempt to find an approximate solution in the form

$$u_n = \sum_{k=1}^{n} a_k \varphi_k; \tag{3.207}$$

the coefficients a_k are determined from the condition that the left-hand side of the given equation, and after substitution of u_n for u, must be orthogonal to the elements $\varphi_1, \varphi_2, \ldots, \varphi_n$. This leads to the system of equations

$$\left.\begin{aligned}
(A\varphi_1, \varphi_1)a_1 + (A\varphi_2, \varphi_1)a_2 + \cdots + (A\varphi_n, \varphi_1)a_n &= (f, \varphi_1), \\
(A\varphi_1, \varphi_2)a_1 + (A\varphi_2, \varphi_2)a_2 + \cdots + (A\varphi_n, \varphi_2)a_n &= (f, \varphi_2), \\
\cdots\cdots\cdots\cdots\cdots\cdots\cdots\cdots\cdots\cdots\cdots\cdots\cdots\cdots \\
(A\varphi_1, \varphi_n)a_1 + (A\varphi_2, \varphi_n)a_2 + \cdots + (A\varphi_n, \varphi_n)a_n &= (f, \varphi_n),
\end{aligned}\right\} \tag{3.208}$$

which has the same form as system (3.24'). It immediately follows that the Bubnov-Galerkin method is exactly the same as the Ritz method when A is positive definite.

The Bubnov-Galerkin method can also be applied to the eigenvalue problem. If, for example, it is required to find the eigenvalues of the equation $Au - \lambda u = 0$, the Bubnov-Galerkin method approximates them as the roots of the equation

$$\begin{vmatrix}
(A\varphi_1, \varphi_1) - \lambda(\varphi_1, \varphi_1) & (A\varphi_2, \varphi_1) - \lambda(\varphi_2, \varphi_1) & \cdots & (A\varphi_n, \varphi_1) - \lambda(\varphi_n, \varphi_1) \\
(A\varphi_1, \varphi_2) - \lambda(\varphi_1, \varphi_2) & (A\varphi_2, \varphi_2) - \lambda(\varphi_2, \varphi_2) & \cdots & (A\varphi_n, \varphi_2) - \lambda(\varphi_n, \varphi_2) \\
\cdots\cdots\cdots\cdots & \cdots\cdots\cdots\cdots & & \cdots\cdots\cdots\cdots \\
(A\varphi_1, \varphi_n) - \lambda(\varphi_1, \varphi_n) & (A\varphi_2, \varphi_n) - \lambda(\varphi_2, \varphi_n) & \cdots & (A\varphi_n, \varphi_n) - \lambda(\varphi_n, \varphi_n)
\end{vmatrix} = 0. \tag{3.209}$$

The approximate value of the eigenvalues of the more general equation $Au - \lambda Bu = 0$ are found as the roots of the equation

$$\begin{vmatrix} (A\varphi_1, \varphi_1) - \lambda(B\varphi_2, \varphi_1) & (A\varphi_2, \varphi_1) - \lambda(B\varphi_2, \varphi_1) & \cdots & (A\varphi_n, \varphi_1) - \lambda(B\varphi_n, \varphi_1) \\ (A\varphi_1, \varphi_2) - \lambda(B\varphi_1, \varphi_2) & (A\varphi_2, \varphi_2) - \lambda(B\varphi_2, \varphi_2) & \cdots & (A\varphi_n, \varphi_2) - \lambda(B\varphi_n, \varphi_2) \\ \cdots & \cdots & \cdots & \cdots \\ (A\varphi_1, \varphi_n) - \lambda(B\varphi_1, \varphi_n) & (A\varphi_2, \varphi_n) - \lambda(B\varphi_2, \varphi_n) & \cdots & (A\varphi_n, \varphi_n) - \lambda(B\varphi_n, \varphi_n) \end{vmatrix} = 0.$$

$$(3.210)$$

9.2 A sufficient condition for convergence. Assume that an operator A is of the form $A = A_0 + B$, where A_0 is positive definite in a given Hilbert space H and $D(B) \supset D(A)$. We also assume that the operator $A_0^{-1}B$ is absolutely continuous in the energy space H_{A_0}. We choose the coordinate elements φ_n so that:

1. they are members of $D(A_0)$;
2. any finite number of coordinate elements is linearly independent:
3. the set of all coordinate elements is complete in H_{A_0}. Under these conditions, we have the following theorems.

Theorem 27. For sufficiently large n, the Bubnov-Galerkin method gives an approximate solution of an equation that converges in the norm of H_{A_0} to the exact solution of the given equation if the given equation has a unique solution.

Theorem 28. The approximate eigenvalues given by the Bubnov-Galerkin method for the equation $A_0u - \lambda Bu = 0$ converge to the corresponding exact eigenvalues.

9.3 Application to problems in mathematical physics. Here we will list several problems to which Theorems 27 and 28 apply.

The equation

$$(-1)^s \frac{d^s}{dx^s}\left(p(x)\frac{d^s u}{dx^s}\right) + Bu = f(x) \tag{3.211}$$

with the boundary conditions

$$\left.\begin{array}{l} u(a) = u'(a) = \cdots = u^{(s-1)}(a) = 0, \\ u(b) = u'(b) = \cdots = u^{(s-1)}(b) = 0 \end{array}\right\} \tag{3.212}$$

permits application of the Bubnov-Galerkin method if $p(x) > p_0$, where p_0 is a positive constant and B is a differential operator of order $\leqslant 2s - 1$ with bounded coefficients.

The Bubnov-Galerkin method is applicable to the nondegenerate elliptic equation

$$-\sum_{j,k=1}^{m} A_{jk} \frac{\partial^2 u}{\partial x_j\, \partial x_k} + \sum_{j=1}^{m} B_j \frac{\partial u}{\partial x_j} + Cu = f(x) \tag{3.213}$$

with the boundary conditions of the Dirichlet problem,

$$u|_S = 0 \tag{3.214}$$

or the boundary conditions of a mixed problem,

$$\left[\sum_{i,k=1}^{m} A_{jk} \frac{\partial u}{\partial x_j} \cos (\nu, x_k) + \sigma u \right]_S = 0; \tag{3.215}$$

Neumann's problem ($\sigma \equiv 0$) is no exception.

Under boundary conditions (3.212), the approximate eigenvalues given by Galerkin's method for the equation

$$(-1)^s \frac{d^s}{dx^s}\left(p(x) \frac{d^s u}{dx^s} \right) - \lambda Bu = 0$$

converge to the corresponding exact values if $p(x)$ and B satisfy the same conditions as for Eq. (3.211). The same holds true for the eigenvalues of the equation

$$-\sum_{j,k=1}^{m} \frac{\partial}{\partial x_j}\left(A_{jk} \frac{u}{\partial x_k} \right) - \lambda \left(\sum_{j=1}^{m} B_j \frac{\partial u}{\partial x_j} + Cu \right) = 0$$

with boundary conditions (3.214) or (3.215).

9.4 A form of the method for the case of natural boundary conditions.

As before, let $A = A_0 + B$, where A_0 and B satisfy the conditions of Section 9.2. In addition, assume that $D(B) \supset H_{A_0}$, so that the operator B is defined everywhere in H_{A_0}. Here it is not necessary to choose coordinate elements in the domain $D(A_0)$ of existence of the operator A_0—it is sufficient for them to belong to H_{A_0}. In applications to problems of mathematical physics, this means, first of all, that the coordinate elements need not satisfy the natural boundary conditions. It is now possible to write the system of equations for the coefficients a_k in Formula (3.207) in the form

$$\{[\varphi_1, \varphi_1] + (B\varphi_1, \varphi_1)\}a_1 + \{[\varphi_2, \varphi_1] + (B\varphi_2, \varphi_1)\}a_2 + \cdots$$
$$+ \{[\varphi_n, \varphi_1] + (B\varphi_n, \varphi_1)\}a_n = (f, \varphi_1),$$
$$\{[\varphi_1, \varphi_2] + (B\varphi_1, \varphi_2)\}a_1 + \{[\varphi_2, \varphi_2] + (B\varphi_2, \varphi_2)\}a_2 + \cdots$$
$$+ \{[\varphi_n, \varphi_2] + (B\varphi_n, \varphi_2)\}a_n = (f, \varphi_2),$$
$$\cdot \; \cdot$$
$$\{[\varphi_1, \varphi_n] + (B\varphi_1, \varphi_n)\}a_1 + \{[\varphi_2, \varphi_n] + (B\varphi_2, \varphi_n)\}a_2 + \cdots$$
$$+ \{[\varphi_n, \varphi_n] + (B\varphi_n, \varphi_n)\}a_n = (f, \varphi_n).$$

Similarly, the following equation is obtained instead of (3.210) for the eigenvalues of the equation $A_0 u - \lambda B u = 0$:

$$
\begin{vmatrix}
[\varphi_1, \varphi_1] - \lambda(B\varphi_1, \varphi_1) & [\varphi_2, \varphi_1] - \lambda(B\varphi_2, \varphi_1) & \cdots & [\varphi_n, \varphi_1] - \lambda(B\varphi_n, \varphi_1) \\
[\varphi_1, \varphi_2] - \lambda(B\varphi_1, \varphi_2) & [\varphi_2, \varphi_2] - \lambda(B\varphi_2, \varphi_2) & \cdots & [\varphi_n, \varphi_2] - \lambda(B\varphi_n, \varphi_2) \\
\cdots & \cdots & \cdots & \cdots \\
[\varphi_1, \varphi_n] - \lambda(B\varphi_1, \varphi_n) & [\varphi_2, \varphi_n] - \lambda(B\varphi_2, \varphi_n) & \cdots & [\varphi_n, \varphi_n] - \lambda(B\varphi_n, \varphi_n)
\end{vmatrix} = 0;
$$

the square brackets denote the energy produce in H_{A_0}.

9.5 A generalization of the Bubnov-Galerkin method (the projection method).

Consider the linear equation

$$ Au = f, \tag{3.216} $$

where $u \in E_1, f \in E_2$, E_1 and E_2 are Banach spaces, and A maps from E_1 into E_2. Choose a sequence of spaces L_n of dimension n, where $n = 1, 2, \ldots$, and $L_n \subset D(A) \subset E_1$ for all n. Moreover, choose a sequence of n-dimensional subspaces $M_n \subset E_2$, and let P_n be the projection operator from the space E_2 into the subspace M_n. The projection method consists in replacing exact equation (3.216) by the approximate equation

$$ P_n A u_n = P_n f, \qquad u_n \in L_n. \tag{3.217} $$

It is clear that the projector P_n is of the form

$$ P_n u = \sum_{k=1}^{n} l_k(u) \psi_k, $$

where $\psi_1, \psi_2, \ldots, \psi_n$ is a basis of the subspace M_n and the $l_k(u)$ are linear functionals that are bounded in E_2. If $\varphi_1, \varphi_2, \ldots, \varphi_n$ is a basis of L_n, then u_n is of the form (3.207) and Eq. (3.217) reduces to the linear system

$$ \sum_{k=1}^{n} l_j(A\varphi_k) a_k = l_j(f) \qquad (j = 1, 2, \ldots, n); \tag{3.218} $$

this notation eliminates the necessity of explicitly writing out M_n—it is sufficient to write out the functionals l_j.

EXAMPLE 37:   *The Ordinary Bubnov-Galerkin Method.*   Let $E_1 = E_2 = H$, where H is a separable Hilbert space. In H, choose an infinite system of linearly independent coordinate elements $\varphi_1, \varphi_2, \ldots$, and let $M_n = L_n$ be the subspace spanned by $\varphi_1, \varphi_2, \ldots, \varphi_n$. Then system (3.218) coincides with system (3.208).

EXAMPLE 38:   *The Generalization of Petrov.*   As before, let $E_1 = E_2 = H$, and consider two sequences $\{\varphi_n\}$ and $\{\psi_n\}$ of elements in the space H such that $\varphi_1, \varphi_2, \ldots, \varphi_n$ and $\psi_1, \psi_2, \ldots, \psi_n$ are linearly independent for all n. Now, let L_n and M_n be the subspaces respectively spanned by $\varphi_1, \varphi_2, \ldots, \varphi_n$ and $\psi_1, \psi_2, \ldots, \psi_n$. System (3.218) now takes the form

$$
\left.
\begin{aligned}
(A\varphi_1, \psi_1)a_1 + (A\varphi_2, \psi_1)a_2 + \cdots + (A\varphi_n, \psi_1)a_n &= (f, \psi_1), \\
(A\varphi_1, \psi_2)a_1 + (A\varphi_2, \psi_1)a_2 + \cdots + (A\varphi_n, \psi_2)a_n &= (f, \psi_2), \\
\cdots\cdots\cdots\cdots\cdots\cdots\cdots\cdots\cdots\cdots\cdots\cdots\cdots \\
(A\varphi_1, \psi_n)a_1 + (A\varphi_2, \psi_n)a_2 + \cdots + (A\varphi_n, \psi_n)a_n &= (f, \psi_n).
\end{aligned}
\right\} \quad (3.219)
$$

Sometimes it is desirable to set $\psi_n = B\varphi_n$, where B is an appropriately chosen operator; in this case, the method is called the *moment method*. When $B = A$, we obtain the method of least squares.

EXAMPLE 39: *The Method of Separating Regions.* Let $E_1 = E_2 = L_2(\Omega)$, where Ω is a region in m-dimensional Euclidean space, and let L_n be a subspace constructed in exactly the same way as in Examples 37 and 38. Now partition the region Ω into n subregions $\Omega_1, \Omega_2, \ldots \Omega_n$ and let $\psi_k(x)$ denote the characteristic function of Ω_k, i.e., the function that is equal to one when $x \in \Omega_k$ and equal to zero when $x \notin \Omega_k$. For M_n we take the subspace spanned by $\psi_1, \psi_2, \ldots, \psi_n$. In this case system (3.218) reduces to the system

$$
\sum_{k=1}^{n} a_k \int_{\Omega_j} A\varphi_k \, dx = \int_{\Omega_j} f \, dx \quad (j = 1, 2, \ldots, n). \quad (3.220)
$$

EXAMPLE 40. *The Collocation Method.* Let A be a differential operator of order s, $E_1 = C^{(s)}(\Omega)$, $E_2 = C(\Omega)$. We choose a sequence of functions $\varphi_1, \varphi_2, \ldots$ satisfying all of the boundary conditions of the problem and, as usual, we require that $\varphi_1, \varphi_2, \ldots, \varphi_n$ be linearly independent for all n. We take the subspace spanned by $\varphi_1, \varphi_2, \ldots, \varphi_n$ for L_n, as a result of which u_n takes the form (3.207). In Ω we choose n points $\xi_1, \xi_2, \ldots, \xi_n$ and set $l_j(u) = u(\xi_j)$. Now system (3.218) takes the form

$$
\sum_{k=1}^{n} a_k (A\varphi_k)_{x=\xi_j} = f(\xi_j) \quad (j = 1, 2, \ldots, n). \quad (3.221)
$$

10. VARIATIONAL METHODS IN NONLINEAR PROBLEMS

10.1 General theorems. Theorem 29 distinguishes a class of nonlinear equations whose solution reduces to solution of some variational problem.

Theorem 29. Let P be a nonlinear operator as defined in a real Hilbert space H on a linear set M that is dense in H, and assume that it is required to solve the equation

$$
Pu = f, \quad f \in H. \quad (3.222)
$$

Assume that the operator P satisfies the following conditions:

1. $PO = 0$;

2. The Gateaux differential $P'(u)h$ exists for all $u, h \in M$, is linear with respect to h, and, as an element of H, is continuous for fixed h in any two-dimensional plane containing u;

3. for all $u \in M$, the operator $P'(u)$ is symmetric and positive so that for $u, h_1, h_2, h \in M$,

$$(P'(u)h_1, h_2) = (h_1, P'(u)h_2),$$

$$(P'(u)h, h) > 0, \quad h \neq 0.$$

If, under the above conditions, Eq. (3.222) is solvable, its solution is unique and minimizes the functional

$$\Phi(u) = \int_0^1 (Ptu, u) \, dt - (f, u). \tag{3.223}$$

Conversely, if M contains an element that minimizes functional (3.223), this element satisfies Eq. (3.222).

Theorem 29 proves that the problems of solving Eq. (3.222) and of minimizing functional (3.223) are equivalent, but does not prove the existence of a solution for any problem. The conditions required for existence of a solution of the variational problem and several properties of such solutions are consequences of the following theorems.

Theorem 30. Assume that Conditions 1–3 of Theorem 29 are satisfied, and assume that, in addition, there exists a constant $\gamma > 0$ such that,

$$(P'(u) h, h) \geqslant \gamma^2 \|h\|^2, \quad u, h \in M. \tag{3.224}$$

Then:

a. functional (3.223) is bounded below;

b. any minimizing sequence for this functional converges in the metric of H to some limit.

The limit whose existence (and uniqueness) follows from Theorem 30 is called the *generalized solution* of the problem of minimizing functional (3.223)

Theorem 31. Assume that Conditions 1–3 of Theorem 29 are satisfied and assume that there exist positive constants β and γ such that for all u, $h \in M$,

$$(P'(u) h, h) \geqslant \beta^2 (P'(0) h, h) \geqslant \gamma^2 \|h\|^2. \tag{3.225}$$

Then the generalized solution of the problem of minimizing functional (3.223) is a member of the space H_A, where $A = P'(0)$.

10.2 The Ritz method.   The Ritz method is usually employed for approximate solution of nonlinear variational problems; more accurately, it is used for construction of a minimizing sequence. Assume that it is required to find the minimum of some functional $\Phi(u)$ whose *domain of existence is linear*. We choose a coordinate system $\{\varphi_n\}$ $(n = 1, 2, \ldots)$ subject to the usual conditions:

1. all elements of the coordinate system belong to the domain of existence of the given functional;

2. any finite number of coordinate elements is linearly independent;

3. the coordinate system is complete in some metric defined on the domain of existence of the given functional. We denote the distance between two elements u and v in this metric by $\rho(u, v)$, and if $D(\Phi)$ with the given metric proves to be a Banach space, we write $\rho(u, v) = \|u - v\|_\rho$.

The set $D(\Phi)$ is linear, so for all $a_1, a_2, \ldots, a_n$

$$u_n = \sum_{k=1}^n a_k \varphi_k \in D(\Phi) \tag{3.226}$$

and the expression for $\Phi(u_n)$ is meaningful and is a function of finite number of variables $a_1, a_2, \ldots, a_n$. We will now find the values of $a_1, a_2, \ldots, a_n$ for which $\Phi(u_n)$ is minimal. To do so, we must solve the system

$$\frac{\partial \Phi(u_n)}{\partial a_j} = 0 \qquad (j = 1, 2, \ldots, n) \tag{3.227}$$

and show that the constants a_k thus found actually minimize $\Phi(u_n)$. Substituting these values into expression (3.226), we obtain an element u_n, which we call the nth Ritz approximation to the solution of the given variational problem.

A functional Φ is said to be increasing in a given metric ρ if

$$\lim_{\rho(u,0) \to \infty} \Phi(u) = +\infty. \tag{3.228}$$

A functional $\Phi(u)$ is said to be upper semicontinuous at a point u in a metric ρ if for any given $\varepsilon > 0$ there exists a $\delta > 0$ such that $\Phi(u) - \Phi(v) > -\varepsilon$, if $\rho(u, v) < \delta$; such a functional is called simply upper semicontinuous (in the metric ρ) if it is upper semicontinuous at any point $u \in D(\Phi)$.

Theorem 32.   Let a functional $\Phi(u)$ be upper semicontinuous and increasing in some metric ρ; moreover, assume that this functional is continuously differentiable in any finite-dimensional linear space in its domain of existence. Then:

1. the functional $\Phi(u)$ is bounded below;

2. the Ritz approximation of the solution can be constructed for all n;

3. a sequence of Ritz approximations is a minimizing sequence for the functional $\Phi(u)$.

10.3 Nonlinear theory of thin shells. The problem of finding the equilibrium configuration of a thin shell under the influence of a normal load $q(x, y)$ reduces to the problem of minimizing the potential energy of the shell:

$$I = \iint_S \left\{ \left(\frac{D}{2} \, \Delta w \right)^2 + \frac{Eh}{2(1 - \mu^2)} \right.$$

$$\times \left. [\varepsilon^2 + \varepsilon_2^2 + 2\mu\varepsilon_1\varepsilon_2 + \tfrac{1}{2}(1 - \mu)\varepsilon_{12}^2] - qw \right\} dx \, dy. \qquad (3.229)$$

Notation: E is the elastic modulus, μ is the Poisson constant, h is the thickness of the shell, $D = Eh^3/12(1 - \mu^2)$ is the rigidity of the shell in the presence of bending, S is the mean surface of the shell,

$$\varepsilon_1 = \frac{\partial u}{\partial x} + k_1 w + \frac{1}{2}\left(\frac{\partial w}{\partial x}\right)^2,$$

$$\varepsilon_2 = \frac{\partial v}{\partial y} + k_2 w + \frac{1}{2}\left(\frac{\partial w}{\partial y}\right)^2,$$

$$\varepsilon_{12} = \frac{\partial u}{\partial y} + \frac{\partial v}{\partial x} + \frac{\partial w}{\partial x}\frac{\partial w}{\partial y},$$

u and v are the tangential displacements, w is the normal displacement, and k_1 and k_2 are the initial curvatures in the cross sections parallel to the zx and zy planes, respectively. The shell is assumed to have a rigidly fixed edge.

Using the equilibrium equation for a shell, we can write u and v in terms of w, which requires us to solve only some linear problem; we can therefore assume that functional (3.229) depends only on w. It can be shown that:

1. this functional is bounded below:
2. the Ritz approximation can be constructed for all n;
3. the set of such approximations is compact in the metric

$$\|w\|^2 = \iint_S (\Delta w)^2 \, dx \, dy;$$

and

4. every limit point of the set under discussion realizes some relative minimum of functional (3.229).

10.4 Functionals in the theory of plasticity and their generalization. Some problems in the theory of plasticity can be reduced to the problem of minimizing a functional of the form

$$\Phi(u) = \int_\Omega \left\{ \sum_{i=1}^k \int_1^{\tau_i^2(u)} \rho_i(\xi)\, d\xi \right\} dx - \int_\Omega fu\, dx, f \in L_2(2). \qquad (2.230)$$

Here the ρ_i are nonnegative functions of ξ that are given in the interval $0 \leqslant \xi < \infty$, Ω is a finite region in the coordinate space, and the $\tau_i^2(u)$ are nonnegative quadratic forms in u and its derivatives of up to some given order; it is assumed that the inequality $\rho_j(\xi) \geqslant \rho_0 = \text{const} > 0$ is satisfied for at least one $i = j$ for functions satisfying the homogeneous boundary conditions of the given problem, and that

$$\int_\Omega \tau_j^2(u)\, dx \geqslant \gamma^2 \int_\Omega u^2\, dx, \quad \gamma = \text{const} > 0. \qquad (2.231)$$

Here are two examples:

EXAMPLE 41:   For the problem of elastic plastic torsion,

$$\Phi(u) = \iint_\Omega \left[\frac{1}{2} \int_0^{T^2} \bar{g}(\xi)\, d\xi - \omega u \right] dx\, dy, \qquad (3.232)$$

where

$$T^2 = \left(\frac{\partial u^2}{\partial x} \right) + \left(\frac{\partial u}{\partial y} \right)^2,$$

Ω is the cross section of the rod, ω is constant, and the function $u(x, y)$ must vanish on the boundary of the region Ω, which is assumed to be singly connected. Finally, the function $\bar{g}(\xi)$ satisfies the inequalities $\bar{g}'(\xi) > 0$ and $\bar{g}(\xi) \geqslant \dfrac{1}{G}$, where G is the shear modulus of the material in the elastic state.

EXAMPLE 42:   Here we will consider the creep of a plate whose edge is fixed. In this case

$$\Phi(w) = \iint_\Omega \left[\frac{1}{2} \int_0^{H^2(w)} g(\xi)\, d\xi - pw \right] dx\, dy, \qquad (3.233)$$

where w is the sag in the normal direction and p is the normal load,

$$H^2 w = \left(\frac{\partial^2 w}{\partial x^2} \right)^2 + \left(\frac{\partial^2 w}{\partial y^2} \right)^2 + \frac{\partial^2 w}{\partial x^2} \frac{\partial^2 w}{\partial y^2} + \left(\frac{\partial^2 w}{\partial x\, \partial y} \right)^2;$$

on the boundary of Ω the function w and its normal derivative vanish. Finally, $g(\xi)$ is some function that is bounded above and below by positive constants.

When the conditions listed above are satisfied, functional (3.230) achieves a minimum and the Ritz process for this functional converges.

10.5 Solution of nonlinear Ritz systems. Kachanov's method. The method proposed by Kachanov for solution of one problem in the theory of plasticity was extended by Rose to certain more general functionals.*

Assume that the given functional is of the form

$$\Phi(u) = \int_\Omega \left\{ \sum_{i=1}^k \int_0^{\tau_i^2(u)} \rho_i(\xi)\, d\xi \right\} dx - (f, u), \qquad (3.234)$$

where the functions $\rho_i(\xi)$ and the forms $\tau_i^2(u)$ satisfy the conditions of Section 10.4 and $f \in L_2(\Omega)$. We will solve the problem of minimizing functional (3.234) with the Ritz method, for which purpose we select a coordinate system $\{\varphi_k\}$ satisfying the conditions of Section 10.2. Set

$$u_{nj} = \sum_{k=1}^n a_k \varphi_k,$$

and write the equations

$$\frac{\partial \Phi(u_n)}{\partial a_j} = 0 \qquad (j = 1, 2, \ldots, n). \qquad (3.235)$$

Solution of this system proceeds in the following manner. In integral (3.234) we substitute constants $\rho_i^{(0)} \geqslant 0$ for $\rho_i(\xi)$, where the constant $\rho_i^{(0)}$ is positive; we denote the quadratic functional thus obtained by $\Phi_1(u)$:

$$\Phi_1(u) = \int_\Omega \sum_{i=1}^k \rho_i^{(0)} \tau_i^2(u)\, dx - (f, u).$$

We set

$$u_{n1} = \sum_{k=1}^n a_{k1} \varphi_k$$

and choose the coefficients a_{kl} so that $\Phi_1(u_{nl})$ is minimal; as we can easily see this only requires us to solve a system that is linear in the coefficients a_{kl}. After these coefficients are determined, we substitute $\rho_i(\tau_i^2(u_{n1}))$, for $\rho_i(\xi)$ in functional (3.234), which leads to a new quadratic functional:

$$\Phi_2(u) = \int_\Omega \sum_{i=1}^k \rho_i(\tau_i^2(u_{n1})) \tau_i^2(u)\, dx = (f, u).$$

We set

$$u_{n2} = \sum_{k=1}^n a_{k2} \varphi_k$$

* See the bibliographic comments at the end of the chapter.

and choose the coefficients a_{k2} so that $\Phi_2(u_{n2})$ is minimal, and we continue the process. If the sequence of solutions

$$(a_{1s}, a_{2s}, \ldots, a_{ns}) \qquad (s = 1, 2, \ldots)$$

has a limit as $s \to \infty$, the limit is the solution of system (3.235).

EXAMPLE 43 ([29, 82]):   The stress function $u(x, y)$ for elastic plastic torsion of a rod having a square cross section with sides of length 2 minimizes the functional

$$\int_{-1}^{1} \int_{-1}^{1} \left[\int_{0}^{T} f(\lambda) \, \lambda d\lambda - 2\omega u \right] dx \, dy$$

over the set of functions that vanish on the contour of the cross section. Here ω is the torsion per unit length, while

$$T = \sqrt{\left(\frac{\partial u}{\partial x}\right)^2 + \left(\frac{\partial u}{\partial y}\right)^2}$$

is the tangential stress, which is related to the deformation rate Γ by the expression $\Gamma = f(T)T$.

If we substitute $\lambda^2 = \xi$ in the integrand, we obtain a functional of the form

$$\int_{-1}^{1} \int_{-1}^{1} \left[\int_{0}^{T_2} \rho(\xi) \, d\xi - 2\omega u \right] dx \, dy, \quad \rho(\xi) = \tfrac{1}{2} f(\sqrt{\xi}).$$

Computations were executed for the case $\omega = 0.015$ and a relationship between T and Γ of the form

$$T = \begin{cases} 8 \cdot 10^5 \Gamma, & \Gamma \leqslant 0.0025, \\ 1940 + 24 \cdot 10^3 \Gamma, & \Gamma \geqslant 0.0025. \end{cases}$$

It follows that

$$\rho(\xi) = \begin{cases} \tfrac{1}{16} \cdot 10^{-5}, & \xi \leqslant 4 \cdot 10^6, \\ \dfrac{1}{48} \cdot 10^{-3}\left(1 - \dfrac{1940}{\sqrt{\xi}}\right), & \xi \geqslant 4 \cdot 10^6. \end{cases}$$

The two coordinate functions

$$\varphi_1 = (x^2 - 1)(y^2 - 1), \qquad \varphi_2 = (x^2 - 1)(y^2 - 1)(x^2 + y^2),$$

were used, so that

$$u_2 = (x^2 - 1)(y^2 - 1)[a_1 + a_2(x^2 + y^2)].$$

Kachanov's method was used to execute 32 iterations with a "Ural" computer. The first approximation corresponds to the elastic state and differs greatly from all subsequent approximations, which are comparatively close; the first five digits stabilized after 30 iterations (see the table).

s	$a_{1s} \cdot 10^{-5}$	$a_{2s} \cdot 10^{-5}$	s	$a_{1s} \cdot 10^{-5}$	$a_{2s} \cdot 10^{-5}$
1	0.0701256598	0.0142167558	17	0.0174171448	−0.0036978272
2	0.0180226718	−0.0033820822	18	0.0174189902	−0.0036991472
3	0.0178718986	−0.0037645918	19	0.0174205806	−0.0037003790
4	0.0177279558	−0.0038018398	20	0.0174219636	−0.0037001506
5	0.0175541842	−0.0036417728	21	0.0174231448	−0.0037025316
6	0.0175513918	−0.0037422022	22	0.0174241668	−0.0037034506
7	0.0175429202	−0.0038871818	23	0.0174250498	−0.0037042658
8	0.0174617178	−0.0037578672	24	0.0174258064	−0.0037049904
9	0.0174521578	−0.0037292512	25	0.0174264580	−0.0037056288
10	0.0174036396	−0.0036996034	26	0.0174270162	−0.0037061862
11	0.0174005660	−0.0036923128	27	0.0174274962	−0.0037066732
12	0.0174035498	−0.0036916262	28	0.0174279068	−0.0037070980
13	0.0174068752	−0.0036924296	29	0.0174282610	−0.0037074664
14	0.0174099386	−0.0036936516	30	0.0174285608	−0.0037077868
15	0.0174126626	−0.0036950292	31	0.0174288402	−0.0037080636
16	0.0174150636	−0.0036964422	32	0.0174290410	−0.0037082982

10.6 Reduction to the Cauchy problem. Another method of solving nonlinear Ritz systems is based on the following idea (see, for example, [19]). Assume that it is required to solve the system

$$f_i(a_1, a_2, \ldots, a_n) = 0 \qquad (i = 1, 2, \ldots, n). \qquad (3.236)$$

We consider functions $F_i(a_1, a_2, \ldots, a_n, \lambda)$ such that

$$F_i(a_1, a_2, \ldots, a_n, 1) = f_i(a_1, a_2, \ldots, a_n)$$

and such that the expression $F_i(a_1, a_2, \ldots, a_n, 0)$ is sufficiently simple; for definiteness, assume that

$$F_i(a_1, a_2, \ldots, a_n, 0) = a_i. \qquad (3.237)$$

The equations

$$F_i(a_1, a_2, \ldots, a_n, \lambda) = 0 \qquad (i = 1, 2, \ldots, n) \qquad (3.238)$$

determine $a_1, a_2, \ldots, a_n$ in terms of λ; for our purposes it is sufficient to know the values of these functions for $\lambda = 1$. Differentiating Eqs. (3.238) with respect to λ, we obtain a system of first-order ordinary differential equations

$$\sum_{k=1}^{n} \frac{\partial F_i}{\partial a_k} \frac{da_k}{d\lambda} + \frac{\partial F_i}{\partial \lambda} = 0 \qquad (i = 1, 2, \ldots, n), \qquad (3.239)$$

for which relations (3.237) yield the initial conditions

$$a_i\big|_{\lambda=0} = 0. \qquad (3.240)$$

If Cauchy problem (3.239)–(3.240) has a solution in the interval $0 \leqslant \lambda \leqslant 1$, we can obtain a solution of system (3.236) by one method or another of solving the Cauchy problem, and setting $\lambda = 1$ in the solution.

Under certain conditions, which we will consider below, this Cauchy problem actually does have a solution.

Consider a functional $\Phi(u)$ that is the potential of some operator $P(u)$ and is given on a linear space that is dense in some real Hilbert space H; this means that

$$\frac{d}{dt} \Phi(u + th)\bigg|_{t=0} = (P(u), h)$$

for all $u, h \in D(\Phi)$.

We will assume that the Gateaux differential $DP(u, h) = P'(u)h$ of the operator $P(u)$ is uniformly positively bounded below. This means that there exists a constant γ such that for all u and h

$$(P'(u) h, h) \geqslant \gamma^2 \|h\|^2.$$

We consider the problem of minimizing the functional $\Phi(u)$, attempting to solve it with the Ritz method, for which we must find a sequence of co-ordinate elements that satisfy the usual conditions; we will attempt to find an approximate solution of the form

$$u_n = \sum_{k=1}^{n} a_k \varphi_k.$$

The Ritz method leads to the following system of equations for the co-efficients a_k:

$$(P(u_n), \varphi_j) = 0 \qquad (j = 1, 2, \ldots, n). \qquad (3.241)$$

We should note that this system is obtained as the result of application of the Bubnov-Galerkin method to the equation $P(u) = 0$, which is the Euler-Lagrange equation for the variational problem of minimizing the functional $\Phi(u)$.

When we apply the method of reduction to the Cauchy problem, we write system (3.238) in the form

$$a_j + \lambda[(P(u_n), \varphi_j) - a_j] = 0 \qquad (j = 1, 2, \ldots, n), \qquad (3.242)$$

which leads to the following Cauchy problem:

$$\frac{da_j}{d\lambda} + (P(u_n), \varphi_j) - a_j + \lambda\left\{\sum_{k=1}^{n}[(P'(u_n)\varphi_k, \varphi_j) - \delta_{jk}]\frac{da_k}{d\lambda}\right\} = 0 \quad (3.243)$$

$$a_j\big|_{\lambda=0} = 0. \qquad (3.244)$$

The determinant Δ_n of the coefficient matrix of the derivatives in system (3.243) is nonzero for all $\lambda \in [0, 1]$, so this system can be solved for the derivatives $da_j/d\lambda$, which, by means of Kramer's formula, can be represented in the form

$$\frac{da_j}{d\lambda} = \frac{\Delta_n^{(j)}}{\Delta_k} = g_j(a_1, a_2, \ldots, a_n, \lambda) \qquad (j = 1, 2, \ldots, n). \qquad (3.245)$$

We assume that:

1. The functions

$$(P(u_n), \varphi_i) \quad \text{and} \quad (P'(u_n)\varphi_k, \varphi_j)$$

of the coefficients $a_1, a_2, \ldots, a_n$ are continuous for all values of the arguments, and have polynomial orders of growth at infinity, so that

$$|(P(u_n), \varphi_j)| \leqslant p_m(|a_1|, |a_2|, \ldots, |a_n|), \qquad (3.246)$$

$$|(P'(u_n)\varphi_k, \varphi_j)| \leqslant p_{m-1}(|a_1|, |a_2|, \ldots, |a_n|); \qquad (3.247)$$

here p_m and p_{m-1} denote polynomials of degrees m and $m - 1$, respectively, where m is some natural number.

2. We have the estimate

$$(P'(u_n)h, h) \geqslant N\left(\sum_{k=1}^{n} a_k^2\right)^{(m-1)/2} \|h\|^2, \qquad N = \text{const} > 0. \qquad (3.248)$$

Then Cauchy problem (3.243)–(3.244) has a solution in the interval $0 \leqslant \lambda \leqslant 1$.

It can be shown that under certain additional assumptions concerning the functions $\rho_i(\xi)$, conditions (3.246) and (3.248) are satisfied for functional (3.230) when $m = 1$.

II. THE LINE METHOD

11.1 Basis of the method. The line method lies midway between analytical and grid methods. The basis of the method is substitution of finite differences for the derivatives with respect to one independent variable, and retention of the derivatives with respect to the remaining variables. This approach replaces a given differential equation by a system of differential equations with a smaller number of independent variables.

We will elucidate the method by means of a second-order equation with two independent variables.

Assume that it is required to integrate the equation

$$A(x, y)\frac{\partial^2 u}{\partial x^2} + 2B(x, y)\frac{\partial^2 u}{\partial x\,\partial y} + C(x, y)\frac{\partial^2 u}{\partial y^2} + D(x, y)\frac{\partial u}{\partial x}$$

$$+ E(x, y)\frac{\partial u}{\partial y} + F(x, y)u = G(x, y) \qquad (3.249)$$

in some region Ω. For definiteness, we assume that the equation is elliptic and that Ω is finite. Some boundary condition must be given on the boundary S of this region. We assume, although it is not necessary, that every line parallel to the x axis either does not intersect the boundary S at all, or shares a line segment with it, or intersects it no more than twice.

We draw lines parallel to the x axis, assuming that the distance between two adjacent lines is constant and equal to h. Assume that the region Ω is intersected by the lines

$$y = y_0 + kh = y_k \qquad (k = 0, 1, 2, \ldots, n). \qquad (3.250)$$

We set $y = y_k$ in Eq. (3.249) and substitute difference ratios for the derivatives with respect to y. For example, we can set

$$\left. \frac{\partial u}{\partial y} \right|_{y=y_k} = \frac{1}{h} [u_{k+1}(x) - u_k(x)],$$

where $u_k(x) = u(x, y_k)$. Similarly,

$$\left. \frac{\partial^2 u}{\partial x \, \partial y} \right|_{y=y_k} = \frac{1}{h} [u'_{k+1}(x) - u'_k(x)],$$

$$\left. \frac{\partial^2 u}{\partial y^2} \right|_{y=y_k} = \frac{1}{h^2} [u_{k+1}(x) - 2u_k(x) + u_{k-1}(x)].$$

We substitute this into Eq. (3.249), in which we have already set $y = y_k$, and thus obtain a system of n ordinary linear equations in $n + 2$ unknown functions $u_0(x), u_1(x), \ldots, u_n(x), u_{n+1}(x)$.

If the region Ω is of the form shown in Fig. 22 (see p. 247), the missing two equations can be obtained from the boundary conditions on the line segments AB and CD of the boundary. The boundary conditions for the unknown functions $u_k(x)$ can easily be obtained from the boundary conditions for the function $u(x, y)$ on AC and BD.

Similarly, we can reduce a higher-order linear (or nonlinear) differential equation or system of partial differential equations to a system of ordinary differential equations; the type of equation (or system) makes no particular difference. It is not difficult to extend the line method to the case of a large number of independent variables.

Application of the line method, say, to Eq. (3.249), is desirable if its coefficients are constant or depend only on y: In this case we are led to a system of ordinary linear differential equations with constant coefficients.

11.2 The line method for the Laplace and Poisson equations. For the Laplace equation

$$\frac{\partial^2 u}{\partial x^2} + \frac{\partial^2 u}{\partial y^2} = 0$$

the line method yields a system of the form

$$\frac{5}{6} u_k''(x) + \frac{1}{12} [u_{k+1}''(x) + u_{k-1}''(x)] + \frac{1}{h^2} [u_{k+1}(x) - 2u_k(x) + u_{k-1}(x)] = 0$$

$$(k = 1, 2, \ldots, n). \quad (3.251)$$

Similarly, for the Poisson equation,

$$\frac{\partial^2 u}{\partial x^2} + \frac{\partial^2 u}{\partial y^2} = f(x, y)$$

we obtain the system

$$\frac{5}{6} u_k''(x) + \frac{1}{12} [u_{k+1}''(x) + u_{k-1}''(x)]$$

$$+ \frac{1}{h^2} [u_{k+1}(x) - 2u_k(x) + u_{k-1}(x)] - F_k(x) = 0$$

$$(k = 1, 2, \ldots, n), \quad (3.252)$$

where

$$F_k(x) = \tfrac{5}{6} f_k(x) + \tfrac{1}{12} [f_{k+1}(x) + f_{k-1}(x)].$$

Consider the case in which the region is of the form shown in Fig. 22 and the boundary condition $u|_S = 0$ is given for the Poisson equation. In this case $u_0(x) = u_{n+1}(x) = 0$ and system (3.252) contains n equations in n unknowns $u_1(x), u_2(x), \ldots, u_n(x)$.

Consider the vectors

$$U = [u_1(x), u_2(x), \ldots, u_n(x)],$$

$$F = [F_1(x), F_2(x), \ldots, F_n(x)]$$

and the matrix

$$M = \begin{pmatrix} -2 & 1 & 0 & \cdots & 0 & 0 \\ 1 & -2 & 1 & \cdots & 0 & 0 \\ \cdots & \cdots & \cdots & \cdots & \cdots & \cdots \\ 0 & 0 & 0 & \cdots & 1 & -2 \end{pmatrix}.$$

System (3.252) can now be written in the form

$$\left(E + \frac{1}{12} M \right) U'' + \frac{M}{h^2} U - F = 0. \quad (3.253)$$

where E is the identity matrix of order n.

It is not difficult to find a matrix B such that the matric $B^{-1}MB$ is diagonal. Namely, if we denote the entries of the matrix B by b_{ks}, then

$$b_{ks} = (-1)^{k+s} \sqrt{\frac{2}{n+1}} \sin \frac{\pi s k}{n+1}.$$

The matrix B is simultaneously orthogonal and symmetric, so $B = B^* = B^{-1}$. Now $BMB = (\lambda_1, \lambda_2, \ldots, \lambda_n)$ and, consequently,

$$M = B(\lambda_1, \lambda_2, \ldots, \lambda_n)B,$$

where, as we can easily show,

$$\lambda_k = -2\left(1 + \cos\frac{k\pi}{n+1}\right).$$

If we use the notation

$$BU = V = (v_{,1}\, v_2, \ldots, v_n),$$

$$BF = G = (g_1, g_2, \ldots, g_n),$$

$$\alpha_k^2 = -\frac{\lambda_k}{h^2\left(1 + \dfrac{\lambda_k}{12}\right)}, \qquad \varphi_k(x) = \frac{g_k(x)}{1 + \dfrac{\lambda_k}{12}},$$

system (3.252) reduces to the n independent equations

$$v_k''(x) - \alpha^2 v_k(x) = \varphi_k(x) \qquad (k = 1, 2, \ldots, n). \tag{3.254}$$

By integrating this equation and returning to the unknowns $u_k(x)$, we find, for example, that in the case of a problem symmetric with respect to the y axis

$$u_k(x) = \sum_{s=1}^{n}(-1)^{k+s}C_s \sin\frac{\pi ks}{n+1}\cosh\alpha_s x$$

$$+\int_0^x \sum_{s}^{n}\frac{(-1)^{k+s}\sqrt{2}\sin\dfrac{k\pi s}{n+1}}{\sqrt{n+1}\,\alpha_s}\sinh\alpha_s(x-t)\varphi_s(t)\,dt. \tag{3.255}$$

The arbitrary constants C_s are determined from the algebraic system obtained by substitution of the boundary conditions into (3.255).

The integrals in Formula (3.255) determine a particular solution of system (3.252). Of course, a simpler particular solution can be constructed in certain special cases. Thus, if $f(x, y) = -1$ in the Poisson equation, such a particular solution is given by the set of constants

$$a_k = \frac{k(n+1-k)}{2}h^2.$$

11.3 Biharmonic equations.   Here we will consider a biharmonic equation in the plane under the assumption that some unknown function and its normal derivative are given on the boundary of a region, assuming that the region is of the form shown in Fig. 22. In this case the equations of the line method take the form

$$\left(E + \frac{1}{6}M\right)U^{(4)} + \frac{2}{h^2}\left(M + \frac{1}{2}M^2\right)U'' + \frac{1}{h^4}M^2U = F; \tag{3.256}$$

the symbols in the left-hand side of this equation have the same meaning as above, while F denotes a vector that depends in some way on the boundary conditions and the still unknown values of $u_1(x)$ and $u_n(x)$. System (3.256) can be approximately replaced by a system in which each equation contains only one unknown. To do so, we set

$$u_1(x) = g_{11}(x) + hg_{21}(x), \qquad u_n(x) = g_{12}(x) + hg_{22}(x),$$

in the expression for the vector F, where g_{11} and g_{12} denote the given values of the unknown biharmonic function $u(x, y)$ on the line segments AB and CD (see Fig. 22), while g_{21} and g_{22} denote the values of the normal derivative of the unknown function on the same segments. The vector F is now known. By setting

$$BU = V = (v_1, v_2, \ldots, v_n), \qquad BF = G = (g_1, g_2, \ldots, g_n),$$

we obtain n independent equations

$$v_k^{(4)} + \beta_k v_k'' + \gamma_k v_k = \frac{g_k}{1 + \frac{1}{6}\lambda_k} \qquad (k = 1, 2, \ldots, n),$$

where we have written

$$\beta_k = \frac{2}{h^2} \frac{\lambda_k + \frac{1}{12}\lambda_k^2}{1 + \frac{1}{6}\lambda_k}, \qquad \gamma_k = \frac{1}{h^4} \frac{\lambda_k^2}{1 + \frac{1}{6}\lambda_k}.$$

11.4 The line method for parabolic equations. Consider the equation

$$\frac{\partial u}{\partial t} = -Lu + f(x, y) = \sum_{j,k=1}^{m} \frac{\partial}{\partial x_j}\left(A_{jk}(x)\frac{\partial u}{\partial x_k}\right) + f(x, y). \qquad (3.257)$$

Assume that x varies in a finite region Ω of the space of coordinates $x_1, x_2, \ldots, x_m$, while the variable t lies in the interval $0 \leqslant t < \infty$. Moreover, assume that on the boundary S of the region Ω we are given the boundary condition

$$u\big|_S = 0, \qquad (3.258)$$

and for $t = 0$ we have the initial condition

$$u\big|_{t=0} = \varphi(x). \qquad (3.259)$$

We suppose that the operator L is positive definite under boundary condition (3.258). Now, consider the sequence of times $t_k = kh$ $(k = 1, 2, \ldots)$ and set $u(t_k, x) = u_k(x)$. In virtue of initial conditions (3.259), the function $u_0(x)$ is known, namely, $u_0(x) = \varphi(x)$. In order to determine the functions $u_k(x)$ for $k > 0$, we replace the time derivative by a difference ratio by means of the formula

$$\frac{\partial u}{\partial t}\bigg|_{t=t_k} = \frac{u_k(x) - u_{k-1}(x)}{h}.$$

This leads to a sequence of equations

$$Lu_k + \frac{1}{h} u_k(x) = f(x, t_k) + \frac{1}{h} u_{k-1}(x), \tag{3.260}$$

which must be solved under the boundary condition

$$u_k|_S = 0. \tag{3.261}$$

The operator of problem (3.260)–(3.261) is positive definite, and this problem can, for example, be solved by the energy method. Thus, since we have the function $u_0(x)$, we can set $k = 1$ in subsequent equations, thus obtaining $u_1(x)$; the same equations with $k = 2$ make it possible to find the function $u_2(x)$, etc.

We should note the following facts concerning the line method for parabolic equations:

1. By using the formula

$$\left.\frac{\partial u}{\partial t}\right|_{t=t_k} = \frac{u_{k+1}(x) - u_k(x)}{h}$$

to substitute for the derivative $\partial u/\partial t|_{t=t_k}$, we could directly determine the function u_{k+1} from an already known function u_k at each step in the problem, without solving any boundary problem. However, this process might be unstable.

2. The line method can also be applied to general equations of the form

$$\frac{\partial u}{\partial t} = Au + f, \tag{3.262}$$

where A is an operator that is positive definite in some Hilbert space. In particular, we can consider higher order equations with boundary conditions that guarantee that the operator of the problem is positive definite.

3. If, instead of being positive definite, the operator A of Eq. (3.262) is merely bounded below, the line method can be applied by choosing a sufficiently small h such that the operator $A + (1/h)I$ is positive definite, where I is the identity operator.

BIBLIOGRAPHIC COMMENTS

The fundamental results obtained prior to 1956 on the theory and applications of variational methods for linear problems are considered in [63]. As a rule, no reference has been made in this chapter to the reference cited in this book.

Much information about variational methods can be found in [25, 46, 70, 97, 119, 122, 131].

Sections 1.4 and 1.5: S. L. Sobolev is responsible for the notion of generalized derivatives, as well as the fundamental results concerning this concept and the embedding theorems. See this author's book [97], as well as [95]. Theorem 6 is a consequence of Ye. P. Kalugina's results; see [20, 21].

Section 3.3: Construction of the Ritz system is usually associated with a large number of analytical computations. Computer execution of these computations is discussed in [96].

Sections 3.7 and 3.8: Concerning bending of a plate with a sharp edge and the spectra of the corresponding problems, see [55, 56].

Section 5.2: Formula (3.147) is rigorously derived in [126].

Section 5.4: Concerning Trefftz' method in its most general form and the results obtained here, see [3].

Section 5.6: Weinstein and Aronszajn's considerations are discussed in detail in [119, 131]. Concerning subsequent considerations, see [121, 127, 128, 132].

Section 7: For determination of strongly minimal systems, see [100]. Problems associated with the stability of the Ritz method are discussed in detail in [65, 68, 109].

Section 8.1: A number of interesting comments on construction of coordinate systems is presented in [25].

Sections 8.2–8.4: Detailed considerations concerning rational selection of coordinate systems for concrete classes are presented in [67].

Section 9.5: The general concept of the projection method and a number of theorems on its convergence are given in [80].

Section 10: Many important problems concerning application of variational methods to nonlinear problems are considered in [7, 12, 14, 15, 19, 27, 28, 39, 40, 66, 82, 123]. This list makes no pretense to completeness.

Section 11: A detailed discussion of the line methods for the Laplace and Poisson equations, as well as for the biharmonic equation, is contained in [63], which contains a bibliography. Concerning application of the method to simple parabolic equations, see [94]; the general case is considered in [37]. In [35] the line method is applied to the more complex equation

$$A \frac{\partial^2 u}{\partial t^2} + B \frac{\partial u}{\partial t} + Cu = f.$$

Chapter Four

APPROXIMATE SOLUTION OF
INTEGRAL EQUATIONS

I. APPROXIMATE COMPUTATION OF THE
EIGENVALUES AND EIGENFUNCTIONS OF A
SYMMETRIC KERNEL

1.1 Introductory remarks. In the present section we will denote a symmetric kernel by $K(x, s)$, so that $K(s, x) = \overline{K(x, s)}$. It is assumed that x and s are real variables confined to the same interval (a, b), which may be infinite. All of what we have to say is, of course, true when x and s are points in the same region of any space, or, in the more general case, of the same measurable set. The kernel is supposed to be such that the integral operator

$$K\varphi = \int_a^b K(x, s)\varphi(s)\,ds \qquad (4.1)$$

is completely continuous in the space $L_2(a, b)$; this occurs, for example, if the double integral

$$B^2 = \int_a^b \int_a^b |K(x, s)|^2\,dx\,ds \qquad (4.2)$$

is finite—and in a number of cases we will make this assumption. Another important class of kernels that make operator (4.1) completely continuous is that of kernels with weak singularities (they are also called weakly polarized kernels), which are of the form

$$K(x, s) = \frac{A(x, s)}{|x - s|^\alpha}, \qquad (4.3)$$

where the constant α lies in the interval $0 < \alpha < 1$ and the function $A(x, s)$ is bounded, and in the case of a symmetric kernel, symmetric. If x and s are points of an m-dimensional manifold instead of real numbers, the exponent α may lie in the interval $0 < \alpha < m$. If the kernel has a weak singularity, the interval (a, b) (in the general case, the region or manifold of values for x and s) must be assumed to be finite—then operator (4.1) is completely continuous in the space $L_1(a, b)$.

An eigenvalue of the kernel $K(x, x)$ is a value of a numerical parameter λ for which the homogeneous integral equation

$$\varphi(x) - \lambda K\varphi = 0 \tag{4.4}$$

has a nontrivial (not identically equal to zero) solution, and this solution is called an eigenfunction of the kernel corresponding to the eigenvalue λ. If the operator (4.1) is completely continuous, each of its eigenvalues has only a finite number of linearly independent eigenfunctions; the set of eigenvalues is finite or countable, and in the latter case it has a unique limit point at infinity.

An eigenvalue is said to be simple if there is only a single linearly independent eigenfunction corresponding to it; otherwise it is said to be multiple. The number of linearly independent eigenfunctions corresponding to a given eigenvalue is called its multiplicity.

The eigenvalues of a given kernel can be written in the form of a sequence in increasing order of absolute values. By convention, this sequence contains each eigenvalue as many times as its multiplicity, and in this notation the set of eigenvalues may contain equal members, but only one linearly independent eigenfunction corresponds to each eigenvalue.

The reciprocals of the eigenvalues of the kernel are called the characteristic values or roots of the kernel.

The eigenvalues of a symmetric kernel are real, and the corresponding eigenfunctions can be assumed to be orthogonal and normalized (briefly, orthonormal).

With any symmetric kernel $K(x, s)$ we can associate the so-called quadratic form of the kernel,

$$(K\varphi, \varphi) = \int_a^b \int_a^b K(x, s)\overline{\varphi(x)}\varphi(s) \, dx \, ds; \tag{4.5}$$

it is real.

Theorem 1. The characteristic roots of a symmetric kernel coincide with the stationary values of its quadratic form, which are the values that it takes on the set of normalized functions $\varphi(x)$; the corresponding eigenfunctions are the functions for which these stationary values are achieved.

In practice, it is frequently desirable to use the following theorems:

Theorem 2. The largest (in absolute value) characteristic root σ_1 of a symmetric kernel $K(x, s)$ has the same absolute value as the maximum of the expression $|K(\varphi, \varphi)|$ under the condition $\|\varphi\|^2 = 1$: the corresponding eigenfunction $\varphi_1(x)$ coincides with the function for which the indicated maximum is achieved.

Theorem 3. Let $\sigma_1, \sigma_2, \ldots, \sigma_n$ be the first n characteristic roots of a symmetric kernel $K(x, s)$, arranged in order of decreasing absolute values, and let $\varphi_1(x)$, $\varphi_2(x)$, ..., $\varphi_n(x)$ be the corresponding orthonormal eigenfunctions. The absolute value of the characteristic root σ_{n+1} with absolute value closest to the given roots σ_1, σ_2, ..., σ_n is equal to the maximum of the expression $|(K\varphi, \varphi)|$ under the conditions

$$\|\varphi\|^2 = 1, \quad (\varphi, \varphi_1) = (\varphi, \varphi_2) = \cdots = (\varphi, \varphi_n) = 0; \qquad (4.6)$$

the corresponding eigenfunction $\varphi_{n+1}(x)$ coincides with a function that satisfies condition (4.6) and causes the indicated maximum to be achieved.

A symmetric kernel is said to be positive definite if its quadratic form has only positive values when $\varphi(x) \not\equiv 0$; such kernels are of much interest, and in this section we will deal primarily with this type of kernel. Theorems 2 and 3 become simpler for such kernels, and take the following forms.

Theorem 2a. The largest characteristic root σ_1 of a positive-definite kernel is equal to the maximum of its quadratic form under the condition $\|\varphi\|^2 = 1$; the corresponding eigenfunction coincides with a function for which this maximum is achieved.

Theorem 3a. Let $\sigma_1, \sigma_2, \ldots, \sigma_n$ be the first n characteristic roots of a positive definite kernel $K(x, s)$, arranged in decreasing order, and let $\varphi_1(x)$, $\varphi_2(x), \ldots, \varphi_n(x)$ be the corresponding orthonormal eigenfunctions. The characteristic root σ_{n+1} closest to them is equal to the maximum of the quadratic form $(K\varphi, \varphi)$ under condition (4.6); the corresponding eigenfunction coincides with a function that satisfies condition (4.6) and causes the indicated maximum to be achieved.

1.2 The Ritz method. We choose a sequence of functions $\{\psi_n(x)\}$, which we call coordinate functions. These functions must satisfy the following three conditions:

1. $\psi_n(x) \in L_2(a, b)$;
2. for all n, the functions $\psi_1(x), \psi_2(x), \ldots, \psi_n(x)$ are linearly independent;
3. the sequence of coordinate functions is complete in $L_2(a, b)$, which means that for any function $f(x) \in L_2(a, b)$ and any given $\varepsilon > 0$ there exists a natural number N and coefficients $\alpha_1, \alpha_2, \ldots, \alpha_n$ such that

$$\left\| f - \sum_{k=1}^{N} \alpha_k \psi_k \right\| < \varepsilon.$$

We should note that all of the above conditions are satisfied by choosing any orthonormal system that is complete in $L_2(a, b)$ as the coordinate system.

According to the Ritz method, we set

$$\varphi_n = \sum_{k=1}^{n} a_k \psi_k; \qquad (4.7)$$

the coefficients a_k are subject to the condition $\|\varphi_n\|^2 = 1$, which yields

$$\sum_{j,k=1}^{n} (\psi_j, \psi_k) a_j \bar{a}_k = 1 \qquad (4.8)$$

and, under these conditions, we write the stationary values of the quadratic form in the form

$$(K\varphi_n, \varphi_n) = \sum_{j,k=1}^{n} (K\psi_j, \psi_k) a_j \bar{a}_k. \qquad (4.9)$$

The Lagrange method now leads to a homogeneous linear system in the coefficients a_k (σ is a Lagrange multiplier):

$$\sum_{k=1}^{n} \{(K\psi_j, \psi_k) - \sigma(\psi_j, \psi_k)\} a_k = 0 \qquad (4.10)$$

$$(j = 1, 2, \ldots, n);$$

the determinant of system (4.10) must be equal to zero:

$$\begin{vmatrix} (K\psi_1, \psi_1)-\sigma(\psi_1, \psi_1) & (K\psi_1, \psi_2)-\sigma(\psi_1, \psi_2) & \cdots & (K\psi_1, \psi_n)-\sigma(\psi_1, \psi_n) \\ (K\psi_2, \psi_1)-\sigma(\psi_2, \psi_1) & (K\psi_2, \psi_2)-\sigma(\psi_2, \psi_2) & \cdots & (K\psi_2, \psi_n)-\sigma(\psi_2, \psi_n) \\ \cdots\cdots\cdots\cdots\cdots\cdots\cdots\cdots\cdots\cdots\cdots\cdots\cdots \\ (K\psi_n, \psi_1)-\sigma(\psi_n, \psi_1) & (K\psi_n, \psi_2)-\sigma(\psi_n, \psi_2) & \cdots & (K\psi_n, \psi_n)-\sigma(\psi_n, \psi_n) \end{vmatrix} = 0.$$

$$(4.11)$$

The roots of Eq. (4.11) yield approximate values for the characteristic roots of the kernel $K(x, s)$. The largest of these roots yields an undersize approximate value of the largest characteristic root, and the approximate value for the smallest characteristic root is oversize. As n approaches infinity, the first k roots of Eq. (4.11), where k is any fixed natural number, approach the first k characteristic roots of the kernel $K(x, s)$.

Once σ is found with Eq. (4.11), it can be substituted into system (4.10); a nontrivial solution substituted into expression (4.7) leads to an approximate expression for the eigenfunction corresponding to the characteristic root that has been found.

EXAMPLE 1: We will use the Ritz method to find an approximate value for the smallest eigenvalue of the positive-definite symmetric kernel

$$K(x, s) = \begin{cases} s, & x \geqslant s, \\ x, & x \leqslant s; \end{cases} \qquad (4.12)$$

integration is from $a = 0$ to $b = 1$.

For the coordinate functions we take the polynomials $\psi_n(x) = P_n(2x - 1)$ ($n = 0, 1, 2, \ldots$), where P_n is the nth Legendre polynomial. The polynomials $\psi_n(x)$ are orthogonal in the interval $(0, 1)$, so that $(\psi_j, \psi_k) = 0, j \neq k$; it is also easy to see that $(\psi_k, \psi_k) = 1/(2k + 1)$. We limit Formula (4.7) to two terms, so

$$\varphi_n(x) = \varphi_2(x) = a_1 P_0(2x - 1) + a_2 P_1(2x - 1) = a_1 + a_2(2x - 1).$$

We have

$$(P_0, P_0) = 1, \quad (P_0, P_1) = 0, \quad (P_1, P_1) = \tfrac{1}{3}.$$

In order to compute the values of (KP_m, P_n), we note that

$$(KP_m, P_n) = \int_0^1 dx \left\{ \int_0^x sP_m(s)P_n(x)\, ds + \int_x^1 xP_m(s)P_n(x)\, ds \right\};$$

if we apply the Dirichlet transformation to the second of the double integrals on the right, we find that

$$(KP_m, P_n) = \int_0^1 dx \int_0^x s[P_m(s)P_n(x) + P_m(x)P_n(s)]\, ds.$$

It follows that

$$(KP_0, P_0) = \tfrac{1}{3}, \quad (KP_0, P_1) = (KP_1, P_0) = \tfrac{1}{12}, \quad (KP_1, P_1) = \tfrac{1}{30}.$$

Equation (4.11) now takes the form

$$\begin{vmatrix} \tfrac{1}{3} - \sigma & \tfrac{1}{12} \\ \tfrac{1}{12} & \tfrac{1}{30} - \tfrac{1}{3}\sigma \end{vmatrix} = 0$$

or

$$\sigma^2 - \tfrac{13}{30}\sigma + \tfrac{1}{80} = 0.$$

It follows that

$$\sigma_1 = \tfrac{1}{60}(13 + \sqrt{124}), \quad \sigma_2 = \tfrac{1}{60}(13 - \sqrt{124}).$$

This yields approximate values for the first two eigenvalues of kernel (4.12):

$$\lambda_1 = \frac{1}{\sigma_1} \approx 2.4859,$$

$$\lambda_2 = \frac{1}{\sigma_2} \approx 32.226.$$

The exact values of the eigenvalues of kernel (4.12) are

$$\lambda_n = \frac{(2n - 1)^2 \pi^2}{4} \quad (n = 1, 2, \ldots);$$

this can easily be shown, if we note that the integral equation

$$\varphi(x) - \lambda \int_0^1 K(x, s)\varphi(s)\, ds = 0,$$

where $K(x, s)$ is the kernel (4.12), is equivalent to the differential equation

$\varphi'' + \lambda\varphi = 0$ and the boundary conditions $\varphi(0) = 0$, $\varphi'(1) = 0$. The exact values of the first two eigenvalues are

$$\lambda_1 = \frac{\pi^2}{4} = 2.4674, \qquad \lambda_2 = \frac{9\pi^2}{4} = 22.2066.$$

Thus, by using two coordinate functions in the Ritz method, we obtain a comparatively accurate value of λ_1, and a relatively crude estimate of λ_2. This last circumstance is not accidental: In order to obtain a sufficiently accurate value of the kth eigenvalue, we must use more (much more) than k coordinate functions.

1.3 The moment method [11]. The moment method is one form of the Ritz method. Let $\psi_1, \psi_2, \ldots, \psi_n$ be the first n coordinate functions, let R_n be the subspace spanned by them, and let P_n be the operator projecting $L_2(a, b)$ into R_n. Application of the Ritz method [Formulas (4.7)–(4.11)] is equivalent to finding, instead of the eigenvalues of the operator K, the eigenvalues of the finite-dimensional operator $P_n K P_n$. The moment method consists in choosing the functions $\psi_m = K^{m+1}\omega$ ($m = 1, 2, \ldots$), for the coordinate functions, where the function $\omega(x)$ is arbitrary; it is only assumed that for the selected n the functions $\omega, K\omega, \ldots, K^{n-1}\omega$ are linearly independent. Computation with the moment method proceeds as follows: The characteristic roots of the operator $P_n K P_n$ are obtained as the roots of the equation

$$\sigma^n + \alpha_{n-1}\sigma^{n-1} + \cdots + \alpha_0 = 0, \tag{4.13}$$

whose coefficients, in turn, are found with the system

$$\sum_{k=1}^{n} (\psi_j, \psi_k)\alpha_{k-1} + (\psi_j, \psi_{n+1}) = 0 \qquad (j = 1, 2, \ldots, n). \tag{4.14}$$

The moment method also applies to asymmetric kernels.

EXAMPLE 2: We will find approximate values for the eigenvalues of the kernel

$$K(x, s) = \begin{cases} \frac{1}{2}(2 - s)x, & x \leqslant s, \\ \frac{1}{2}(2 - x)s, & x \geqslant s. \end{cases}$$

We set $\omega(x) = \sin \pi x$ and $n = 3$. We have

$$\psi_1(x) = \omega = \sin \pi x,$$

$$\psi_2(x) = \frac{x}{2\pi} + \frac{1}{\pi^2}\sin \pi x,$$

$$\psi_3(x) = \frac{x}{6\pi}\left(1 + \frac{3}{\pi^2}\right) - \frac{x^3}{12\pi} + \frac{1}{\pi^4}\sin \pi x,$$

$$\psi_4(x) = \left(\frac{31}{720\pi} + \frac{1}{6\pi^3} + \frac{1}{2\pi^5}\right)x - \frac{x^3}{36\pi}\left(1 + \frac{3}{\pi^2}\right) + \frac{x^5}{240\pi} + \frac{1}{\pi^6}\sin \pi x.$$

For the constants α_k we obtain the system

$$0.5000000\alpha_0 + 0.1013212\alpha_1 + 10^{-2} \cdot 2.384240\alpha_2 + 10^{-3} \cdot 5.761453 = 0,$$

$$0.1013212\alpha_0 + 10^{-2} \cdot 2.384240\alpha_1 + 10^{-3} \cdot 6.761453\alpha_2 + 10^{-3} \cdot 1.398529 = 0,$$

$$10^{-2} \cdot 2.384240\alpha_0 + 10^{-3} \cdot 5.761453\alpha_1 + 10^{-3} \cdot 1.398529\alpha_2$$
$$+ 10^{-4} \cdot 3.397373 = 0,$$

which yields

$$\alpha_0 = -10^{-4} \cdot 1.249, \quad \alpha_1 = 10^{-2} \cdot 1.35979, \quad \alpha_2 = -0.296814.$$

Equation (4.13) takes the form

$$\sigma^3 - 0.296814\sigma^2 + 10^{-2} \cdot 1.35979\sigma = 10^{-4} \cdot 1.249 = 0,$$

and has roots

$$\sigma_1 = 0.242963, \quad \sigma_2 = 10^{-2} \cdot 4.145, \quad \sigma_3 = 10^{-2} \cdot 1.2,$$

from which it follows that

$$\lambda_1 = 4.11585, \quad \lambda_2 = 24.20, \quad \lambda_3 = 80.$$

With accuracy up to the number of digits we have written, the exact values of the eigenvalues are

$$\lambda_1 = 4.11585, \quad \lambda_2 = 24.14, \quad \lambda_3 = 63.61.$$

1.4 Kellogg's method.   Let $K(x, s)$ be a symmetric kernel, which, for simplicity, we assume to be positive definite, and let $\omega(x)$ be an arbitrary function in $L_2(a, b)$. Kellogg's method calls for construction of a sequence of functions $\omega_n(x) = K^n\omega$ $(n = 1, 2, 3, \ldots)$ and a sequence of numbers

$$\frac{\|\omega_{n-1}\|}{\|\omega_n\|}. \tag{4.15}$$

Let $\varphi_1(x), \varphi_2(x), \ldots$ be the orthonormal eigenfunctions of the kernel $K(x, s)$, and let $\lambda_1 \leqslant \lambda_2 \leqslant \cdots$ be the corresponding eigenvalues. Now, suppose that the function $\omega(x)$ is orthogonal to the eigenfunctions $\varphi_1(x), \ldots,$ $\varphi_{k-1}(x)$, but not to the eigenfunction $\varphi_k(x)$. Then sequence (4.15) has the kth eigenvalue λ_k as its limit, and the sequence of functions

$$\frac{\omega_n(x)}{\|\omega_n\|}$$

has, for its limit, some linear combination of the eigenfunctions corresponding to the eigenvalue λ_k. In particular, if the function $\omega(x)$ is not orthogonal to the eigenfunction $\varphi_1(x)$, the limit of sequence (4.15) is λ_1.

The sequence

$$\frac{1}{\sqrt[n]{\|\omega_n\|}}$$

approaches the same limit as sequence (4.15).

Under the assumption that $(\omega, \varphi_1) \neq 0$, we obtain two approximate formulas for the smallest eigenvalue:

$$\lambda_1 \approx \frac{\|\omega_{n-1}\|}{\|\omega_n\|} \; ; \tag{4.16}$$

$$\lambda_1 \approx \frac{1}{\sqrt[n]{\|\omega_n\|}} \; ; \tag{4.17}$$

we also obtain an approximate formula for the first eigenfunction:

$$\varphi_1(x) \approx \frac{\omega_n(x)}{\|\omega_n\|} \; . \tag{4.18}$$

Formula (4.16) yields an oversize value of λ_1. We should also note that Formula (4.17) can be used for sufficiently large n.

If the given kernel is symmetric but not positive definite, Formulas (4.16) and (4.17) yield approximate values of the smallest absolute value of the eigenvalues of the given kernel.

EXAMPLE 3: We will use Kellogg's method to compute the smallest eigenvalue of kernel (4.12). We choose $\omega(x) = x$ and $n = 3$. Note that

$$Kx^n = \int_0^1 K(x, s)s^n \, ds = \frac{1}{n+1}\left(x - \frac{x^{n+2}}{n+2}\right),$$

from which it immediately follows that

$$\omega_1(x) = K\omega = \tfrac{1}{2}x - \tfrac{1}{6}x^3,$$

$$\omega_2(x) = K\omega_1 = \tfrac{5}{24}x - \tfrac{1}{12}x^3 + \tfrac{1}{120}x^5,$$

$$\omega_3(x) = K\omega_2 = \tfrac{61}{720}x - \tfrac{5}{144}x^3 + \tfrac{1}{240}x^5 - \tfrac{1}{5040}x^7.$$

Thus,

$$\|\omega_1\| = 0.23238, \quad \|\omega_2\| = 0.09396, \quad \|\omega_3\| = 0.03792.$$

If we successively set $n = 2$ and $n = 3$ in Formula (4.16), we obtain two oversize approximations of λ_1:

$$\lambda_1 \approx 2.475, \quad \lambda_1 \approx 2.477.$$

1.5 The trace method. By the mth trace of the kernel $K(x, s)$ we mean the number

$$A_m = \int_a^b K_m(s, s) \, ds,$$

where $K_m(x, s)$ denotes the mth iterated kernel. If the kernel is symmetric and satisfies condition (4.2), its traces, beginning with the second, are finite. The traces of a kernel are related to its eigenvalues by the expression

$$A_m = \sum_{n=1}^{\infty} \frac{1}{\lambda_n^m} \; ;$$

which yields approximate formulas for the smallest eigenvalue that are usable if m is sufficiently large:

$$|\lambda_1| \approx \sqrt{\frac{A_{2m}}{A_{2m+2}}}, \tag{4.19}$$

$$|\lambda_1| \approx \frac{\sqrt[2m]{r}}{\sqrt[2m]{A_{2m}}}. \tag{4.20}$$

In Formula (4.20) the number r is the multiplicity of the eigenvalue λ_1. If, together with λ_1, the number $-\lambda_1$ is also an eigenvalue of a given kernel, r must be taken to mean the sum of the multiplicities of the eigenvalues λ_1 and $-\lambda_1$.

Formula (4.19) yields an oversize value of $|\lambda_1|$, while Formula (4.20) yields an undersize value.

Approximate formulas of the same type can be obtained for subsequent eigenvalues, but such formulas prove to be rather cumbersome. Thus, if the eigenvalues λ_1 and λ_2 are simple, where the numbers $-\lambda_1$ and $-\lambda_2$ are not eigenvalues of the given kernel (this occurs, for example, if the given kernel is positive definite), we have the approximate formulas

$$|\lambda_2| \approx \frac{1}{|\lambda_1|} \sqrt{\frac{B_{2m}}{B_{2m+2}}}, \tag{4.21}$$

$$|\lambda_2| \approx \frac{1}{|\lambda_1|} \sqrt[2m]{\frac{2}{B_{2m}}}, \tag{4.22}$$

where

$$B_{2m} = A_{2m}^2 - A_{4m}; \tag{4.23}$$

Formula (4.21) yields an oversize value of $|\lambda_2|$, while Formula (4.22) yields an undersize value.

Under similar assumptions, we find that

$$|\lambda_3| \approx \frac{1}{|\lambda_1^2 \lambda_2|} \sqrt[2m]{\frac{8}{B_{2m}^2 - 2B_{4m}}}. \tag{4.24}$$

We should also note that even-order traces for a symmetric kernel can be computed with the formula

$$A_{2m} = \int_a^b \int_a^b |K_m(x, s)|^2 \, dx \, ds = 2 \int_a^b \int_a^x |K_m(x, s)|^2 \, ds \, dx, \qquad (4.25)$$

which requires only half as many iterations.

EXAMPLE 4: We will use the trace method to find the first eigenvalue of kernel (4.12). It is easy to show that

$$K_2(x, s) = xs - \frac{x^2 s}{2} - \frac{s^3}{3}, \quad s \leqslant x,$$

and, by Formula (4.25),

$$A_2 = \tfrac{1}{6}, \quad A_4 = \tfrac{131}{5040}.$$

The eigenvalues of kernel (4.12) are all positive, so, by setting $m = 1$ in Formula (4.19), we find that

$$\lambda_1 \approx \sqrt[2m]{\frac{A_2}{A_4}} = 2.532.$$

Moreover, the eigenvalues of kernel (4.12) are also simple, so we must set $r = 1$ in Formula (4.20); if we set $m = 2$ in this formula, we find that

$$\lambda_1 \approx \frac{1}{\sqrt[4]{A_4}} = 2.460.$$

EXAMPLE 5: The squares of the roots of the Bessel function $J_0(x)$ are the eigenvalues of the symmetric kernel

$$L(x, s) = \begin{cases} -\sqrt{xs} \ln s, & x \leqslant s, \\ -\sqrt{xs} \ln x, & x \geqslant s, \end{cases} \quad a = 0, \quad b = 1.$$

We will use the trace method to find the first two roots of the function $J_0(x)$. It is easy to show that for the second interated kernel we have

$$L_2(x, s) = \frac{\sqrt{xs}}{4} [(x^2 + s^2) \ln x + 1 - x^2], \quad x \geqslant s.$$

Now, by Formula (4.25),

$$A_2 = \tfrac{1}{32}, \quad A_4 = \tfrac{11}{12288}, \quad B_2 = \tfrac{1}{12288}.$$

Setting

$$\lambda_1 \approx \frac{1}{\sqrt[4]{A_4}}, \quad \lambda_2 \approx \frac{1}{\lambda_1} \sqrt{\frac{2}{B_2}},$$

we find that

$$\lambda_1 \approx 5.7813, \quad \lambda_2 \approx 27.117.$$

It follows that we obtain the approximations of the first two roots of the function $J_0(x)$:

$$\alpha_1 \approx 2.4044, \quad \alpha_2 \approx 5.2702;$$

more exact values of these roots are

$$\alpha_1 = 2.4048, \quad \alpha_2 = 5.5200.$$

1.6 Substitution of a degenerate kernel. If the kernel is degenerate,

$$K(x, s) = \sum_{\alpha=1}^{n} u_\alpha(x)v_\alpha(s),$$

its characteristic roots coincide with the eigenvalues of the matrix $\| A_{\alpha\beta} \|_{\alpha,\beta=1}^{\alpha,\beta=n}$, where

$$A_{\alpha\beta} = \int_a^b v_\alpha(x)u_\beta(x) \, dx.$$

Determination of these eigenvalues is an algebraic problem that yields to well-known methods. If, therefore, some method (see below, Section 4) of approximating a given kernel by a degenerate kernel is known, finding the characteristic roots of a given kernel reduces, for purposes of approximation, to the algebraic problem of finding the eigenvalues of the corresponding matrix.

1.7 Application of Fredholm's determinant. The eigenvalues of a kernel $K(x, s)$ [that is not necessarily symmetric] can be found as the roots of its Fredholm determinant

$$D(\lambda) = \sum_{n=0}^{\infty} \frac{(-1)^n c_n}{n!} \lambda^n. \tag{4.26}$$

The coefficients c_n can be computed by using the following relations:

$$\left. \begin{array}{l} c_0 = 1, \quad B_0(x, s) = K(x, s) \\[2mm] c_{n+1} = \int_a^b B_n(x, x) \, dx, \\[2mm] B_n(x, s) = c_n K(x, s) - n \int_a^b K(x, t)B_{n-1}(t, s) \, dt. \end{array} \right\} \tag{4.27}$$

Using Formulas (4.27) to compute the first several coefficients c_n, we replace series (4.26) by a segment of it, which is a polynomial in λ; the roots of this polynomial yield approximate values for the eigenvalues of the given kernel. In practice, this method is of little use.

2. ITERATION METHODS

2.1 Simple iteration. Consider the equation

$$\varphi(x) - \lambda K\varphi = f(x), \tag{4.28}$$

where

$$K\varphi = \int_a^b K(x, s)\varphi(s)\, ds;$$

here and everywhere below the kernel $K(x, s)$ is not necessarily assumed to be symmetric. The method of simple iteration, which is also called the method of successive approximations, proceeds by using the recursion formula

$$\varphi_{n+1}(x) = f(x) + \lambda \int_a^b K(x, s)\varphi_n(s)\, ds = f(x) + \lambda K\varphi_n \tag{4.29}$$

to construct a sequence of functions $\{\varphi_n(x)\}$ that can be treated as an approximation of the solution of Eq. (4.28); the initial approximation $\varphi_0(x)$ can be chosen arbitrarily.

If the free term of the equation is used as the initial approximation, so that $\varphi_0(x) = f(x)$, we find that

$$\varphi_n(x) = \sum_{m=0}^n \lambda^m K^m f.$$

2.2 Conditions for convergence. Assume that

$$\left.\begin{aligned}
B^2 &= \int_a^b \int_a^b |K(x, s)|^2\, dx\, ds < \infty, \\
&\int_a^b |f(x)|^2\, dx < \infty;
\end{aligned}\right\} \tag{4.30}$$

these requirements are not necessary, but when they are satisfied it is easier to state conditions for convergence of the method of simple iteration.

Theorem 4. Assume that conditions (4.30) are satisfied. Sequence (4.29) converges in the metric of $L_2(a, b)$ to the solution of Eq. (4.28) if $|\lambda| < |\lambda_1|$, where λ_1 is the smallest (in absolute value) eigenvalue of the kernel $K(x, s)$. If the kernel satisfies the additional condition

$$\int_a^b |K(x, s)|^2\, ds \leqslant A = \text{const}, \tag{4.31}$$

then sequence (4.29) converges to the solution of Eq. (4.28) uniformly in the closed interval $[a, b]$.

We also have a theorem that is, in some sense, the converse of Theorem 4: *If the simple iteration process converges for some λ, then $|\lambda| < |\lambda_1|$, no matter what the free term of the equation.*

It is not always easy to verify satisfaction of the condition $|\lambda| < |\lambda_1|$, so we will give several simpler sufficient conditions for convergence of simple iteration.

Simple iteration converges in the metric of $L_2(a, b)$ if

$$|\lambda| < B^{-1}. \qquad (4.32)$$

If the kernel satisfies condition (4.31), the convergence is uniform in $[a, b]$.

If the interval (a, b) is finite and the kernel is bounded,

$$|K(x, s)| \leqslant M = \text{const},$$

the process of simple iteration converges uniformly if

$$|\lambda| < \frac{1}{M(b - a)}. \qquad (4.33)$$

Here it is necessary for the free term $f(x)$ to satisfy condition (4.30); it is sufficient for the integral

$$\int_a^b |f(x)| \, dx$$

to be finite.

For a kernel with a weak singularity,

$$K(x, s) = \frac{A(x, s)}{|x - s|^\alpha}, \quad |A(x, s)| \leqslant M = \text{const}, \quad 0 < \alpha < 1,$$

the simple iteration process converges if

$$|\lambda| < \frac{1 - \alpha}{2^\alpha M(b - a)^{1-\alpha}}.$$

If the interval (a, b) is finite and the kernel is a Volterra kernel, the simple iteration process converges for all λ. If, moreover, the kernel is bounded, the process converges uniformly if the free term is summable, i.e., if the integral

$$\int_a^b |f(x)| \, dx$$

exists.

Formula (4.29) contains the quadrature

$$K\varphi_n = \int_a^b K(x, s)\varphi_n(s) \, ds,$$

which depends on x; well-known quadrature formulas can be used to compute this integral. Assume that the quadrature formula is of the form

$$\int_a^b F(x) \, dx = \sum_{i=1}^n A_i F(x_i).$$

Then the value of the functions $K\varphi_n$ at the points x_i can be computed with the formula

$$(K\varphi_n)_{x_i} = \sum_{j=1}^{m} A_j K(x_i, x_j)\varphi_n(x_j);$$

a useful computation scheme is given in Kantorovich and Krylov's monograph ([25], Chapter Three, p. 127).

2.3 Modified forms of the iteration method. Modifications can be made, for example, for a positive-definite symmetric kernel [23].

a. *The Method of Steepest Descent* [23]. Consider the integral equation

$$A\varphi = \varphi(x) + \int_a^b K(x, s)\varphi(s)\, ds = f(x) \tag{4.34}$$

with a symmetric positive positive definite kernel $K(x, s)$. Equation (4.34) can be replaced by the equivalent variational problem of minimizing the functional

$$F(\varphi) = (\varphi, \varphi) + (K\varphi, \varphi) - (f, \varphi) - (\varphi, f)$$

$$= \int_a^b |\varphi(x)|^2\, dx + \int_a^b \int_a^b K(x, s)\overline{\varphi(x)}\varphi(s)\, dx\, ds$$

$$- 2\,\mathrm{Re} \int_a^b \varphi(x)\overline{f(x)}\, dx.$$

In the method of steepest descent, we choose an arbitrary zeroth approximation $\varphi_0(x)$ and then select an element φ' with fixed norm, so that

$$\frac{d}{d\varepsilon} F(\varphi_0 + \varepsilon\varphi')\bigg|_{\varepsilon=0} = \text{max.}$$

We construct the element φ' and choose an ε so that

$$F(\varphi_0 + \varepsilon\varphi') = \text{min.}$$

We now take the element $\varphi_1 = \varphi_0 + \varepsilon\varphi'$ as the first approximation and repeat the process. The computation continues until two adjacent approximations coincide to within the required accuracy. The element φ' and the number ε are given by the formulas

$$\varphi' = A\varphi_0 - f, \qquad \varepsilon = \frac{\|\varphi'\|^2}{(A\varphi', \varphi')}.$$

The process converges with the same rate as a progression with mean

$$\left(\frac{\sigma_1}{2 + \sigma_1}\right)^2,$$

where σ_1 is the largest characteristic root of the kernel $K(x, s)$.

b. *Application of Simple Iteration to a Transformed Equation* [74].   Assume that, as before, the kernel of Eq. (4.34) is symmetric and positive definite. We rewrite Eq. (4.34) in the form

$$\varphi = \varphi - \frac{\sigma_1}{(1 + \sigma_1)(2 + \sigma_1)} A\varphi + \frac{\sigma_1}{(1 + \sigma_1)(2 + \sigma_1)} f, \qquad (4.35)$$

where σ_1 is the largest characteristic root of the kernel $K(x, s)$, and we apply the method of simple iteration to Eq. (4.35). This leads to the recurrence relation

$$\varphi_{n+1} = \varphi_n - \frac{\sigma_1}{(1 + \sigma_1)(2 + \sigma_1)} A\varphi_n + \frac{\sigma_1}{(1 + \sigma_1)(2 + \sigma_1)} f.$$

The process converges with the same rate as a progression with mean

$$q = \max\left(\frac{2}{2 + \sigma_1}, \frac{2 + 2\sigma_1 + \sigma_1^2}{2 + 3\sigma_1 + \sigma_1^2}\right);$$

since, by hypothesis, the kernel $K(x, s)$ is positive definite, we have $\sigma_1 > 0$ and $q < 1$.

2.4 Integral equations of the first kind with symmetric kernels [105].   Let $K(x, s)$ be a symmetric positive-definite kernel, and assume that the equation

$$K\varphi = \int_a^b K(x, s)\varphi(s)\, ds = f(x) \qquad (4.36)$$

is solvable. We choose an arbitrary function $\varphi_0(x) \in L_2(a, b)$ and a number λ in the integral $0 < \lambda < 2\lambda_1$, where λ_1 is the smallest eigenvalue of the kernel $K(x, s)$. The sequence of functions defined by the recurrence relation

$$\varphi_{n+1}(x) = \varphi_n(x) + \lambda[f(x) - K\varphi_n]$$

converges in the metric of $L_2(a, b)$ to the solution of Eq. (4.36).

3. APPLICATION OF QUADRATURE FORMULAS

3.1 Volterra equations of the second kind.   Assume that in the Volterra equation

$$\varphi(x) - \int_a^x K(x, s)\varphi(s)\, ds = f(x) \qquad (4.37)$$

x varies in a finite interval $[a, b]$, the free term is continuous in this interval, and the kernel is continuous in the triangle $a \leqslant x \leqslant b$, $a \leqslant s \leqslant x$. We replace the integral in Eq. (4.37) by some quadrature formula that does not contain the value of the integrand at the right end of the range of integration. If the quadrature formula is of the form

$$\int_a^{x_n} F(x)\, dx = \sum_{m=0}^{n-1} A_m^{(n)} F(x_m),$$

then, by setting $x = x_n$ in Eq. (4.37), we replace this equation by the equation

$$\varphi(x_n) - \sum_{m=0}^{n-1} A_m^{(n)} K(x_n, x_m)\varphi(x_m) = f(x_n). \qquad (4.38)$$

Equation (4.38) is a recurrence relation that makes it possible to determine the values of $\varphi(x_n)$, beginning with $\varphi(a) = f(a)$.

It may occur that the kernel $K(x, s)$ is not continuous; then, as a preliminary, it is desirable to transform Eq. (4.37) so that the integrand becomes continuous, and then to apply a quadrature formula. Assume, for example, that the kernel has a weak singularity at $x = s$, so that the equation takes the form

$$\varphi(x) - \int_a^x \frac{A(x, s)}{(x - s)^\alpha}\, \varphi(s)\, ds = f(x). \qquad (4.39)$$

In this case it is desirable to pass to an iterated kernel, continuing the iteration until the new kernel is continuous.

3.2 Volterra equations of the first kind.   The equations

$$\int_a^x K(x, s)\varphi(s)\, ds = f(x), \qquad f(a) = 0, \qquad (4.40)$$

reduce to an equation of the second kind if the kernel $K(x, s)$ and the free term $f(x)$ are continuously differentiable and $K(x, x) \neq 0$. Application of quadrature formulas makes it possible to avoid such a reduction. Assume that the quadrature formula contains the value of the integrand at the end of the range of integration, so that

$$\int_a^{x_n} F(x)\, dx = \sum_{m=0}^{n} A_m^{(n)} F(x_m), \qquad A_n^{(n)} \neq 0.$$

We replace Eq. (4.40) by the system

$$\sum_{m=0}^{n} A_m^{(n)} K(x_n, x_m)\varphi(x_m) = f(x_n),$$

which recurrently determines the values of $\varphi(x_m)$ at all mesh points of the quadrature formula, except for $x_0 = a$; for this value we have

$$\varphi(a) = \frac{f'(a)}{K(a, a)}.$$

3.3 Fredholm equations. In the equation

$$\varphi(x) - \int_a^b K(x, s)\varphi(s)\, ds = f(x) \tag{4.41}$$

we replace the integral by some quadrature formula. Assume that this formula is of the form

$$\int_a^b F(x)\, dx = \sum_{m=1}^n A_m F(x_m).$$

Equation (4.41) is approximately replaced by the equation

$$\varphi(x) - \sum_{m=1}^n A_m K(x, x_m)\varphi(x_m) = f(x). \tag{4.42}$$

Here we set $x = x_j$ ($j = 1, 2, \ldots, n$), thus obtaining an algebraic system for the unknown values of $\varphi(x_j)$:

$$\varphi(x_j) - \sum_{m=1}^n A_m K(x_j, x_m)\varphi(x_m) = f(x_j) \tag{4.43}$$

$$(j = 1, 2, \ldots, n).$$

Solving this equation and substituting the values thus obtained into Formula (4.42), we obtain an approximate solution for the given integral equation. The unknown function $\varphi(x)$ can also be constructed without reference to Formula (4.42) by using some interpolation formula.

The Gauss and Chebyshev formulas can be recommended as the most accurate; if the kernel and the free term are periodic with period $b - a$, it is possible to use the rectangle formula, which, in this case, also provides sufficient accuracy.

EXAMPLE 6: The plane interior Dirichlet problem for the region lying inside a sufficiently smooth closed contour L can be reduced to solution of the integral equation

$$\mu(t) - \frac{1}{\pi} \int_L \frac{\cos (\nu, r)}{r} \mu(\tau)\, d\sigma = f(t). \tag{4.44}$$

Here t and τ are parameters that determine the position of points on the curve L, r is the distance between points corresponding to values of these parameters, ν is the exterior normal to L at τ, $d\sigma$ is an arc-length element, $\mu(t)$ is the unknown function, and $f(t)$ is given. Integral equation (4.44) is obtained if a harmonic function is sought in the form of the potential of a double layer with density $\mu(\tau)$.

We will find an approximate solution for Eq. (4.44) for the case in which L is the ellipse

$$x = a \cos t, \quad x = b \sin t;$$

for definiteness, we set $a = 5$, $b = 3$, and, for the same reason, we set

$$f(t) = x^2 + y^2 = 25 - 16 \sin^2 t.$$

It is easy to reduce the integral in Eq. (4.44) to the form

$$\int_L \frac{\cos(v, r)}{r} \mu(\tau)\, d\sigma = -\frac{b}{2a} \int_{-\pi}^{\pi} \frac{\mu(\tau)\, d\tau}{1 - \varepsilon^2 \cos^2 \dfrac{t + \tau}{2}},$$

where ε is the eccentricity of the ellipse; for the above values of a, b, and $f(t)$, Eq. (4.44) takes the form

$$\mu(t) + \frac{3}{10\pi} \int_{-\pi}^{\pi} \frac{\mu(\tau)\, d\tau}{1 - 0.64 \cos^2 \dfrac{t + \tau}{2}} = 25 - 16 \sin^2 t; \qquad (4.45)$$

the exact solution of this equation is

$$u(t) = \tfrac{17}{2} + \tfrac{128}{17} \cos 2t = 8.50 + 7.53 \cos 2t.$$

In Eq. (4.45), the constant before the integral sign is $3/(10\pi) = 0.0958$; in order to simplify the computation, we round it off to 0.1 and, consequently, we will solve the equation

$$\mu(t) + \int_{-\pi}^{\pi} \mu(\tau) \frac{d\tau}{6.8 - 3.2 \cos(t + \tau)} = 25 - 16 \sin^2 t. \qquad (4.46)$$

It is not difficult to see that

$$\mu(-t) = \mu(\pi - t) = \mu(t). \qquad (4.47)$$

We replace the integral in (4.46) by means of the rectangle formula, using $n = 12$ ordinates. Notation:

$$\mu(0) = y_1, \quad \mu\left(\frac{\pi}{6}\right) = y_2, \quad \mu\left(\frac{\pi}{3}\right) = y_3, \quad \mu\left(\frac{\pi}{2}\right) = y_4.$$

Now system (4.43) reduces to the system

$$1.19y_1 + 0.35y_2 + 0.31y_3 + 0.15y_4 = 25,$$
$$0.18y_1 + 1.34y_2 + 0.32y_3 + 0.16y_4 = 21,$$
$$0.16y_1 + 0.32y_2 + 1.34y_3 + 0.18y_4 = 13,$$
$$0.15y_1 + 0.31y_2 + 0.35y_3 + 1.19y_4 = 9,$$

from which it follows that

$$\left. \begin{array}{ll} y_1 = \dfrac{1701}{106} \approx 16.038, & y_2 = \dfrac{1301}{106} \approx 12.274, \\[4mm] y_2 = \dfrac{501}{106} \approx 4.726, & y_4 = \dfrac{101}{106} \approx 0.953. \end{array} \right\} \qquad (4.48)$$

We will construct the function $\mu(t)$ by means of a Fourier series, which, in virtue of (4.47) takes the form

$$\mu(t) = \sum_{n=0}^{\infty} a_n \cos 2nt.$$

It is possible to use (4.48) to compute the coefficients of the first four terms in this series:

$$a_0 = \tfrac{901}{106} = 8.500, \quad a_1 = \tfrac{400}{53} \approx 7.547, \quad a_2 = a_3 = 0.$$

Eliminating the remaining terms of the Fourier series, we find that

$$\mu(t) = 8.50 + 7.55 \cos 2t,$$

which is little different from the exact solution.

4. SUBSTITUTION OF A DEGENERATE KERNEL

Assume that the equation

$$\varphi(x) - \int_a^b K(x, s)\varphi(s) \, ds = f(x) \tag{4.49}$$

is solvable for all $f \in L_2(a, b)$. Now, assume that the kernel $K(x, s)$ splits into the sum

$$K(x, s) = L(x, s) + R(x, s), \tag{4.50}$$

where the kernel $R(x, s)$ has a small norm in the metric of $L_2(a, b; a, b)$:

$$\int_a^b \int_a^b |R(x, s)|^2 \, dx \, ds < \varepsilon^2, \tag{4.51}$$

where ε is sufficiently small. Then the equation

$$\psi(x) - \int_a^b L(x, s)\psi(s) \, ds = f(x) \tag{4.52}$$

has a solution for all $f \in L_2(a, b)$ and $\|\varphi - \psi\| = O(\varepsilon)$. If it is possible to find a partition (4.50) such that the kernel $L(x, s)$ is degenerate, Eq. (4.52) reduces to a linear algebraic system. If the kernel $K(x, s)$ satisfies inequality (4.31) and the partition is executed so that $R(x, s)$ satisfies not only inequality (4.51), but the inequality

$$\int_a^b |R(x, s)|^2 \, ds < c\varepsilon^2, \qquad c = \text{const}, \tag{4.53}$$

as well, then not only is the above estimate in mean true, but we have the uniform estimate $|\varphi(x) - \psi(x)| = O(\varepsilon)$ which, for convenience, can be represented in the form $\|\varphi - \psi\|_C = O(\varepsilon)$.

The estimate for $\|\varphi - \psi\|$ can be refined. Let $\Gamma_K(x, s)$ and $\Gamma_L(x, s)$ denote the resolvents of the kernels $K(x, s)$ and $L(x, s)$, and let $\|R\|$, $\|\Gamma_K\|$, $\|\Gamma_L\|$ denote the norms of the operators with the corresponding kernels. Then

$$\|\varphi - \psi\| \leqslant \|R\| (1 + \|\Gamma_K\|)(1 + \|\Gamma_L\|) \|f\|. \tag{4.54}$$

The norm in Formula (4.54) can be taken in any functional space. If this norm is taken in the space $L_2(a, b)$ then, in virtue of inequality (4.51) we have $\|R\| < \varepsilon$, and, consequently,

$$\|\varphi - \psi\| < \varepsilon(1 + \|\Gamma_K\|)(1 + \|\Gamma_L\|) \|f\|. \tag{4.54'}$$

Partition (4.50) can be constructed in many ways, as long as the kernel $L(x, s)$ is degenerate. Below are several such methods.

1. Suppose that the sequence $u_\alpha(x)$ $(\alpha = 1, 2, \ldots)$ is orthonormal and complete in $L_2(a, b)$. Then the kernel $K(x, s)$ splits into a double Fourier series that converges in mean,

$$K(x, s) = \sum_{\alpha,\beta=1}^{\infty} A_{\alpha\beta} u_\alpha(x) u_\beta(s),$$

where

$$A_{\alpha\beta} = \int_a^b \int_a^b K(x, s)\overline{u_\alpha(x)}\,\overline{u_\beta(s)}\, dx\, ds;$$

if n is sufficiently large, we can set

$$L(x, s) = \sum_{\alpha,\beta=1}^{n} A_{\alpha\beta} u_\alpha(x) u_\beta(s).$$

2. We can also construct the expansion

$$K(x, s) = \sum_{\alpha,\beta=1}^{\infty} B_{\alpha\beta} u_\alpha(x)\overline{u_\beta(s)},$$

where

$$B_{\alpha\beta} = \int_a^b \int_a^b K(x, s)\overline{u_\alpha(x)} u_\beta(s)\, dx\, ds,$$

and set

$$L(x, s) = \sum_{\alpha,\beta=1}^{n} B_{\alpha\beta} u_\beta(x)\overline{u_\beta(s)}.$$

3. Assume that the sequence $u_\alpha(x)$ $(\alpha = 1, 2, \ldots)$ is complete but not orthonormal in $L_2(a, b)$. Then the sequence $u_\alpha(x)\, u_\beta(s)$ is complete but not orthonormal in $L_2(a, b; a, b)$. We can set

$$L(x, s) = \sum_{\alpha,\beta=1}^{n} A_{\alpha\beta} u_\alpha(x)\overline{u_\beta(s)},$$

choosing the coefficients $A_{\alpha\beta}$ so that

$$\int_a^b \int_a^b |K(x, s) - L(x, s)|^2 \, dx \, ds = \min; \qquad (4.55)$$

to do so, it is sufficient to determine the above-noted coefficients from the system

$$\sum_{\alpha,\beta=1}^n A_{\alpha\beta} \int_a^b u_\alpha(x)\overline{u_{\alpha'}(x)} \, dx \int_a^b \overline{u_\beta(s)u_{\beta'}(s)} \, ds$$

$$= \int_a^b \int_a^b K(x, s)\overline{u_{\alpha'}(x)}u_{\beta'}(s) \, dx \, ds \qquad (\alpha', \beta' = 1, 2, \ldots, n).$$

We can also set

$$L(x, s) = \sum_{\alpha,\beta=1}^n B_{\alpha\beta}u_\alpha(x)u_\beta(s)$$

and determine the coefficients $B_{\alpha\beta}$ from the system

$$\sum_{\alpha,\beta=1}^n B_{\alpha\beta} \int_a^b u_\alpha(x)\overline{u_{\alpha'}(x)} \, dx \int_a^b u_\beta(s)\overline{u_{\beta'}(s)} \, ds$$

$$= \int_a^b \int_a^b K(x, s)\overline{u_{\alpha'}(x)u_{\beta'}(s)} \, dx \, ds \qquad (\alpha', \beta' = 1, 2, \ldots, n).$$

4. Both methods of Section 4.3 are special cases of the following more general method. Let two sequences $\{u_\alpha(x)\}$ and $\{v_\alpha(x)\}$, $1 \leqslant \alpha < \infty$, be complete but, generally speaking, not orthonormal in $L_2(a, b)$. We can set

$$L(x, s) = \sum_{\alpha,\beta=1}^n A_{\alpha\beta}u_\alpha(x)v_\beta(s),$$

choosing the coefficients $A_{\alpha\beta}$ so that condition (4.55) is satisfied; for the coefficients $A_{\alpha\beta}$, we obtain the system

$$\sum_{\alpha,\beta=1}^n A_{\alpha\beta} \int_a^b u_\alpha(x)\overline{u_{\alpha'}(x)} \, dx \int_a^b v_\beta(s)\overline{v_{\beta'}(s)} \, ds = \int_a^b \int_a^b K(x, s)\overline{u_{\alpha'}(x)}\overline{v_{\beta'}(s)} \, dx \, ds.$$

5. If the interval (a, b) is finite and the kernel is continuous in the square $a \leqslant x, s \leqslant b$, the kernel can be approximated uniformly by a polynomial in x and s, and this polynomial can be taken for $L(x, s)$.

6. The Bubnov-Galerkin method and the method of least squares, which we shall discuss in the next section, are special methods of replacing a given kernel by a degenerate kernel.

EXAMPLE 7:   Consider the equation

$$\varphi(x) - \int_0^1 \sin xs \; \varphi(s) \, ds = f(x). \tag{4.56}$$

We set

$$L(x, s) = xs - \frac{x^3 s^3}{6},$$

as a result of which we find that

$$R(x, s) = \sin xs - xs + \frac{x^3 s^3}{6} = \frac{x^5 s^5}{120} - \cdots$$

The approximate equation

$$\psi(x) - x \int_0^1 s\psi(s) \, ds + \frac{x^3}{6} \int_0^1 s^3 \psi(s) \, ds = f(x)$$

yields

$$\psi(x) = f(x) + c_1 x + c_2 x^3, \tag{4.57}$$

where

$$c_1 = \int_0^1 s\psi(s) \, ds, \qquad c_2 = -\frac{1}{6} \int_0^1 s^3 \psi(s) \, ds.$$

Multiplying Eq. (4.57) approximately by x and $-x^3/6$, and integrating, we find that

$$\tfrac{2}{3}c_1 - \tfrac{1}{5}c_2 = f_1, \quad \tfrac{1}{30}c_1 + \tfrac{43}{42}c_2 = f_2,$$

where

$$f_1 = \int_0^1 xf(x) \, dx, \qquad f_2 = -\frac{1}{6} \int_0^1 x^3 f(x) \, dx;$$

we find the approximate solution $\psi(x)$ by solving this system.

We will now estimate the difference $\varphi - \psi$ by means of Formula (4.54). We first note that the norm is taken in the metric of the space C of functions continuous on the segment [0, 1]. Then, for example,

$$\|R\| = \underset{x}{\mathrm{Max}} \int_0^1 |R(x, s)| \, ds;$$

the norms of the other integral operators are similarly defined. We have $|R(x, s)| < \dfrac{x^5 s^5}{120}$ from which it follows that

$$\|R\| \leqslant \underset{x}{\mathrm{Max}} \int_0^1 \frac{x^5 s^5}{120} \, ds = \frac{1}{720}.$$

Moreover,

$$\|\Gamma_K\| \leqslant \frac{\|K\|}{1 - \|K\|}.$$

But

$$\| K \| = \max_{0 \leqslant x \leqslant 1} \int_0^1 \sin xs \, ds = \max_{0 \leqslant x \leqslant 1} \frac{1 - \cos x}{x}$$

$$= 1 - \cos 1 < 1 - \cos \frac{\pi}{3} = \frac{1}{2}.$$

It follows that

$$\| \Gamma_K \| < 1.$$

Similarly,

$$\| L \|' = \max_{0 \leqslant x \leqslant 1} \int_0^1 \left(xs - \frac{x^3 s^3}{6} \right) ds = \max_{0 \leqslant x \leqslant 1} \left(\frac{x}{2} - \frac{x^3}{24} \right) = \frac{1}{2} - \frac{1}{24} = \frac{11}{24}$$

and

$$\| \Gamma_L \| < \tfrac{11}{13}.$$

Now, by Formula (4.54),

$$\| \varphi - \psi \| < \tfrac{1}{720} \cdot 2 \cdot \tfrac{24}{13} \| f \| = 0.00513 \| f \| = 0.00513 \max_{0 \leqslant x \leqslant 1} | f(x) |.$$

We will now estimate the difference $\varphi - \psi$ in the metric of $L_2(0, 1)$. As we know, the norm of an integral operator with kernel $K(x, s)$ in the space $L_2(a, b)$ is no larger than the quantity B defined by Formula (4.2). It thus follows that since

$$| R(x, s) | < \frac{x^5 s^5}{120}.$$

we have

$$\| R \| \leqslant \frac{1}{120} \left\{ \int_0^1 \int_0^1 x^{10} s^{10} \, dx \, ds \right\}^{1/2} = \frac{1}{1320}.$$

Moreover,

$$\| K \| \leqslant \left\{ \int_0^1 \int_0^1 \sin^2 xs \, dx \, ds \right\}^{1/2} \leqslant \left\{ \int_0^1 \int_0^1 x^2 s^2 \, dx \, ds \right\}^{1/2} = \frac{1}{3},$$

$$\| L \| \leqslant \left\{ \int_0^1 \int_0^1 \left(xs - \frac{x^3 s^3}{6} \right)^2 dx \, ds \right\}^{1/2} = \left(\frac{1}{9} - \frac{1}{75} + \frac{1}{1764} \right)^{1/2} < \frac{1}{3}.$$

It follows that

$$\| \Gamma_K \| \leqslant \tfrac{1}{2}, \quad \| \Gamma_L \| < \tfrac{1}{2}$$

and

$$\| \varphi - \psi \| < \tfrac{1}{1320} \cdot \tfrac{9}{4} \| f \| = 0.00170 \| f \|.$$

5. THE BUBNOV-GALERKIN METHOD AND THE METHOD OF LEAST SQUARES

5.1 The Bubnov-Galerkin method. To use the Bubnov-Galerkin method to solve the equation

$$\varphi(x) - \lambda \int_a^b K(x, s) \varphi(s) \, ds = f(x). \tag{4.58}$$

we select a sequence of functions $u_\alpha(x)$ ($\alpha = 1, 2, \ldots$) in $L_2(a, b)$ such that for any n the functions $u_1(x)$, $u_2(x)$, $\ldots$, $u_n(x)$ are linearly independent, and we attempt to find an approximate solution in the form

$$\varphi_n(x) = \sum_{\alpha=1}^{n} a_\alpha u_\alpha(x), \qquad (4.59)$$

where the coefficients a_α are determined from the condition requiring that the residual of Eq. (4.58) be orthogonal to the functions $u_1(x)$, $u_2(x)$, $\ldots$, $u_n(x)$. This yields the linear system

$$\sum_{\alpha=1}^{n} a_\alpha \int_a^b \left[u_\alpha(x) - \lambda \int_a^b K(x, s)u_\alpha(s)\, ds \right] \overline{u_\beta(x)}\, dx$$

$$= \int_a^b f(x)\overline{u_\beta(x)}\, dx \qquad (\beta = 1, 2, \ldots, n). \quad (4.60)$$

If λ is not an eigenvalue, system (4.60) has a unique solution when n is sufficiently large; as $n \to \infty$, approximate solution (4.59) approaches the exact solution $\varphi(x)$ of Eq. (4.58) in the metric of $L_2(a, b)$. We have the estimate

$$\| \varphi - \varphi_n \| \leqslant (1 + \varepsilon_n) \| \varphi - P_n\varphi \|, \qquad (4.61)$$

where P_n is the projection operator into the space spanned by the functions $u_1, u_2, \ldots, u_n$, and $\varepsilon_n \xrightarrow[n \to \infty]{} 0$.

Sometimes the following generalization of the Bubnov-Galerkin method can be used. In $L_2(a, b)$, two complete systems $\{u_n(x)\}$ and $\{v_n(x)\}$ are chosen so that for any n the functions $u_1, u_2, \ldots, u_n$ and $v_1, v_2, \ldots, v_n$ are linearly independent; a solution is sought in the form (4.59), but the coefficients a_α are determined from the condition requiring that the residual be orthogonal to the functions $v_1, v_2, \ldots, v_n$. This leads to the following system for determination of the coefficients a_α:

$$\sum_{\alpha=1}^{n} a_\alpha \int_a^b \left[u_\alpha(x) - \lambda \int_a^b K(x, s)u_\alpha(s)\, ds \right] \overline{v_\beta(x)}\, dx$$

$$= \int_a^b f(x)\overline{v_\alpha(x)}\, dx \qquad (\beta = 1, 2, \ldots, n). \quad (4.62)$$

We will now state conditions for convergence of the generalized Bubnov-Galerkin method. First of all, we assume that the sequences $\{u_n\}$ and $\{v_n\}$ are bases of $L_2(a, b)$. Let U_n and V_n denote the spaces spanned by $u_1, u_2, \ldots, u_n$ and $v_1, v_2, \ldots, v_n$, respectively, and let P_n be the projection operator into the space U_n. We also assume that there exists a constant $C > 0$ such that for all $v \in V_n$ we have $\|v\| \leqslant C \|P_n v\|$. Then:

1. system (4.62) has a unique solution when n is sufficiently large;
2. $\varphi_n \to \varphi$ in the metric of $L_2(a, b)$;
3. estimate (4.61) holds.

5.2 The method of least squares. We choose a sequence of coordinate functions $\{u_\alpha(x)\}$ satisfying the same conditions as in Section 5.1, choose an approximate solution of the form (4.59), and determine the coefficients a_α from the condition requiring that the residual of Eq. (4.58) have a minimal norm in $L_2(a, b)$:

$$\|\varphi_n - \lambda K\varphi_n\|^2 = \int_a^b \left| \varphi_n(x) - \lambda \int_a^b K(x, s)\varphi_n(s) \, ds \right|^2 dx = \min.$$

This leads to the linear algebraic system

$$\sum_{\alpha=1}^n a_\alpha(Au_\alpha, Au_\beta) = (f, Au_\beta) \qquad (\beta = 1, 2, \ldots, n), \qquad (4.63)$$

in which we have set

$$Au = u(x) - \lambda Ku = u(x) - \lambda \int_a^b K(x, s)u(s) \, ds.$$

In more detail, the coefficients and free terms of system (4.63) can be written as

$$(Au_\alpha, Au_\beta) = \int_a^b u_\alpha(x)\overline{u_\beta(x)} \, dx$$

$$-2 \, \text{Re} \left\{ \lambda \int_a^b \int_a^b K(x, s)u_\alpha(s)\overline{u_\beta(x)} \, dx \, ds \right\}$$

$$+ |\lambda|^2 \int_a^b \int_a^b \int_a^b K(x, s)\overline{K(x, t)}u_\alpha(s)u_\beta(t) \, dx \, ds \, dt,$$

$$(f, Au_\beta) = \int_a^b f(x)\overline{u_\beta(x)} \, dx - \overline{\lambda} \int_a^b \int_a^b \overline{K(x, s)}f(x)\overline{u_\beta(s)} \, dx \, ds.$$

If the given λ is not an eigenvalue of the kernel $K(x, s)$, then system (4.63) has a solution for all n and $\varphi_n \to \varphi$ in the metric of $L_2(a, b)$, where φ is the solution of Eq. (4.58); if the approximate solution φ_n has been constructed, its error can be approximated with the formula

$$\|\varphi_n - \varphi\| \leqslant M \|\varphi_n - \lambda K\varphi_n - f\|;$$

where M is a constant equal to the norm of the operator A^{-1}.

It may occur that λ is an eigenvalue of the kernel $K(x, s)$; then the homogeneous equation

$$Au = u(x) - \lambda \int_\Omega K(x, y)u(y) \, dy = 0 \qquad (4.64)$$

has nontrivial solutions, of which, as we know, there are only a finite number of linearly independent solutions, which we denote by $\omega_1(x), \omega_2(x), \ldots, \omega_p(x)$. The adjoint homogeneous equation $A^*u = 0$ has exactly the same number of linearly independent solutions. Equation (4.58) is solvable if and only if the function $f(x)$ is orthogonal to all of the solutions of the equation $A^*u = 0$. Assume that this requirement is satisfied—then Eq. (4.58) has an uncountable set of solutions. This set of solutions contains one, and only one, solution that is orthogonal to all of the functions $\omega_1(x)$, $\omega_2(x)$, ..., $\omega_p(x)$. If these functions are known, the above-noted solution can be constructed with the method of least squares. To do so, we choose coordinate functions $u_k(x)$ and, as shown above, we choose $n > p$ and set

$$\varphi_n(x) = \sum_{k=1}^{n} a_k u_k(x).$$

We require that

$$(\varphi_n, \omega_j) = \sum_{k=1}^{n} a_k(u_k, \omega_j) = 0 \qquad (j = 1, 2, \ldots, p).$$

These relations can be used to choose p coefficients a_k as functions of the other coefficients; we now require that $\|Au_n - f\|^2 = \min$. This leads to a new linear algebraic system, which we use to find the remaining n-p coefficients a_k.

6. APPROXIMATE SOLUTION OF SINGULAR INTEGRAL EQUATIONS

6.1 Statement of the problem.   Consider the equation

$$A\varphi = a(t)\varphi(t) - b(t)S\varphi + \int_\Gamma K(t, \tau)\varphi(\tau)\, d\tau = f(t), \qquad (4.65)$$

where

$$S\varphi = \frac{1}{\pi i} \int_\Gamma \frac{\varphi(\tau)}{\tau - t}\, d\tau.$$

For simplicity, we assume that the given functions in Eq. (4.65) satisfy a Lipschitz condition with positive exponent for all variables on which these functions depend. We also assume that the contour of integration Γ is a simple closed curve with continuous curvature; the curve Γ partitions the complex plane into two regions: an interior region D^+, and an exterior region D^-.

We subject the coefficients $a(t)$ and $b(t)$ to the condition

$$\min_{t \in \Gamma} |a^2(t) - b^2(t)| > 0, \qquad (4.66)$$

which plays a special role in the theory of singular integral equations.

Under these conditions, any solution (if one exists) of Eq. (4.65) that is summable with power greater than one satisfies the Lipschitz condition with positive exponent.

Let $\alpha(A)$ denote the number of linearly independent solutions of the homogeneous equation $A\varphi = 0$; correspondingly, let $\alpha(A^*)$ denote the number of linearly independent solutions of the adjoint homogeneous equation $A^*\psi = 0$. Both $\alpha(A)$ and $\alpha(A^*)$ are finite. We will call the difference $m = \alpha(A) - \alpha(A^*)$ the *index* of the operator A or Eq. (4.65); the index is independent of the kernel $K(t, \tau)$ and is computed with the formula

$$m = \frac{1}{2\pi} \int_\Gamma d \arg \frac{a(t) + b(t)}{a(t) - b(t)}. \qquad (4.67)$$

Equation (4.65) is solvable if, and only if, the free term $f(t)$ is orthogonal to all solutions of the equation $A^*\psi = 0$. If this condition is satisfied, and if, moreover, the solutions of the homogeneous equation $A\varphi = 0$ are known, then Eq. (4.65) can be' solved approximately with the method of least squares in exactly the same way as Fredholm's equation (see the end of the preceding section).* Another method for approximate solution of Eq. (4.65) can be based on the fact that if $K(t, \tau) \equiv 0$, this equation can be solved in closed form by means of quadratures; if, however, $K(t, \tau)$ is a degenerate kernel, evaluation of quadratures must be supplemented by solution of some linear algebraic system. Methods for approximate substitution of degenerate kernels for Fredholm kernels are discussed in Section 4; here therefore we will only show how to solve Eq. (4.65) for the case in which the kernel $K(t, \tau)$ is degenerate.

6.2 Solution of a singular equation with degenerate kernel. Let

$$K(t, \tau) = \sum_{\alpha=1}^{n} u_\alpha(t) v_\alpha(\tau).$$

Equation (4.65) takes the form

$$a(t)\varphi(t) - b(t)S\varphi = f(t) - \sum_{\alpha=1}^{n} c_\alpha u_\alpha(t), \qquad (4.68)$$

where

$$c_\alpha = \int_\Gamma v_\alpha(\tau)\varphi(\tau) \, d\tau. \qquad (4.69)$$

Treating the right-hand side of Eq. (4.68) as known, we will apply Carleman's method to this equation. Briefly, the method proceeds as follows: The right-hand side of Eq. (4.68) is denoted by $f_1(t)$, and we set

$$\Phi(z) = \frac{1}{2\pi i} \int_\Gamma \frac{\varphi(\tau)}{\tau - z} \, d\tau,$$

---

* For a detailed discussion, see the author's article, "The method of least squares in mathematical physics." Uch. Zap. LGLI, No. 111, Ser. matem. Nauk, **16**(1949) pp. 167–206. Singular equations are considered on pp. 174–176 of this article.

where z is any point of the complex plane that does not lie on the contour Γ. If we place the coordinate origin inside Γ, we find that

$$\ln \frac{a(t) + b(t)}{a(t) - b(t)} = \theta(t) + m \ln t,$$

where the function $\theta(t)$ is single valued on Γ; this function satisfies a Lipschitz condition with positive exponent. Equation (4.68) reduces to the form

$$\Phi^+(t) - t^m e^{\theta(t)} \Phi^-(t) = \frac{f_1(t)}{a(t) - b(t)}, \qquad (4.70)$$

where $\Phi^+(t)$ and $\Phi^-(t)$ are the limits of the function $\Phi(z)$ as $z \to t$, $t \in \Gamma$, from inside and outside Γ, respectively. We set

$$\psi(z) = \frac{1}{2\pi i} \int_\Gamma \frac{\theta(\tau)}{\tau - z} \, d\tau$$

and introduce a new unknown function $F(z)$, setting $\Phi(z) = F(z)e^{\psi(z)}$. Let $\omega(t)$ denote the singular integral

$$\omega(t) = \frac{1}{2\pi i} \int_\Gamma \frac{\theta(\tau)}{\tau - t} \, d\tau = \frac{1}{2} S\theta.$$

Then Eq. (4.70) takes the form

$$F^+(t) - F^-(t)t^m = \frac{f_1(t)e^{-\omega(t)}t^{m/2}}{\sqrt{a^2(t) - b^2(t)}}. \qquad (4.71)$$

The procedure now depends on the value of m.

If $m = 0$, Eq. (4.68) has a unique solution, which can be represented in the form

$$\varphi(t) = \varphi_0(t) - \sum_{\alpha=1}^n c_\alpha \varphi_\alpha(t), \qquad (4.72)$$

where

$$\varphi_0(t) = \frac{a(t)f(t)}{a^2(t) - b^2(t)} + \frac{b(t)e^{\omega(t)}}{\sqrt{a^2(t) - b^2(t)}} \frac{1}{\pi i} \int_\Gamma \frac{e^{-\omega(\tau)}f(\tau) \, d\tau}{\sqrt{a^2(\tau) - b^2(\tau)}(\tau - t)}, \qquad (4.73)$$

and $\varphi_\alpha(t)$ is determined with the same Formula (4.73) with $u_\alpha(t)$ substituted for $f(t)$.

Formulas (4.72) and (4.69) give us a system for the unknowns c_α:

$$c_\beta + \sum_{\alpha=1}^n a_{\alpha\beta} c_\alpha = b_\beta \qquad (\beta = 1, 2, \ldots, n). \qquad (4.74)$$

Here

$$a_{\alpha\beta} = \int_\Gamma \varphi_\alpha(t)v_\beta(t) \, dt, \qquad b_\beta = \int_\Gamma f(t)v_\beta(t) \, dt. \qquad (4.75)$$

If the determinant of system (4.74) is nonzero, Eq. (4.65) is solvable and has a unique solution; if, however, this determinant is equal to zero, Eq. (4.65) is solvable if, and only if, the column of free terms in system (4.74) satisfies the appropriate orthogonality conditions; this is equivalent to having the free term of Eq. (4.65) satisfy some orthogonality condition. In this case, if Eq. (4.65) has a solution, it is not unique.

If $m > 0$, the solution of Eq. (4.68) is of the form

$$\varphi(t) = \varphi_0(t) - \sum_{\alpha=1}^{n} c_\alpha \varphi_\alpha(t) + \sum_{\gamma=1}^{n} g_\gamma \Phi_\gamma(t). \tag{4.76}$$

Here the g_γ are arbitrary constants and $\Phi_\gamma(t)$ is the solution of the homogeneous equation

$$a(t)\Phi_\gamma(t) - b(t)S\Phi_\gamma(t) = 0;$$

this time the function $\varphi_0(t)$ is determined by the formula

$$\varphi_0(t) = \frac{a(t)}{a^2(t) - b^2(t)} f(t)$$

$$+ \frac{b(t)e^{\omega(t)}}{\sqrt{t^m[a^2(t) - b^2(t)]}} \frac{1}{\pi i} \int_\Gamma \frac{\tau^{m/2}e^{-\omega(\tau)}f(\tau)}{\sqrt{a^2(\tau) - b^2(\tau)}} \frac{d\tau}{\tau - t}, \tag{4.77}$$

while the $\varphi_\alpha(t)$ are obtained by substituting $u_\alpha(t)$ for $f(t)$ in Formula (4.77). For the constants c_α and g_γ we obtain the system

$$c_\beta + \sum_{\alpha=1}^{n} a_{\alpha\beta} c_\alpha - \sum_{\gamma=1}^{m} A_{\gamma\beta} g_\gamma = b_\beta \qquad (\beta = 1, 2, \ldots, n), \tag{4.78}$$

where $a_{\alpha\beta}$ and b_β have their previous values (4.75) and

$$A_{\gamma\beta} = \int_\Gamma \Phi_\gamma(t)v_\beta(t) \, dt.$$

If the rank of the coefficient matrix for the unknowns in system (4.78) is n, Eq. (4.68) is always solvable and the corresponding homogeneous equation has m linearly independent solutions. If, however, the rank of this matrix $r < n$, Eq. (4.68) is solvable only when $f(t)$ satisfies $n - r$ orthogonality conditions; the number of linearly independent solutions of the corresponding homogeneous equation is $m + n - r$.

Now let $m < 0$, $m = -\mu$. If Eq. (4.65) has a solution, it must be of the form

$$\varphi(t) = \varphi_0(t) - \sum_{\alpha=1}^{n} c_\alpha \varphi_\alpha(t),$$

where $\varphi_0(t)$, as before, is determined by Formula (4.77) and $\varphi_\alpha(t)$ is obtained from Formula (4.77) by substituting $u_\alpha(t)$ for $f(t)$. The function

$$f(t) - \sum_{\alpha=1}^{n} c_\alpha u_\alpha(t)$$

must satisfy the following orthogonality conditions:

$$\int_\Gamma \frac{e^{-\omega(\tau)}\tau^{\mu/2-k}}{\sqrt{a^2(\tau) - b^2(\tau)}} \left[f(\tau) - \sum_{\alpha=1}^n c_\alpha u_\alpha(\tau) \right] d\tau = 0 \qquad (4.79)$$

$$(k = 0, 1, 2, \ldots, \mu - 1).$$

The coefficients c_α must also satisfy conditions (4.74). Equation (4.65) has a solution if Eqs. (4.74) and (4.79) are consistent; otherwise it does not. The solution is unique if the rank of the matrix of system (4.74) and (4.79) is $r = \mu$, and not unique if $r < \mu$; in this case homogeneous equation (4.65) has $\mu - r$ linearly independent solutions.

BIBLIOGRAPHIC COMMENTS

Problems on approximate solution of integral equations are discussed in detail in [30, 64, 25].

The method of simple iterations for transformed equations (see Section 2.3) was developed in [74] by Natanson for the equations of a larger class. More general transformations are discussed in [4].

For a detailed discussion of the Bubnov-Galerkin method, see Chapter Three of the present book, as well as [63].

For solution of singular integral equations with one independent variable, see [8, 71, 72].

BIBLIOGRAPHY

1. I. S. Bakhvalov, An error estimate for numerical integration of differential equations by means of the Adams method, Dokl. Akad. Nauk, SSSR, Vol. **104**, No. 5 (1955).
2. I. S. Berezin and N. P. Zhidkov, Computational Methods [in Russian], Vol. II, Moscow, Fizmatgiz, 1960.
3. M. Sh. Birman, Variational methods for solution of boundary-value problems similar to the Trefftz method Vestn. LGU, No. 13, Ser. matem., mekh. i astr., 3 (1956).
4. M. Sh. Birman, One modified form of the method of successive approximations, Vestn. LGU, No. 9 (1952), pp. 69–76.
5. B. M. Budak and A. D. Gorbunov, A difference method for solution of the Cauchy problem for the equation $y'' = f(x, y)$ and the system $x_i' = X_i(t, x_1, \ldots x_n)(i = 1, \ldots, n)$ with discontinuous right sides, Vestn, MGU, Ser. matem., No. 5 (1958), pp. 7–11.
6. E. D. But, Numerical Methods [in Russian], Moscow, Fizmatgiz, 1959.
7. M. M. Vaynberg, Variational methods for Investigation of Nonlinear Operators [in Russian], Moscow, Gostekhizdat, 1956.
8. N. P. Vekua, Systems of Singular Integral Equations [in Russian], Moscow-Leningrad, 1940.
9. Ye. A. Volkov, The grid method for solution of the interior Dirichlet problem for the Laplace equation, Collection: Computer Mathematics, No. 1 (1957).
10. Ye. A. Volkov, The grid method for boundary-value problems with directional or normal derivatives, Zh. vych. matem. i matem. fiz., Vol. **1**, No. 4 (1961), pp. 607–621.
11. Yu. V. Vorob'yev, The Moment Method in Applied Mathematics [in Russian], Moscow, Fizmatgiz, 1958.
12. I. I. Vorovich, The existence of solutions in the nonlinear theory of shells, Izvestiya Akad. Nauk., Ser. matem., **19** (1955), pp. 173–186.
13. B. Z. Vulikh, Introduction to Functional Analysis [in Russian], Moscow, Fizmatgiz, 1958.
14. L. N. Gagen-Torn, Solvability of the Ritz system for functionals in the theory of plasticity, Trudy Matem. Inst. im. V. A. Steklova, **66** (1962), pp. 190–195.
15. L. N. Gagen-Torn and S. G. Mikhlin, Solvability of nonlinear Ritz systems, Dokl. Akad. Nauk SSSR, Vol. **138**, No. 2 (1961).
16. A. V. Gel'fand, Approximate integration of systems of first-order ordinary differential equations, Izvestiya Akad. Nauk, Ser. matem, (1938), pp. 483–594.
17. S. K. Godunov and V. S. Ryaben'kiy, Introduction to the Theory of Difference Schemes [in Russian], Moscow, Fizmatgiz, 1962.
18. E. Goursat, A Course in Mathematical Analysis [in Russian], Vol. II, Moscow-Leningrad, ONTI, 1936.
19. D. F. Davidenko, One new method for numerical solution of systems of nonlinear equations, Dokl. Akad. Nauk. SSSR, Vol. 88, No. 4 (1953).
20. Ye. P. Kalugina, The class L_Φ as a convex manifold, Dokl. Akad. Nauk SSSR, **98** (1954), pp. 13–16.
21. Ye. P. Kalugina, On the classes $H_\Phi(r_1, r_2, \ldots r_n)$, Dokl. Akad. Nauk SSSR, **96** (1954), pp. 13–15.
22. E. Kamke, A Handbook on Ordinary Differential Equations, Moscow, IL, 1950.
23. L. V. Kantorovich, Functional analysis in applied mathematics, Uspekhi Matem. Nauk, Vol. 3, No. 6(28) (1948).
24. L. V. Kantorovich and G. P. Akilov, Functional Analysis in Normed Spaces [in Russian], Moscow, Fizmatgiz, 1959.
25. L. V. Kantorovich and V. I. Krylov, Approximate Methods for Higher Analysis [in Russian], Moscow-Leningrad, Gostekhizdat, 1949.

26. L. V. Kantorovich and V. I. Krylov, Numerical methods, Collection: Thirty Years of Soviet Mathematics, Moscow-Leningrad, 1948.
27. L. M. Kachanov, Variational methods for solution of problems in the theory of plasticity, Prikl. matem. i mekh. Vol. 23, No. 3 (1959).
28. L. M. Kachanov, Foundations of the Theory of Plasticity [in Russian], Moscow, Gostekhizdat, 1956.
29. L. M. Kachanov, Examples of solutions given by variational methods to problems in the theory of elastic-plastic torsion, Collection: Research on Elasticity and Plasticity, No. 1, LGU (1961), pp. 157–161.
30. L. Collatz, Numerical Methods for Solution of Differential Equations [Russian translation], Moscow, IL, 1953.
31. A. N. Krylov, Lectures on Approximate Computation [in Russian], Moscow, AN SSSR, 1949.
32. V. I. Krylov, The convergence and stability of numerical solutions of first-order differential equations, Dokl. Akad. Nauk BSSR, Vol. 4, No. 5 (1960), pp. 187–189.
33. R. Courant and D. Hilbert, Methods of Mathematical Physics [Russian translation], Vol. I, Moscow-Leningrad, GTTI, 1933.
34. R. Courant, K. Friedrichs and G. Levy, Difference equations for mathematical physics, Uspekhi. Matem. Nauk, VIII (1941).
35. O. A. Ladyzhenskaya, Finite difference methods for the theory of partial differential equations, Uspekhi. Matem. Nauk. Vol. 12, No. 5(77) (1957), pp. 123–148.
36. O. A. Ladyzhenskaya, Nonstationary homogeneous equations and their applications to linear problems in mathematical physics, Matem. sb. 45(87): 2 (1958), pp. 123–158.
37. O. A. Ladyzhenskaya, Solution of nonstationary operator equations, Matem. sb. 39(81): 4 (1956), pp. 491–524.
38. O. A. Ladyzhenskaya, The Mixed Problem for Hyperbolic Equations [in Russian], Moscow, Gostekhizdat, 1953.
39. A. Lagenbakh, Certain nonlinear operators of the theory of elasticity in Hilbert space, Vestn. LGU., No. 1, Ser. matem., mekh. i astr., 1 (1961).
40. A. Lagenbakh, Application of variational methods to certain nonlinear differential equations, Dokl. Akad. Nauk SSSR, Vol. 121, No. 2 (1958).
41. J. N. Lans, Numerical Methods for High-Speed Computers [Russian translation], Moscow, IL, 1962.
42. V. I. Lebedev, The grid method for the second boundary-value problem for the Poisson equation, Dokl. Akad. Nauk, Vol. 127, No. 4 (1959).
43. V. I. Lebedev, The finite-difference analog of the Neumann problem, Dokl. Akad. Nauk SSSR, Vol. 126, No. 3 (1959), pp. 494–497.
44. V. I. Lebedev, Estimating the error of the grid method for the Dirichlet and Neumann problems, Dokl. Akad. Nauk SSSR, Vol. 128, No. 4 (1959).
45. V. I. Lebedev, Estimating the error of the grid method for the two-dimensional Neumann problem, Dokl. Akad. Nauk SSSR, Vol. 132, No. 5 (1960).
46. L. S. Leybenzon, Variational Methods in the Theory of Elasticity [in Russian], Moscow-Leningrad, Gostekhizdat, 1943 (see also the Collected Works of Academician L. S. Leybenzon [in Russian], Vol. I, AN SSSR, 1951).
47. S. M. Lozinskiy, Approximate solution of systems of ordinary differential equations, Dokl. Akad. Nauk SSSR, Vol. 97, No. 1 (1954), pp. 29–32.
48. S. M. Lozinskiy, On the interval of existence for solutions of ordinary differential equations, Dokl. Akad. Nauk SSSR, Vol. 94, No. 1, 1954, pp. 17–19.
49. S. M. Lozinskiy, On variational equations, Dokl. Akad. Nauk SSSR, Vol. 93, No. 4 (1953).
50. S. M. Lozinskiy, An estimate for the error of approximate solutions of systems of ordinary differential equations, Dokl. Akad. Nauk SSSR, Vol. 92, No. 2 (1953), pp. 225–228.
51. S. M. Lozinskiy, An estimate of the error in numerical integration of ordinary differential equations, Izvestiya VUZOV, Matematika, 5 (1958).
52. N. N. Luzin, On S. A. Chaplygin's method of approximate integration, Uspekhi Matem. Nauk, Vol. 6, No. 6(46) (1951), pp. 2–27.

53. L. A. Lyusternik, Remarks on numerical solution of boundary-value problems for the Laplace equation and computation of eigenvalues with the grid method, Trudy Matem. Inst. im. V. A. Steklova, **20** (1947), pp. 49–64.
54. L. A. Lyusternik, Difference approximations of the Laplace operator, Uspekhi Matem. Nauk, Vol. **9**, No. 2(60) (1954).
55. Ye. V. Makhover, Bending of a sharp-edged plate with variable thickness, Uch. Zap. Leningrad ped. Inst. fiz.-matem. f-t, Vol. **17**, No. 2 (1957), pp. 28–39.
56. Ye. V. Makhover, On the spectrum of natural frequencies of a sharpedged plate, Uch. zap. Leningrad ped. Inst. Vol. **197** (1958), pp. 113–118.
57. Sh. Ye. Mikeladze, New Methods of Integrating Differential Equations [in Russian], Moscow-Leningrad, Gostekhizdat, 1951.
58. Sh. Ye. Mikeladze, Numerical integration of elliptic and parabolic equations, Izvestiya Akad. Nauk, Ser. materm., Vol. **5**, No. 1 (1941), pp. 57–73.
59. W. E. Milne, Numerical Analysis [Russian translation], Moscow, IL, 1951.
60. W. E. Milne, Numerical Solution of Differential Equations [Russian translation], Moscow, IL, 1955.
61. K. Miranda, Elliptic Partial Differential Equations [Russian translation], Moscow, IL, 1958.
62. V. M. Mitkevich, Application of the Ritz method to the problem of the bending of a cantilever plate, collection: Research at the Hydraulics Laboratory of the Academy of Sciences UkSSR, No. 9 (1961), pp. 48–57.
63. S. G. Mikhlin, Variational Methods in Mathematical Physics [in Russian], Moscow, Gostekhizdat, 1957.
64. S. G. Mikhlin, Integral Equations and Their Applications [in Russian], Moscow-Leningrad, Gostekhizdat, 1949.
65. S. G. Mikhlin, Some conditions for stability of the Ritz method, Vestn. LGU, No. 13, Ser. matem., maekh., i astr., 3 (1961).
66. S. G. Mikhlin, The Ritz method for nonlinear problems, Dokl. Akad. Nauk SSSR, Vol. **142**, No. 4 (1962).
67. S. G. Mikhlin, Rational selection of coordinate functions for the Ritz method. Zh. vych. matem. i matem. fiz, Vol. **2**, No. 3 (1962).
68. S. G. Mikhlin, The stability of the Ritz method, Dokl. Akad. Nauk SSSR, Vol. **135**, No. 1 (1961).
69. S. G. Mikhlin, Execution of the Ritz method, Dokl. Akad. Nauk SSSR, Vol. **106**, No. 3 (1956).
70. S. G. Mikhlin, The Problem of Minimizing a Quadratic Functional [in Russian], Moscow-Leningrad, Gostekhizdat, 1952.
71. S. G. Mikhlin, Singular integral equations, Uspekhi Matem. Nauk, Vol. **3**, 3(25) (1948).
72. N. I. Muskhelishvili, Singular Integral Equations [in Russian], Moscow, Fizmatgiz, 1962.
73. I. P. Mysovskikh, Lectures on Computer Methods [in Russian], Moscow, Fizmatgiz, 1962.
74. I. P. Natanson, On the theory of approximate solution of equations, Uch. zap. Leningrad ped. Inst., **64** (1948), pp. 3–8.
75. D. Yu. Panov, A Handbook on Numerical Solution of Partial Differential Equations [in Russian], Moscow-Leningrad, Gostekhizdat, 1951.
76. D. Yu. Panov, Numerical Solution of Systems of Quasi-linear Hyperbolic Partial Differential Equations [in Russian], Moscow, Gostekhizdat, 1957.
77. I. G. Petrovskiy, Lectures on Partial Differential Equations [in Russian], Moscow, Gostekhizdat, 1953.
78. N. I. Pol'skiy, Generalizations of Galerkin's method, Dokl. Akad. Nauk SSSR, Vol. **86**, No. 3 (1952).
79. N. I. Pol'skiy, On the convergence of the method of B. G. Gal'orkin, Dokl. Akad. Nauk, URSR, Ser. Fiz.-matem., Khim. Nauk, No. 6 (1949), 7–12.
80. N. I. Pol'skiy, On a general scheme for application of approximate methods, Dokl. Akad. Nauk SSSR, Vol. **111**, No. 6 (1956).

81. R. D. Richtmyer, Difference Methods for Solutions of Boundary-Value Problems [Russian translation], Moscow, IL, 1956.

82. S. N. Rose, On the convergence of L. M. Kachanov's method, Vestn. LGU, No. 19 (1961).

83. V. S. Ryaben'kiy and A. F. Filippov, On the Stability of Difference Equations [in Russian], Moscow, Gostekhizdat, 1956.

84. M. G. Salvadori, Numerical Methods for Engineers [Russian translation], Moscow, IL, 1955.

85. A. A. Samarskiy, A priori estimates for difference equations, Zhurn. vych. matem. i matem. fiz., Vol. 1, No. 6 (1961).

86. A. A. Samarskiy, A priori estimates for solutions of the difference analog of parabolic differential equations, Zh. vych. matem. i matem. fiz., Vol. 1, No. 3 (1961).

87. A. A. Samarskiy, Homogeneous difference schemes for nonlinear parabolic equations, Zh. vych. matem. i matem. fiz., Vol. 2, No. 1 (1962).

88. A. A. Samarskiy and I. V. Fryazinov, The convergence of homogeneous difference schemes for heat-transfer equations with discontinuous coefficients, Zh. vych. matem. i matem. fiz, Vol. 1, No. 5 (1961).

89. J. Sansone, Ordinary Differential Equations [Russian translation], Vol. II, Moscow, IL, 1954.

90. V. K. Saul'yev, Integration of Parabolic Equations with the Grid Method [in Russian], Moscow, Gostekhizdat, 1960.

91. V. K. Saul'yev, The problem of solving eigenvalue problems with finite-difference methods; Collection: Computer Mathematics and Computer Technology, No. 2, 1955.

92. M. G. Slobodyanskiy, An estimate of the error in approximate solutions of linear problems, Prikl. matem. i mekh., Vol. 17, No. 2 (1953).

93. V. I. Smirnov, A Course in Higher Mathematics [in Russian], Vol. II, Moscow, Fizmatgiz, 1958.

94. V. I. Smirnov, A Course in Higher Mathematics [in Russian], Vol. IV, Moscow, Fizmatgiz, 1958.

95. V. I. Smirnov, A Course in Higher Mathematics [in Russian], Vol. V, Moscow, Gizmatgiz, 1959.

96. T. N. Smirnova, Polynomial supervision and execution of analytical computations with a computer, Trudy matem. Inst. im. V. A. Steklova, 66 (1962), pp. 77–112.

97. S. L. Sobolev, Applications of Functional Analysis in Mathematical Physics [in Russian], LGU, 1950.

98. S. L. Sobolev, The Equations of Mathematical Physics [in Russian], Moscow, Gostekhizdat, 1954.

98a. P. Ye. Sobolevskiy, On equations with operators forming acute angles, Dokl. Akad. Nauk SSSR, Vol. 116, No. 5, 1957.

99. V. V. Stepanov, A Course in Ordinary Differential Equations [in Russian], Moscow, Gostekhizdat, 1953.

100. A. T. Taldykin, Systems of elements in Hilbert spaces and series in them, Matem. sb. 29(71): 1 (1951).

101. A. N. Tikhonov and A. A. Samarskiy, Homogeneous difference schemes, vych. matem. i matem. fiz., Vol. 1, No. 1 (1961).

102. A. N. Tikhonov and A. A. Samarskiy, Homogeneous difference schemes of greater accuracy on nonuniform grids, Zh. vych. matem. i matem. fiz., Vol. 1, No. 3 (1961).

103. A. N. Tikhonov and A. A. Samarskiy, The Stürm-Liouville difference problem, Zh. vych. matem. i matem. fiz., Vol. 1, No. 5 (1961).

104. D. K. Faddeyev and V. N. Faddeyeva, Computer Methods for Linear Algebra [in Russian], Moscow, Fizmatgiz, 1963.

105. V. M. Fridman, The method of successive approximations for integral equations of the first kind, Uspekhi Matem. Nauk, Vol. 11, No. 1(67) (1956).

106. S. A. Chaplygin, A New Method for Approximate Integration of Differential Equations [in Russian], Moscow-Leningrad, Gostekhizdat, 1950.

107. M. R. Shura-Bura, An estimate of the error of numerical integration of ordinary differential equations, Prik. matem. i mekh., Vol. 16, No. 5 (1952).

108. D. M. Eydus, On solution of boundary-value problems with the finite-difference method, Dokl. Akad. Nauk SSSR, Vol. 83, No. 2 (1952), pp. 191–194.
109. G. N. Yaskova and M. N. Yakovlev, Conditions for stability of the Pertov-Galerkin method, Trudy Matem. Inst. im. V. A. Steklova, 66 (1962), pp. 182–189.
110. E. Batschelet, Über die numerische Auflösung von Randwertproblemen bei elliptischen partiellen Differentialgleichungen, Zeits. angew. Math. und Phys., Bd. III, No. 3 (1952), 165–193.
111. L. Bers, On mildly nonlinear partial difference equations of elliptic type, Journ. Res. Nat. Bur. Standards 51, No. 5 (1953), 229–236.
112. G. G. O'Brien, M. A. Hyman and S. Kaplan, A study of the numerical solution of partial differential equations, Journ. Math. and Phys. 29, No. 4 (1951), 223–251.
113. J. W. Carr, Error bounds for the Runge–Kutta single-step integration process, Journ. Assoc. Comput. Mach. 5, No. 39 (1958).
114. G. Dahlquist, Convergence and stability in the numerical integration of ordinary differential equations, Math. Scand. 4, No. 1 (1956), 33–53.
115. Jim Douglas and T. M. Gallie, On the numerical integration of a parabolic differential equation subject to a moving boundary condition, Duke Math. Journ. 22, No. 4 (1955), 557–571.
116. G. E. Forsythe and W. R. Wasow, Finite-difference Methods for Partial Differential Equations, New York-London 1960 (Russian translation available).
117. S. Gerschgorin, Fehlerabschätzungen für Differenzenverfahren bei Lösung partiellen Differentialgleichungen, Zeits, angew. Math. und Mech. 10 (1930), 373–382.
118. J. H. Giese, On the truncation error in a numerical solution of the Neumann problem for a rectangle, Journ. Math. and Phys. 37, No. 2 (1958), 169–177.
119. S. H. Gould, Variational methods for eigenvalue problems, University of Toronto Press, 1957.
120. J. Horn, Gewönliche Differentialgleichungen, Berlin und Leipzig, 1937.
121. T. Kato, On the upper and lower bounds of eigenvalues, Journ. Phys. Soc. Japan 4, No. 1 (1949), 334–339.
122. N. Kryloff, Les méthodes de solution approchée des problèmes de la physique mathématique, Mémor. Sci. Math. 49 (1931).
123. A. Langenbach, Variationsmethoden in der nichtlinearen Elastizität- und Plastizitäts-theorie, Wiss. Z. Humboldt-Univ. Berlin, Math-Nath. R., IX, 1959/60, 145–164.
124. v. Mises, R., Zur numerischen Integration von Differentialgleichungen, Zeits. angew. Math. und Mech. 10 (1930), 81–92.
125. T. S. Motzkin and W. Wasow, On the approximation of linear elliptic differential equations by difference equations with positive coefficients, Journ. of Math. and Phys. 31, No. 4 (1953), 253–259.
126. L. E. Synge, The method of the hypercircle in functionspace for boundary value problems, Proc. Royal Soc., ser. A, No. 1027, 191 (1947), 447–466.
127. G. Temple, The computation of characteristic numbers and characteristic functions, Proc. London Math. Soc. 29 (1928).
128. G. Temple, The theory of Rayleigh's principle as applied to continuous systems, Proc. Royal Soc. 119 (1928).
129. H. F. Weinberger, Upper and lower bounds for eigenvalues by finite difference methods, Comm. Pure and Appl. Math. 9 (1956).
130. H. F. Weinberger, Lower bounds for higher eigenvalues by finite difference methods, Pacific. Journ. Math. 8, 339–368.
131. A. Weinstein, Étude des spectres des équations aux dérivées partielles de la théorie des plaques élastiques, Mémor. Sci. Math. 88 (1937).
132. D. H. Weinstein, Modified Ritz method, Proc. Nat. Acad. Sci. USA 20 (1934), 529–532.

INDEX